RUTH ROBINSON'S YEAR OF MIRACLES

Frances Garrood

RUTH ROBINSON'S YEAR OF MIRACLES

Published by Sapere Books.

11 Bank Chambers, Hornsey, London, N8 7NN,
United Kingdom

saperebooks.com

ISBN: 978-1-912786-09-1

For Claire, with my love

ACKNOWLEDGEMENTS

Particular thanks are due to Alis Hawkins, who believed in this novel and encouraged me to persevere with it, and Alex Hammond of Cornerstones Literary Consultancy, who helped me to make it a better book. I would also like to thank the team at Sapere Books, who once again have been such a pleasure to work with.

PROLOGUE

My Uncle Eric is telephoning the zoo to ask how many Thomson's gazelles a lion can eat in a fortnight.

Uncle Silas is stuffing a weasel on the kitchen table by candlelight (we have a power cut).

A respectful knock at the front door heralds the arrival of yet another minibus full of pilgrims hoping for a miracle.

Outside it is raining — a typical, nasty, dank November drizzle — and a piglet is trying to get in through the cat flap.

In the midst of all this, I am trying to cobble together something for our supper (the weasel is being prepared for posterity rather than for consumption).

I pause to take stock.

Six months ago, I had a regular job, a monthly salary and a comfortable flat to go home to.

How on earth have I got into all this?

PART I: SUMMER

In the first three months following conception, the embryo develops from a single cell into a tiny recognisable human being. By the end of that time, it will measure up to 10cms in length and weigh about one ounce. Its head is almost half the size of its entire body, it has begun to move independently, and it will have fingernails and toenails. All its major organs will be in place.

CHAPTER ONE

Many women the wrong side of thirty-five seem to want a baby but not necessarily a man. I am on the wrong side of thirty-five, and all I ever wanted was the man. But it seems that I have got the baby instead.

I sit on the lavatory and cry. How many other women all over the country are also at this moment sitting on the lavatory and crying, either because they are pregnant or because they are not? The pregnancy testing kit is uncompromisingly positive. Good news, it seems to say. You're going to have a baby!

But I don't want a baby, I sob. I never wanted a baby. I don't even like babies! And I've always been so careful. Besides, aren't I supposed to be past my child-bearing best? There seems to be a proliferation of articles and programmes about the ticking of body clocks and the folly of women who Leave It Too Late. My body clock has kept a tactful silence for as long as I can remember, and apart from the monthly (and expected) reminder that I am not pregnant — that one more disappointed egg has gone unfertilised to its tiny grave — I have never given it a thought. But I have made one slip; one tiny slip; and now this. A cruel reminder that behind every sexual act between fertile couples of opposite sexes there lurks a baby waiting to be conceived.

I flush away the evidence and wipe my eyes. Maybe the test is wrong. They can be wrong sometimes. And I don't feel pregnant. My stomach is still washboard flat, my breasts small and firm, and I don't feel in the least bit sick. How can a silly little strip of paper be right when my body (not to mention my head) is in denial?

But I am not stupid. I know how these things work. And my oh-so-reliable period is a week late. Barring accident or interference, I am going to have a baby.

It couldn't have come at a worse time. The orchestra in which I play the violin has recently had to make cuts, and as a lesser player in one of the back desks, I have been 'let go', as they kindly put it. This was a blow indeed, although not entirely unexpected, and to cheer myself up, I planned to award myself a belated gap year on the strength of a small legacy from my grandmother. And why not? I have no responsibilities, my mortgage is small and my life my own. My good friend Mikey — solid, dependable and reassuringly gay — was going to accompany me. We were going to scuba dive in the Red Sea, trek at the foot of the Himalayas and visit Petra. We had it all worked out. My small bedroom is littered with atlases and brochures, phrase books and useful telephone numbers. I was going to let my flat (the contract is already signed; a nice young Norwegian couple would look after it and feed the cat as well) and go off with a rucksack and my violin on my back (Mikey took issue with the violin, but as I explained, I wouldn't dream of going anywhere without it. I could always lock it up in a safe somewhere if we did anything really exotic). I was going to be free from the constraints and expectations of the world of work. I was going to have an *adventure.*

I spend a sleepless night worrying about my new and unwelcome condition. I know life isn't fair, and I've never expected it to be, but do I really deserve this? I've always tried to be responsible, such relationships as I have had have nearly all been long term and monogamous, and I have always practised safe sex. Except this once. Just the once.

His name is Amos (his parents, like mine, are religious) and he is an old friend; a big bearded trombonist with hands like shovels and arms made to hug. I needed a hug — so, it seemed, did he — and this is the result.

Do I tell Amos? Over my second cup of Horlicks, I ponder the question, and decide that I shall not. Amos has his own problems; he has endured a recent and very messy divorce, and he too has lost his job (violinists are not the only ones getting the push). Besides, I know that whatever happens this will tie me to Amos, and I'm not sure this is something either of us will want. This is my pregnancy; my problem. Especially since I told Amos that I was on the pill (by that stage we were in a state of reckless undress, and lying seemed a much easier option than waiting for Amos to 'pop to the chemist', as he had kindly offered to do).

By four fifty-three am, having worked my way through the prospect of keeping the baby and, fleetingly, the possibility of having it adopted, I consider taking advantage of the Woman's Right to Choose. It is not something I have ever given much thought to since I never expected to find myself in this position, but now it seems the least unattractive of my alternatives. I sit up in bed and switch the light on. Yes! I am a woman, and I shall choose. My gap year isn't lost; it's merely postponed. I feel faint stirrings of hope, thinking with satisfaction that with a bit of luck they are the only stirrings I am going to feel, for I shall have an abortion. After all, it's a small procedure at this stage, neither I nor my unborn child will feel a thing, and in a week or so I will be back to normal. Fortunately, Mikey and I were leaving it until the last minute to book our tickets (Mikey likes nothing better than a bargain), so

I can allow myself a little leeway. I'm sure the Norwegians can make alternative arrangements for a couple of weeks, and then everything will be back on track.

A week later, having persuaded two doctors that this unwanted pregnancy will seriously compromise my sanity, I am sitting in the waiting-room of the clean, clinical building where I shall be divested of my little problem. I decided to go to a private clinic because they could see me at once, and I thought I would be unlikely to bump into anyone I know. My gap year fund is shrinking by the minute, but I have some savings which will help. Mikey (who had to be told, for obvious reasons) has insisted on coming with me. Mikey is being unusually silent.

'Are you all right?' I ask him, thinking that really it should be the other way round. 'You're being very quiet.'

'I feel quiet.' Mikey turns the pages of a glossy magazine.

'What's up?'

'Nothing.' He examines the price of a very expensive country mansion, and whistles through his teeth.

'Are you sure?'

'Quite sure.'

'You're behaving like a woman,' I tell him.

'What do you mean?'

'That's what women do. They say nothing's wrong when it is, and then get cross if no-one tries to get to the bottom of the problem.'

'Okay.' Mikey puts down his magazine. 'I don't think you should be doing this.'

'Doing what?'

'The abortion.'

'*Now* you tell me! Anyway, it's not your baby, so it's none of your business.'

'It is my business. You've made it my business.'

'No I haven't!'

'Yes you have.'

A passing nurse gives us as funny look, and it occurs to me that of course she assumes that Mikey is the baby's father.

'You insisted on coming with me. I didn't make you. I didn't even ask you.'

'You had to have someone.'

'No I didn't!'

'Yes you did. No-one should go through something like this alone.'

'So you accept that I'm going through with it?'

'I know you mean to. But Ruth, have you really considered what you're doing?'

'Of course I have.' This is not entirely true. I have tried hard to push the whole baby thing to the back of my mind and look upon this in the same way as I would a visit to the dentist.

Mikey reaches into his pocket and takes out a small booklet. On the cover is a joyously pregnant woman, her hands smugly clasped round her bump. Inside are graphic illustrations of foetal development.

'Look at this.' He jabs a finger at a picture of a seven-week foetus. 'Eyes and little arms, and a heart.'

'So?' The foetus looks like a cross between a seahorse and a new-born rabbit.

'So, it's a human being.'

'Hardly.'

'You know what I mean.' Mikey sighs. 'It has all the potential to be a person. It could be a brain surgeon or a nuclear physicist or —'

'A chimney sweep?'

'That too.'

'Mikey, I can't. Apart from anything else, I can't let you down. We fly in a fortnight —'

'Not necessarily. And anyway, a baby is more important than cavorting around the world with me.'

'Mikey, please. This is hard enough as it is.'

'Is it?'

I hesitate. If I'm honest, this hasn't been hard at all. Apart from when I found out, I've been in very successful denial. It annoys me that Mikey is disturbing my comfort zone and putting unwelcome thoughts into my head.

Mikey wheels out his trump card.

'I would give anything — *anything* — to be a father,' he says. 'But I never shall be.'

'You could be.'

'No I couldn't. I shall never be able to have straight sex, and I certainly have no intention of looking for a willing woman and a turkey baster. I've accepted my lot. Perhaps you should accept yours.'

'Mikey, you're not being fair.'

'Neither are you.' He returns to his magazine, and we maintain a sullen silence. The minutes tick by.

'Miss Robinson?' A starched nurse comes into the waiting room. 'Would you come this way, please?'

I stand up and pick up my bag. Mikey looks up from his magazine, but he doesn't say anything.

'Good luck?' I prompt him.

Mikey shakes his head.

'There's nothing good about this,' he says. 'But — be safe.'

Fifteen minutes later, I am lying on a trolley awaiting my turn on what I imagine to be some kind of surgical conveyor belt. I am wearing one of those backless hospital gowns, and I feel naked and defenceless. I have been given an injection to help me relax, but all it's done is make me feel strange and floaty and very slightly sick. I wish very much that I was anywhere but here.

I must have dozed off, because through a drug-induced haze, I can see my small seahorse/rabbit hovering somewhere near the ceiling. Perhaps I have had the operation, and my little embryo is having one of those out-of-body experiences on its way to the hereafter, only with me watching it rather than the other way round. It reaches the window, where it scrabbles hopelessly for a few moments, and then it slithers down in a streak of pink ectoplasm and disappears.

I wake up as the trolley begins to move, and for a few moments I rather enjoy the sensation of being transported somewhere; of other people taking charge and of everything being out of my hands. Someone is pushing me with brisk, business-like footsteps. Soon, all this will be over. I open my eyes, and the ceiling (palest cream, with little decorative swirls. You don't get those on the National Health) moves backwards above me. We go round corners and someone opens and closes doors. I begin to drift again.

'No. *No!*'

Who was that? The voice sounds panicky and very close. Very like mine, in fact.

'No what?' Another voice, soothing and female. The trolley rumbles on its way.

'No!' This voice is quite definitely mine.

'It'll soon be over, dear. Just you relax.'

'NO!' I clutch the edges of the trolley and try to sit up. 'Let me off! Let me out of here! I want to go home!'

The trolley comes to an abrupt halt.

'You've signed the consent form, dear. Everything's arranged. Mr. Buxton is waiting for you.'

'Bugger Mr. Buxton! I just want to go home. You can't keep me here against my will!'

'If you're going to talk like that, I'm sure we don't want to keep you at all.' The voice is stern, like that of a very cross nanny. 'I'll have to go and speak to Mr. Buxton.'

A minute later, a masked face is leaning over me. I can tell from its eyebrows that it is not pleased.

'Now then, Miss Robinson. What's all this about?' Mr. Buxton's voice is that of a busy man who is not used to having his day disrupted.

'I want to go home.'

'You mean you've changed your mind?'

'I suppose so.'

'Well, have you or haven't you? We haven't got all day. We talked this through —' up to a point — 'and you had counselling —' five minutes with a rather bored nurse — 'You've had every chance to think about your decision.'

My eyes fill with sudden tears. Oh, where is the smooth-talking, kindly Mr. Buxton of three days ago? What has happened to the gentle fatherly figure who "understood how hard these decisions are" and who offered me his support, whatever I decided? I didn't need him then, when I felt strong and determined and grown up. I need him now, when I am confused and unhappy and vulnerable. But that Mr. Buxton seems to have been left behind in his consulting rooms, together with his smart charcoal suit and spotted bow tie, and the peaceful watercolours of lakes and fields and woods on his dove grey walls.

'Well,' he continues, 'if you've changed your mind, then that's that. But of course, there will still be a fee to pay. Someone else could have had your appointment.'

His voice goes on, calm but reproachful, but I am no longer listening. I imagine my little seahorse/rabbit drifting away from its window and snuggling back into my womb, where it belongs. There is the ghost of a smile on its round featureless face, but the smile is grateful rather than smug.

'Your partner is waiting for you,' a nurse tells me, as she helps me dress and collect up my things.

'He's not my partner,' I tell her, emerging from the changing room.

'No,' says Mikey, who loves this kind of situation. 'I bat for the other side. Can't you tell?' He minces towards us, holding out his hand for my bag. 'What made you change your mind?'

'Not you, if that's what you were hoping,' I tell him, rather unkindly.

'I was hoping nothing of the sort.'

'No. I'm sorry.'

'That's all right.' He pats my knee.

'I just — well, I just couldn't do it. That's all.' I hesitate. Should I tell him about my vision (if that's what it was)? No. Better not. 'You were right. I hadn't really thought about it. I hadn't thought what it *meant*. And when I was lying there waiting, I knew it wasn't for me. Maybe for other people, but not me.' I feel unutterably tired, and just want to get home.

'You won't regret it,' Mikey says.

'It's okay for you to say that.'

'I mean it. And I'll be godfather.'

'Oh, would you?' Mikey would make the perfect godfather, and for a moment, I feel quite excited.

'I'd be honoured. I shall buy it lovely presents for its birthday, and take it to the zoo.'

I have a vivid mental picture of Mikey, hand-in-hand with my seahorse/rabbit, looking at camels and monkeys, and I giggle.

'I don't know what they gave you in there, but we need to get you home,' Mikey says sternly. 'Before you become hysterical.'

CHAPTER TWO

A week later — how things can change in a week! — things are not looking good. Since Mikey has managed to persuade me that the gap year must at the very least be postponed, I'm sure that with a bit of luck I'll be able to stay on in my flat, take on some violin students and make some kind of living for myself and the seahorse/rabbit. The Norwegians will understand. After all, this is an emergency.

The Norwegians do not understand. Neither are they nearly as nice as they once appeared to be. They tell me, in impeccable English, that they have rights. I have signed a piece of paper. My flat — *my* flat — is theirs for the next twelve months.

I explain that something has cropped up, and I have nowhere to live. The Norwegians tell me that they also have nowhere to live, and that where I go is my problem. They are moving in on Tuesday. Please can I make sure that the flat is clean and that I have defrosted the fridge.

Couldn't they make it Thursday? I plead. Even Wednesday? No, they could not. The Norwegians have made nice tidy little Norwegian plans, and these plans include moving into my flat on Tuesday. It appears that they are still prepared to do right by the cat, for that is in the agreement, but not to give me even one extra day, which is not. If I ever get to go on my gap year, I shall definitely not visit Norway.

In desperation, I ring round my friends. Surely someone, somewhere, will take me in, if only temporarily. I shan't take up much room, and I promise to play my violin very quietly. I can even busk until I get some students. But everyone seems to have some reason or other why they can't put me up. Of those who might have been able to have me, two friends are having marriage problems, one is moving house herself, and another is about to have twins. As for my orchestra friends, they are mostly poor and living out of suitcases, quite apart from worrying about their jobs. It would be churlish to add to their problems.

Feeling desperate, and very sick (the morning sickness has now kicked in with a vengeance) I reach the bottom of the accommodation barrel and find my parents. I shall go and spend the night with them, and break my news to them as gently as I can. It's not something I am looking forward to.

Now, perhaps I should explain about my parents. They are nice enough people, but they are stuck in a nineteen fifties time warp; an age when nice girls got sensible jobs (teaching, nursing, social work; that kind of thing) and then married, had children and led unblemished lives of dedicated domesticity, after which they went trustingly to their reward (they are also strict Evangelical Christians). My parents are undoubtedly good people — they give generously to charity, help (if not actually love) their neighbours, and lead generally blameless lives — but there is a lack of joy or humour which I find very hard to take in all but the smallest of doses. My childhood was bordered by strict rules and narrow boundaries, and as an only child, I was very lonely. Sundays — for me, the worst day of the week — were days of mind-numbing boredom, involving two church services, plus Sunday school, and I was not permitted to do anything which could be called work. Occasionally, I would sneak out with my violin and practise in the garden shed, but if I was discovered, retribution inevitably followed, so it was rarely worth the bother. Sundays apart, approved friends were allowed to come and play, but not stay overnight, and parties were regarded with suspicion. I remember our annual holiday (a fortnight by the sea) as dull and uneventful; a cliché of Englishness, with my father dozing in a deckchair and my mother doing nothing more adventurous than paddling discreetly at the water's edge. We ate cheese and tomato sandwiches and Penguin biscuits and drank stewed tea from a flask, and I was allowed the occasional ice-cream, but on the whole, I would infinitely have preferred to have stayed at home.

I am a mystery and a disappointment to my parents. My musical ability is something they seem to see as a threat rather than a gift; the pursuit of hedonism rather than of art. True, they paid for my violin lessons, clapped politely at school concerts, and when I was awarded a place at music college, they didn't exactly stand in my way, but neither did they encourage me.

'Are you sure, Ruth? Are you quite sure?' my mother said, when I finally left to take up my place. 'It seems such a — such a *risky* way of life.'

'Quite sure, Mum. I've never been surer of anything.'

For how could I explain to her that music was my world, my life? That music flowed in and through me like the air I breathed, and that I could no more live without it than I could transform myself into the kind of daughter they wanted?

No-one understood where my musical ability had come from. My mother played the piano a little, and my father sang (badly) in the church choir, but otherwise, apart from light music on the radio and Songs of Praise on a Sunday evening, music played no part in their lives. A great uncle was reputed to have been a reasonably proficient cellist, but by the time I knew him he was old and arthritic, his days of music-making long gone, together, sadly, with his memory.

But worse by far than the idea of living at home is the prospect of telling my mother and father that I am pregnant. For a start, I know for a fact that they still believe me to be a virgin; they have always taken my word for it that when I go on holiday with a boyfriend we sleep in separate rooms, and that any man staying at my flat occupies the sofa. My fall from grace is going to come as a dreadful and most unexpected blow.

In the event, their reaction is worse than even I could have anticipated. I have read about people turning pale, but I have never actually seen it happen until now.

'Oh, Ruth! How could you do this to us?' My mother exclaims, after a few moments' horrified silence.

'Mum I haven't done anything to *you*. If I've done anything to anyone, I've done it to *myself*.'

'What will people think?' My father joins in. He has not gone pale so much as red. He does a good line in what he sees as righteous indignation, citing Jesus among the moneylenders as his example, and he is very, very angry. 'Have you thought about our reputation?'

'This isn't about you.' I too am getting angry. 'It's about *me*! Do you think it's easy for me? Do you think this is what I want?'

'I don't know —'

'No. You don't know. You know very little about me, as it happens. You've never really understood me, have you?'

'We've tried —'

'No, you haven't! You've never tried. You've never tried to *know* me. My music, my friends, *my* way of life — all of it. You treat me like a — like some kind of foreigner!'

'What on earth can you mean?' My mother seems to be recovering herself. 'We've given you everything you need. We've cared for you, loved you —'

'Have you? Have you really? Isn't loving someone all about accepting them for what they are? Years ago, you created a mould, and you've been trying to fit me into it ever since. But it doesn't work that way. I know I'm a disappointment to you, and I'm sorry about that. Believe me, at the moment I'm a disappointment in myself. But there have been so many times when I've needed you — needed your support — and you haven't really been there for me.' I know I'm being unfair, but having got going, I'm finding it hard to stop. All the anger and disappointment over the years seem to be coming to the surface in an unstoppable tide. 'I am who I am, Mum. I try — as you do — to live my life as best I can. But I'm different. Different from you. Can't you understand that?'

'Oh, we understand that all right. You're most certainly different from us.' It's my father's turn. 'We understand that in spite of every opportunity, in spite of a good Christian upbringing, you can go and behave like this. It seems we've been wasting our time all these years.'

'Dad, I'm thirty-six years old! You finished bringing me up years ago. What I do now is my responsibility, not yours. Besides, it's the *twenty-first century*. Things have changed. You mightn't like it, and of course you're entitled to your opinion, but nowadays there's no stigma to being a single parent. No-one *minds* anymore.'

'Well, they should mind. They should. It's a disgrace, that's what it is. I've always said so, haven't I, Rosemary?' (turning to my mother). 'But I never thought anything like that would happen in this family. I never thought it would happen to us.'

'*It's not happening to you!*' I yell. 'It's happening to me! My baby, my life, *my disgrace*, if you like. All mine. You don't have to have any part in any of it if you don't want to. You can disown me if it makes you feel better.'

'There's no need to be silly, Ruth. Of course we wouldn't disown you,' my father says. 'We'd never disown our own flesh and blood.'

The argument rumbles on, to the exhaustion of all parties and the benefit of none. The divide between my mother and father and myself is as wide and as deep as it ever was, and it seems that none of us has the power to change it. There have been occasions when I would genuinely have liked to be what my parents want me to be — for a start, it would have made life so much easier — but with the best will in the world, it could never happen. Years ago, I even wondered whether I could have been adopted, but my dark hair and eyes (my mother's) and stubborn chin (my father's) have long since put paid to that theory.

'Well, I'll go and put the cocoa on,' says my mother, when everything has been said that could possibly be said, and I have enraged them even further by refusing to divulge the paternity of my unborn child. 'Would you like some, Ruth?'

Cocoa? At a time like this? But for my parents, their routine is a lifeline second only to God, and it would take more than their daughter's downfall to prise them away from their bedtime cocoa (half milk, half water, with one teaspoon of sugar).

'No thanks. I think I'll just go to bed.'

I give them each a dutiful kiss, and go upstairs. Maybe Mum and Dad will see things differently in the morning.

CHAPTER THREE

Breakfast at my parents' house is a dignified affair. Not for them the dripping tea bag dredged from its mug, the burnt toast eaten on the hoof. The table is laid with a white cloth, tea is brewed under its smug knitted tea cosy, and neat triangles of toast stand to attention in the toast rack (my parents are the only people I know who own — never mind use — a toast rack). Most families that I know come down to breakfast in relays and grab what they can find, but in my parents' house we are expected to breakfast together (cereal and toast on weekdays; a boiled egg on Sundays). As I unfold my table napkin and wait for my father to say Grace, I imagine days or even weeks of these breakfasts and this atmosphere (today, an enveloping thick grey blanket of reproach and disappointment), and resolve to find myself somewhere to rent as soon as possible. True, it would be convenient to stay on here, at least until I have enough students to enable me to make some kind of living, but it would be at the expense of the sanity of all concerned, and hence simply not worth it.

But in the event, the decision is taken out of my hands.

'Your mother and I have been talking.' My father butters a small piece of toast, looks at it for a moment as though it might be in some way unclean, and then puts it carefully in his mouth. 'Haven't we, Rosemary?'

My mother nods unhappily.

'And we think it best if you don't stay here.'

'What?' This is something I hadn't expected.

'Yes.' He continues, as though I hadn't spoken. 'Best all round, really.'

'How can it be best?'

'We have our reputation to think of. It may sound old-fashioned to you, Ruth, but the church is very important to us. People respect us. Look up to us, really. Your mother teaches at Sunday School; I still preach the occasional sermon. And then there's the Youth Group. What kind of example would it be if we had — if you — well, if people saw you living here?'

'You mean — you mean you're actually throwing me out? Like a Victorian father? Is that what you're doing?' I am incredulous. I didn't think even *my* father would do anything like this. I am fortunate indeed that he's not a Victorian father, for if he were, no doubt it would be the workhouse for me.

'Well of course we're not. We can't throw you out if you don't live here, can we, even if we wanted to? We're just saying that it would be — awkward if you lived here at the moment. We're asking you to find somewhere else to live.'

'But surely I can stay just until I find somewhere to rent? After all, I don't look pregnant. No-one need even know. And I'll pay my way.'

'It's not about money, and it doesn't matter that you don't look — well that things aren't obvious. People will ask questions, and we'll have to tell them the truth.' Ah. The truth. Far be it for me to stand between my parents and the truth. 'I'm sorry Ruth, but there it is. This problem is not of our making.'

Looking at my father, his heightened colour, the way he is stabbing at the butter, I can see that he's still very angry, and I know what all this is about. I'm being punished. I've been a bad girl, and this is my punishment; to be banished from my parents' house. It may well have something to do with what people think, but it's got a lot more to do with how my father feels.

'And the baby? Are you going to disown that, too?'

'We'll have to cross that bridge when we come to it.' My father holds out his cup for more tea.

'My baby isn't a bridge to be crossed! It's a human being; your grandchild. None of this is the baby's fault. "Suffer the little children —"'

'Please don't try quoting Holy Scripture at me, Ruth. Especially out of context. As I said, we'll have to see.'

'What about you, Mum? What do you think?' I see my last straw, and grasp at it, but without much hope.

'I'll do as your father says, naturally.' My mother looks uncomfortable. 'It's probably best that you go away. Just for the time being.'

'And the baby?'

'As your father says, we'll — we'll see.'

I am filled with sudden rage. Hitherto, I have dwelt on my situation rather than my unborn child. My baby, to whom I have yet to give more than a few glancing thoughts since my visit to the clinic, suddenly becomes enormously important, and for the first time in my life, I feel I am not alone in my battle against my parents. I now have someone on my side. It may be tiny — still at the seahorse/rabbit stage — but it is mine. We are a unit. My baby and I against the world. I feel empowered and protective and — yes — even maternal, and I smile, in spite of myself.

'This is nothing to smile about, Ruth.' My father dabs at his mouth with his napkin, and then folds it neatly and replaces it by his plate. 'However, just to let you know that we want to do right by you, we have an idea.' He pauses to make sure he has my full attention. 'We thought you might go and stay with the twins for a while.'

'Applegarth's huge. They've got plenty of room,' my mother offers.

'Yes,' my father continues. 'I'm sure they'll be glad to help.'

Why on earth should they be glad to help, when my parents are not? But it's an interesting idea.

My uncles — my mother's elder brothers — are identical twins. Eric and Silas have remained unmarried, and have always lived together, occupying their parents' old home, a huge rambling Victorian house in the middle of nowhere, together with a menagerie of animals and a chaotic amount of clutter. They are gentle eccentrics, devoted to each other and all living things. They have never, as far as I know, made any kind of living, existing comfortably on their inheritance (my grandfather made a lot of money in wool. Needless to say, my mother has divided most of her share between her church and various charities) and such food as they are able to grow themselves. Although nowadays I see little of them, I have always been fond of my uncles, seeing them as the most human (and by far the most interesting) members of my small family. However, I'm not at all sure how they will feel about having their disgraced niece thrust upon them at short notice.

'When were you thinking of asking them?' I say, folding my own napkin in an attempt at insouciance.

'I already have.'

'But it's only half-past eight!'

'They get up early to do the milking.'

Milking? 'And?'

'They're thinking about it.'

'I'll bet they are.'

'They're ringing back at eleven.'

'And you didn't think to consult me before you did this?'

'No. I didn't.' My father stands up, drawing a line under our conversation. 'Since you are so irresponsible, and that is putting it kindly, as to get yourself into this — situation, you can't really expect us to trust you to make a wise decision as to what to do next.'

By half-past eleven, the expected phone call still hasn't come, and my father is pacing up and down the hallway looking at his watch and tutting like the White Rabbit (although of course, unlike the White Rabbit, it is not he who is late). My father hates unpunctuality, and although he has known his brothers-in-law all these years, and they have never considered time-keeping to be a priority, their behaviour never fails to surprise and infuriate him. Accepting other people's modi vivendi is not my father's forte.

It is twelve fifteen when the expected phone call finally comes, and my father shuts himself in his study to take it. Lingering in the hallway outside, I hear little of what he says, although such words as 'shame' and 'waste' and 'disappointment' give me a taster of the tone of the conversation. When he finally emerges, it is not without an air of triumph.

'All settled,' he says, his relief palpable. 'They're happy to have you for as long as you need to stay, and there are no neighbours to gossip, so they have nothing to worry about on that score.'

Eric and Silas have always seemed to me to be the last people on earth to worry about gossiping neighbours — or anything else, come to that — but I let it pass.

'I don't believe they're churchgoers,' he continues (he knows very well that they aren't), 'but I'm afraid that can't be helped.'

'What a shame,' I murmur.

'What was that?'

'Nothing.'

Two days later, I have finished clearing out my flat, packed up those things I want to take with me, said a fond (and unreciprocated) farewell to the cat, and am on my way. The Norwegian invasion is just hours away, and I don't trust myself not to tell my new tenants all the things which are still fuelling my indignation. Suffice it to say that I hope the boiler makes its early-morning howling noise (an occasional but very alarming occurrence) and that the neighbours throw one of their more boisterous parties. After their uncharitable behaviour, the Norwegians do not deserve any consideration from me.

My father drives me the forty miles to my uncles' house (I sold my car to help pay for the gap year). It is not a comfortable journey.

'So,' he says, after about fifteen minutes. 'What plans do you have?'

Plans? I haven't had time to plan anything, and my parents seem to have taken care of my immediate future.

'Well…' I hesitate.

'I thought as much.' The car veers violently to the left. 'You haven't given this much thought, have you, Ruth?'

'I need time,' I tell him lamely.

'You don't have much time.'

'I believe these things take about nine months,' I say, in a weak attempt at humour.

'Not funny, Ruth.'

'I never said this was funny.' My father's not the only one feeling angry. 'But it's happening. It's a done deal. I'm having a baby. Lots of people have babies, and yes —' because I know what's coming next — 'many of them are out of wedlock. Dad, it's not the end of the world!'

'It's the end of your reputation.'

I can't believe I'm hearing this. 'I'm a *violinist*, Dad. My reputation — such as it is — rests on my musicianship, not on my virginity!'

'Well, really!' The car screeches to a halt at traffic lights.

'I'm only saying what you're thinking.'

'I think we'd better end this conversation before one of us says something we regret,' my father says, as the car starts up again.

And I think he's right. Looking at his stern profile, his neat collar and tie, his highly polished shoes, I find it hard to believe that this man is related to me at all. Parents are supposed to love their children unconditionally, but where my father is concerned, this seems to be very much in doubt.

Will I love the seahorse/rabbit unconditionally? Only time will tell.

CHAPTER FOUR

We arrive at my uncles' house late, since my father has had to stop the car twice for me to be sick. My copious vomiting took place without comment from either of us, which was probably just as well. My father has never felt comfortable with illness of any sort.

It always amazes me that the open countryside inhabited by my uncles can exist so near to relative civilisation. It is hard to believe that these sweeping hills and wide skies and lack of any neighbouring habitation are a mere three miles from a respectably-sized town, but so it is. The house itself, known as Applegarth, is situated at the end of a rutted track. It is well-built but run down, with a wilderness of a garden adjoining a paddock occupied by what look like several broken-down agricultural implements and a variety of livestock. Eric and Silas call it a smallholding. My father calls it a mess.

'What would their dear mother say?' he mutters, as he drives cautiously round bumps and through puddles. 'She was so fond of this place.'

'I expect Silas and Eric are fond of it too, in their own way,' I say.

'In that case, they should look after it.' My father stops the car so that I can get out to open a gate, causing several chickens to run squawking into the bushes. 'I suppose that's what you call free range,' he remarks. 'It's a wonder they don't get stolen or run over.'

'They're more likely to be eaten by foxes here,' I point out.

When we reach the house, Eric and Silas greet us on the doorstep.

'Welcome, welcome!' They kiss me and shake my father's hand. 'Come on in. We've made soup.'

'Ruth probably won't have any. She's got an upset tummy.' Dad has obviously decided not to acknowledge the cause of my indisposition. He scrapes something unpleasant off his foot and then, after hesitating for a moment, takes of his shoes.

'I'm fine now, and I'd love some soup.' I deposit my case in the entrance hall, and look around me. Coats and caps hang several deep on hooks inside the porch and some, having given up the unequal struggle, are lying in heaps on the floor. There are wellingtons and walking boots, sticks and galoshes, and even a rifle propped up casually in a corner.

'Is that safe?' Dad asks, indicating the rifle.

Silas (or Eric) laughs.

'It's not loaded. And we only use it for rabbits.'

'How comforting,' my father mutters.

In the large kitchen, every available surface is occupied with clutter. There are unwashed pots and pans, old newspapers, tools, clothes and bags of animal feed. A large dog is sleeping by the very grimy Aga and two cats are curled up on the draining board. Something which could be soup is bubbling away in a kind of cauldron. It smells interesting.

'I'll have to say no to the soup,' Dad says, backing away nervously, as though he might catch something. 'Rosemary's expecting me home.'

I know this isn't true since today is Mum's day for doing meals-on-wheels, and I'm surprised. Dad glances at me, and there is mute appeal in his eyes. He looks out of place and rather pathetic standing there in his stockinged feet, and I take pity on him.

'Yes. She did tell him to hurry home,' I say. My father looks at me suspiciously, and I smile at him. 'Mustn't keep her waiting.'

'No. No. I'd best be going.' He hesitates for a moment. 'Thank you for having Ruth.'

'No problem.' Eric/Silas grins. 'It'll be nice to have a woman around the house.'

I walk back down the track to open the gate for Dad, and he winds down the car window.

'We've done the right thing.' He hesitates. 'Take care of yourself.' This is the nearest he gets to an endearment, and I'm touched.

'You too. Love to Mum.'

As I watch the car making its cautious way back down the track, its usually gleaming paintwork now generously splattered with mud, there's a lump in my throat. Poor Dad. While I find his attitude hard to understand, I am his only child, and such a disappointment. Perhaps families are destined to disappoint each other; all those expectations, those cosy stereotypes, those impossible hopes. How can anyone begin to live up to them?

Back at the house, Eric and Silas are glowing with good cheer. They introduce me to the dog ('we call him Mr. Darcy') who opens one eye in acknowledgement, and the cats, who appear to have no names and who ignore me. The soup ('Nettle and rabbit. Don't worry — it's much nicer than it sounds!') is delicious, and I have two helpings. Afterwards, we eat early cherries from the garden and slices of rather stale bought cake, after which I'm taken on a tour of the grounds.

When I was a child, I used to stay regularly with my uncles. My parents' apparent ambivalence about the domestic set-up was countered by their need to pursue various church activities for which at the time I was considered too young. Since my only grandparent lived two hundred miles away, Eric and Silas were the obvious people to have me, and they were always more than willing. They didn't put themselves out or make any special arrangements; they simply absorbed me into their way of life, treating me as an equal (and expecting me to behave like one), and I adored my visits. Free from any injunctions to keep my clothes clean, wash my hands before meals or go to bed at seven, I ran wild (as much as one little girl on her own can do such a thing). I helped with the animals and the cooking, I climbed trees and paddled in the stream and rode the one-eared donkey in the orchard before returning home with a healthy suntan, scratched and bruised knees, filthy clothes and a head full of interesting information. I may not have known where human babies came from, but the provenance of piglets and kittens was no longer a mystery to me, and if my parents objected, there wasn't much they could do about it. As I once heard Silas explaining to my mother, 'The child sees what she sees. It's only nature.' And they had to put up with it.

The grounds surrounding the house haven't changed much, although the quantity of livestock has increased. There is now a pretty doe-eyed jersey cow, two goats, some sheep and several pigs, including a very pregnant sow called Sarah. There are also at least two dozen chickens, four beehives, some ducks in a very muddy pond and a peacock. The peacock just arrived one day, I'm told, and is ornamental rather than useful. A selection of ramshackle sheds and outhouses provides shelter for the animals, and while their surroundings leave a lot to be desired, the animals look well-cared-for.

The garden is a riot of flowers, weeds and vegetables, all coexisting in apparent harmony. There are cabbages and nettles, broad beans and nasturtiums, roses and tomatoes. The white bells of bindweed can be seen flourishing among the raspberry canes and there are fruit trees and brambles in the orchard.

'It's like the *Secret Garden*,' I say, as I pick my way across this jungle while Mr. Darcy, who has woken up and joined us, chases exciting smells among the bushes.

'Yes. It's a bit of a mess,' admits Silas/Eric.

'Oh, I didn't mean that.'

'We don't mind.' He pauses, 'One day we'll have to sort it all out, but we always seem to run out of time.' They both laugh, as though at some private joke. 'I hope you'll be able to put up with us.'

Back at the house, I feel a bit like Snow White entering the home of the seven dwarfs. She didn't *have* to do all that cleaning (although with a merry band of Disney rabbits and birds to help her she seemed to make light work of it), but I can understand why she did it. I have a feeling that I shall have Snow White urges before I've been here long, for while I'm not a particularity tidy person, I think I'll find it hard to live in this chaos. Will my uncles mind if I do a bit of tidying up? I'll leave it a day or two before I suggest it, since I would hate to do anything which implied criticism of my hosts.

'Oh, you've brought your violin with you!' Eric/Silas cries, as we re-enter the house. 'How lovely! We've got an old piano, but we can't play it. Silly, isn't it? But you will play for us, won't you, Ruth? We love a bit of live music, don't we, Silas?'

His brother nods and smiles, and I notice again the slight dimple in Silas's chin and the way Eric's eyebrows sweep up at the corners, and resolve to make sure that from now on I shall remember who is who.

When I am shown up to my room, I find that I have been promoted from the tiny attic bedroom I slept in as a child to the big front bedroom, with its heavy dark furniture, worn carpet and ancient brocade curtains.

'We were born in this room,' Silas tells me, as he brings up my suitcase. 'In this bed, actually.'

The bed is huge, with an elaborately carved headboard and great sunken mattress which dips alarmingly in the middle. It has probably hosted the couplings and births of whole generations of my mother's family, and I try to look enthusiastic.

'We thought about buying a new mattress,' he adds. 'But I'm told the this one's quite cosy.'

The mattress certainly turns out to be cosy, for once I've given up any attempt to climb out of the dip in its middle, I find that it envelops me like a womb, and that first night I sleep better than I have in weeks. It occurs to me that it would have been very hard to keep up even the most severe of marital disputes if the protagonists had to retire to this bed afterwards, because close — not to say intimate — physical contact must be unavoidable if both parties were to get any sleep. Maybe all beds should be like this, in the interests of domestic harmony.

When I awake the next morning to the sounds of birdsong and the insistent crowing of a cockerel, I wonder whether I shall ever have someone to roll into a dip with me; someone to cuddle up to at night and laugh (or cry) at the day's happenings; someone to share my life, and be a father to the baby. Even Snow White got her man in the end, and with very little effort on her own part. I, however, am unlikely to find myself a prince (or anyone else, come to that) so long as I remain hidden away in this outpost of civilisation.

I determine that at the earliest opportunity, I shall start looking for a more permanent place to live.

CHAPTER FIVE

When I come down to breakfast, I find that my uncles have already eaten, and I am invited to help myself to 'whatever takes my fancy'. At the moment, nothing much takes my fancy, especially as the idea of trying to find something edible amid the chaos is more than a little daunting (Eric and Silas appear to have breakfasted on the remains of the soup).

'Goat's milk,' they advise, when I explain about the morning sickness. 'It never fails.' *How on earth do they know?* Silas pours me a generous glassful.

The milk is obviously fresh as it's still warm, and as I struggle to swallow it, I wonder why the thought of milk warmed by a goat is so much less appetising than milk warmed in a saucepan. It's somehow too intimate, like sitting on a seat recently occupied — and warmed — by a stranger. Maybe it would help if I were acquainted with the goat in question. But wherever the milk came from, it appears to do the trick, for while I'm still not up to breakfasting on soup, I eat two slices of bread and honey and some of yesterday's cherries.

'There.' Eric and Silas regard me with satisfaction, as though I am a child who has finished up her greens. 'Not so bad, was it?'

I agree that it wasn't bad at all, and also have to admit that I'm feeling considerably better.

'Would you mind if I did a bit of — well just a little bit of tidying up?' I ask them. 'Just so that I feel I'm doing my bit.'

My uncles roar with laughter.

'She wants to sort us out,' says Eric. 'That'll be a job and a half. But help yourself if it makes you feel better. Just don't throw anything away.'

I try not to feel offended. After all, my offer was intended to help them, not me. I shan't be staying for long, so it's not my problem if my uncles want to live like pigs.

Three hours later, I am totally exhausted, but I've found (and cleaned) most of the kitchen floor and some of the surfaces. Things which are obviously rubbish are piled in one corner; things which may be of some use in another. The washing machine (Snow White may have found her prince, but she didn't have a washing machine) is whirring merrily away, and the cats have gone out into the garden to sulk as I've removed their cosy little nest of old jumpers from the draining board. When Eric and Silas come in for lunch, I have found bread and cheese and pickled onions, and laid them out nicely on the table.

'Goodness.' Eric goes over to the sink to wash his hands. 'You didn't have to do this, you know. You're our guest. Besides,' he adds, 'Blossom comes in tomorrow.'

'Blossom?'

'Our cleaner. She doesn't really do much housework —' I'll say she doesn't — 'but she needs the money, and she's magic with the animals. That's really why we keep her on. We couldn't manage them all and the garden on our own.'

Blossom. I imagine a lovely cuddly woman with a wide welcoming bosom and equally wide smile; someone I can talk to, and maybe even someone who will know something about babies, even if she's lacking in the cleaning skills department. I look forward very much to meeting her.

How wrong can I be.

When Blossom arrives next morning, she turns out to be a small skinny woman, with eyes like darting black beads in a face taut with disapproval.

'What's all this, then?' she asks, before she's even taken off her coat.

'Our niece has come to stay,' Eric/Silas tells her (I still can't tell them apart from behind). 'Blossom, meet Ruth.' He disappears into the garden, leaving Blossom and me to get acquainted.

'How do you do?' I hold out my hand.

'Hmm.' Blossom ignores the hand. 'How long you staying?'

'I don't really know. Not long. Just until I find somewhere else.'

'What have you done to the kitchen?'

'I tidied it a bit.'

'Hmm. They won't like that.'

'They didn't seem to mind. And at least we can find everything now.'

'They could find everything before. That's the way they like it. I don't interfere in the kitchen.' (Now there's a surprise.)

I try to overcome the temptation to ask what it is that Blossom actually does, and wait to see. She fetches brooms and brushes from under the stairs, and clears a kind of runway through the clutter in the hall, thus giving easier access to the stairs, various doorways and the downstairs lavatory. The coats and caps she leaves where they've fallen, presumably because she isn't tall enough to replace them. She shakes the doormat, polishes the door knocker, and then repairs to the kitchen to make herself some coffee. She doesn't offer me any, so I make my own.

'Where do you live?' I try to make conversation.

'Village.' Blossom slurps her coffee, and adds more sugar.

'How do you get here?'

'Bike.'

'And — your husband?' I notice her wedding ring. 'What does he do?'

'Dead.' Blossom wipes her mouth on the back of her hand.

'Oh, I'm so sorry.'

'Don't be. Miserable bugger, he was.' There is the ghost of a smile. 'Well rid of him.'

'And — children?'

'Son. And daughter. No better than she ought to be.'

'Oh dear.' I suspect that in Blossom's book that probably applies to me, too. 'Do you see much of her?'

'Nope.' Blossom gets up from the table and deposits her empty coffee cup in the sink. I notice that she doesn't wash it up. She picks up a bucket and opens the back door. 'You expecting?' She turns, her hand still on the door handle.

'Yes. Yes, I am. How did you know?'

'Can always tell.' Blossom looks pleased. 'Knack,' she explains.

'Oh. That's — handy.'

'Can tell you the sex, and all.'

'Really?'

'Stand up and turn around.'

I do as I'm told.

'Boy,' she says, and goes out into the garden, banging the door shut behind her.

'How did you get on with our Blossom?' Silas asks when they come in at lunch time.

'I don't think she likes me very much.'

'Don't mind Blossom. She doesn't like anybody.' He laughs at my expression. 'You're wondering why we have her, aren't you?'

'Well, it did cross my mind.'

'Sometimes we ask ourselves, don't we, Eric? I suppose she's become a habit. And she doesn't chatter or expect us to look after her.'

'How on earth did she come to be called Blossom?'

'She doesn't look much like a Blossom, does she? I believe it was one of those baptismal mix-ups — a deaf priest, a mother who didn't like to point out a mistake. Something like that. Her father was Welsh and wanted her to be Blodwyn, but it wasn't to be.'

'She told me my baby would be a boy.'

'Then that's what it'll be. Blossom's always right.'

'How does she do it?'

'I've no idea.' Silas cuts himself a slice of bread. 'She says it's a knack, but she won't tell us her secret. She does it with piglets, too.'

'What, all the sexes?'

'No, but she can tell us how many there will be. She says Sarah's going to have thirteen, and she'll be right, give or take a piglet or two. Thirteen's a lot, though, poor old girl. Sarah's getting on a bit. We may have to drown a couple.' He butters his bread. 'I might stuff one,' he adds thoughtfully.

'*Stuff* one?'

'It's a hobby.'

'Stuffing things?'

'Taxidermy. I'm teaching myself,' he says, through a mouthful of bread and cheese. 'I've never done a piglet. It might be rather fun.'

'Do you — stuff things too?' I turn to Uncle Eric.

'Good Lord, no. Not my kind of thing at all.'

'No. He's much too busy disproving Noah's Ark,' Silas says.

'Noah's Ark?' This conversation is becoming weirder by the minute.

'The Creationist theory,' Eric says. 'Noah and the Ark; animals going in two by two; all that. Some people actually believe it. Every word of it. So I'm doing some research.'

'Gosh. My parents wouldn't approve of that at all,' I laugh. 'Do they know?'

'Certainly they know. And you're right. They don't approve. But there's not a lot they can do about it. Your father asked me "not to pollute your mind with my theories", but I said you were old enough to decide for yourself.'

'To be honest, I haven't given it a lot of thought,' I said. 'Well, not since I left home, anyway.'

'Well, do. It's very interesting. I started with Adam and Eve. That bit was quite easy.'

'And the talking serpent and the apple?'

'Ah.' He looks pleased. 'It wasn't an apple, for a start. You have another look at your Bible. There's no mention of an apple. Just the fruit of the tree of knowledge. It could have been an apricot, or a fig.' He cuts himself more bread, and offers me a slice. 'I like the idea of mankind being seduced with a fig. They're so much more sexy than apples. We've got a marvellous fig tree in the garden.' He takes a large bite of his bread. 'There's nothing to say it was an apple.'

'I never thought of that.'

'People don't. And then there's Jonah and the whale. If you look at the physiology of whales, you'll find that Jonah would have been destroyed by its gastric juices within twenty minutes, and that's if he could find any air to breathe while it was happening. He certainly wouldn't have lived to tell the tale.'

'And Noah?'

'Don't get him started,' Silas says, peeling a rather mottled banana. It reminds me of the hide of a giraffe, but maybe that's the Noah's Ark effect.

'Noah's the best of all,' Eric says. 'At least, it's the most interesting — and by far the most impossible. Just imagine. All those creatures, all that fodder, all the extra animals to feed to the carnivores, all that mucking out. Quite impossible. Pass the pickle, please. But I'm having this discussion with a — friend, and he wants proof, so I'm going to prove it.'

'How?'

'Research, Ruth. Research. He wants facts and figures; he shall have facts and figures.' He smiles at me. 'You can help if you like.'

'I think I'd better not. My parents would never speak to me again. Besides,' I add carefully, 'isn't it possible that someone's done all this before.'

'Done all what before?'

'Disproving the Ark. You could look it up on the internet and find out.'

'We haven't got a computer. Besides, I'd like to do it myself. It makes it more fun. Computers may be wonderful things, but I think they tend to make people lazy.'

'You're probably right.'

We finish our lunch, and I make coffee.

'Give us a tune, then,' says Silas.

'What, now?'

'Why not?'

So I get out my violin and tune it, after which I play them a Bach gavotte. I realise with dismay how out of practice I am, and resolve to put in at least two hours every day. My uncles, however, are delighted, and applaud enthusiastically.

'That was wonderful, Ruth,' Silas says. 'I'd no idea you were so good.'

'Not good enough, though.' I put my violin back in its case. 'You have to be exceptional to get anywhere these days. I didn't even manage to stay in the back desk of the seconds in a third-rate orchestra.'

'But you love it.' It was a statement rather than a question.

'Oh, yes!'

'Well then. How many people find — and do — something they really love? That's what matters.'

'What about you? Do you both love what you do?'

My uncles exchange glances and smile.

'I think we've always been happy,' Eric says. 'We love this place, our animals, our way of life. We're very lucky to be able to do it.'

'And you — get on?' For a moment, I wonder if I have overstepped the mark, but they don't seem to mind.

'We have the odd tiff, but yes. We get on,' Silas says. 'We've never been apart for more than a night or two. People think we're odd, but then I suppose we *are* a bit odd. It doesn't bother us what other people think.'

'I don't think it's odd. I think it's wonderful,' I say with feeling. And I mean it. To live your whole life with someone you really care about, doing something you love; what more could anyone ask?

'What will you do now, Ruth? What are your plans?' Eric asks.

Oh dear, that question again.

'I don't know. I still haven't got used to the idea of the baby yet. But I won't be under your feet for long, I promise. I'm going to start looking for a place to rent, and then get myself some pupils and start teaching.'

'But we thought you were staying here,' Silas says.

'Is that what Dad said?'

'Well, no. But we assumed you would. As you've nowhere else at the moment.'

'I couldn't possibly —'

'Why not? We've got plenty of room, and you're more than welcome.'

'But my teaching. What about that?'

'There must be people around here who need violin lessons. You could advertise.'

'Well ... you're awfully kind.' It's certainly an attractive proposition. On the other hand, I don't want to take advantage of my uncles' generosity, and with no mobile signal or internet (the house is surrounded by thick woodland) I would be terribly cut off. 'Can I think about it? In the meantime, I'll pay my way, and do what I can to help.'

'You think about it, then. No hurry.' Silas picks up his plate and dumps it in the sink. 'But you're very welcome.'

So it would seem. And if this particular Snow White has to wait a little longer for her prince, then the way I'm feeling at the moment, it seems a small price to pay.

CHAPTER SIX

As the weeks go by, I find it hard to believe that I have ever lived anywhere else. It seems to have taken me no time at all to settle into my uncles' way of life, and almost for the first time in my life, I feel truly at home. Even Blossom seems to have accepted me as a member of the household, and while never overtly friendly, she condescends to exchange a few brief words — Blossom's words are nothing if not brief — when she stops for coffee. Of course, I loved living in my flat, but (unless you count the cat) I have never had anyone to share it with, and living with Eric and Silas has made me realise how much I enjoy being with other people. Even at home with my parents before I went to college, I used to feel lonely, because there was so much about me that they didn't understand.

'You've already practised once today, Ruth,' my father would say. 'Do you really need to start doing it again? That bit sounds fine to me.'

'I just need to get this phrase right. Just ten more minutes.'

'If you must,' he would sigh. 'But I can't see what another ten minutes is going to do.'

'Dad, you've never liked Bach, so you wouldn't understand.' He wasn't the only one to get irritated.

'Too many notes. Far too many notes.' And thus, arguably the greatest composer who has ever lived would be briskly dismissed.

Here, I feel accepted and perhaps even loved, and my music is actively encouraged. My uncles have no expectations of me, nor I of them, and in the relaxed, comfortable atmosphere of this shambolic house, I believe that I am becoming a nicer person. I enjoy having to consider the needs of other people; to fit in with their routine and their way of life. I like helping around the house and garden, and I have accomplished skills which I could never have dreamed of. Not only have I learnt that it's perfectly possible to live happily without wanting to tidy up every five minutes, but more usefully, I have learnt to milk a goat, skin a rabbit, and make delicious soups and salads out of ingredients I have hardly ever seen, never mind eaten, before. As for the internet, which I once thought essential to any kind of civilised life, I no longer give it a thought.

'Just stretch out your middle finger,' Eric says now. He is measuring my forearm with a rather frayed tape measure. 'By the way, you're looking much better.'

'Am I?'

'Oh, yes. You looked thin and pasty when you arrived. The fresh air must be doing you good.' He puts down his tape measure. 'I make it nineteen inches. Damn. It does seem to vary. Silas's was twenty inches. And it's meant to be eighteen. Eighteen doesn't seem very much somehow.'

'Very much for what?'

'A cubit. It's supposed to be the measurement from the elbow to the middle finger. Noah measured his Ark in cubits.'

'Why?'

'God told him to.'

'God doesn't seem a measuring sort of person, somehow.'

'I know what you mean.' Eric makes notes on a piece of paper and refers to a battered Bible on the kitchen table. 'I think I'll make it eighteen inches, which fits nicely into yards. It's much easier if we can do it all in yards.'

'We?'

'Well you're helping now, aren't you?' He makes more notes. 'The Ark had to be three hundred cubits long, so that's — let me see — about a hundred and fifty yards. Not nearly big enough. I can see that already.'

'Wouldn't it have been easier for you to start with the size of the Ark, rather than the habits of the animals?' I ask, for Eric has already done some research into the diets of a variety of species.

'In a way, but the animals are more fun, so I shall alternate.'

'But if you can see straight away that there isn't room for them all, then that's that, isn't it?'

'Oh, Ruth, Ruth. We have to *prove* it. We need *proof.* Facts, figures, that sort of thing. We've got to show him *exactly* why there isn't enough room. And we've not just got to tell him how impossible it all is, but how ridiculously impossible. We've got to blow him — and his Ark — right out of the water.'

'Oh. I see.' I hesitate for a moment. 'Who's "he"?'

'Well, as a matter of fact, it's your father.'

'Oh dear.'

'Yes. Oh dear indeed. But I didn't know you were coming when we had our — discussion, and I don't want to give up on it now.'

'I can see that.'

'If you don't mind, that is.'

'Oh, I don't mind at all. Dad thrives on this sort of thing. And if anyone can provide a successful argument in favour of all those animals living in even the tiniest of Arks, then my father's your man.' I watch Eric leafing through his Bible, making notes and chewing his pen. 'Is it all right if I go now?'

'My dear girl, of course you may go. I've kept you too long as it is.'

He does have a point, for quite apart from routine house and animal duties, I've already spent an hour on the phone to the zoo trying to get answers to a list of questions ranging from whether zebras eat hay to the gestation of the rhinoceros. The man at the zoo is kindly and tries to be helpful, but he is bewildered by all these questions.

Upstairs in my room I get out my violin and warm up with some scales. I'm not doing nearly enough practice, but without a goal, much of the incentive has gone. I shall never be a soloist, and now not even an orchestral player. So what (or who) am I playing for? My pupils? Even if I manage to get any, they won't mind whether I practise or not. My public? Unless you count Eric and Silas, I don't have a public. Myself? As I watch my fingers moving up and down the fingerboard, I remember practising these same scales for the exams I did as a schoolgirl, and my parents even then questioning the point of all that work. And I can see my small, furious, foot-stamping self trying to explain.

'It's for me, me, me! *I do it for me*! I love it. Can't you see? Can't you *hear*?'

But all they could see was that their daughter was wasting hours of her time (and quite a lot of their money) doing something which they saw as trivial; a hobby perhaps, a pastime, but certainly not a career which would earn any kind of living. They didn't like the sound that I made and couldn't fathom why I enjoyed making it, and even the high marks I achieved in my examinations (invariably with distinction) failed to impress them. It was as though I had burst into another language and expected them to converse with me. It was totally foreign. *I* was totally foreign.

I put down my violin and sit on the bed. Over the years, I have devoted thousands of hours to my music; hours of scales and exercises, of pieces and studies, and once, gloriously, a violin concerto with a full orchestra. They have been hours of toil, hours of weeping frustration but also moments of indescribable pleasure. Am I going let all that hard work go, just because I have no immediate goal? I told Eric and Silas that I love what I do, and of course it's true. But like every love affair, my relationship with the violin is going through a rough patch; a period when it might be tempting to let it go, at least for the time being. Is that what I really want?

I pick up my violin again, running my fingers along the grain of the wood, feeling the smooth polished back, stroking its familiar ribs and surfaces. I bought it with money left to me by a godfather, and it's old and quite valuable. Far better musicians than I shall ever be have owned and played this instrument, and I often wonder who they were, how they came by it and how or why they passed it on. Maybe one day it will pass into the hands of my own child — my son, if Blossom is to be believed — and he in his turn will give it to one of his own children. Or perhaps he will sell it. Who knows? But one thing is certain. So long as I can play, I will. Not for audiences or even for money, but, as I told my parents all those years ago, for me. Because I have to. Because, quite simply, it's what I do. I stand up and riffle through a pile of music, then I take out one of the Bach unaccompanied suites and painstakingly start to practise the first movement.

'Any phone calls?' I ask, when much later I come downstairs for a cup of tea (with no mobile signal, I'm now dependent on the landline).

'None for you,' Silas says. 'Don't worry. Someone will reply sooner or later.'

'But I really need to be earning now,' I say, getting milk from the fridge. 'I put the advertisement in ten days ago.'

'It's probably the wrong time of year, August. Who needs violin lessons in August?'

He's right, of course. I should wait until the autumn and the new school year. But my savings are beginning to dip alarmingly, and while I've long since said goodbye to any hope of a gap year, I'm going to need things for the baby. Eric and Silas have said they're quite happy to keep me, but I value my independence. Besides, it would be wrong to take advantage of their generosity.

'I shall busk,' I say, pouring boiling water onto a teabag. 'I shall take my fiddle and go into town and busk. Someone's bound to throw me a coin or two if I wait long enough. I did it on the underground when I was at college. There were three of us together at the bottom of the escalator at Paddington Station.' Oh, happy days. 'I did all my Christmas shopping one year out of my busking money.'

'What on earth did your parents say?' Silas asks. He is examining his latest acquisition, a dead squirrel, on the draining board.

'I didn't tell them. They would have been appalled. They would have considered it to be no better than begging, and the thought of their daughter begging on the streets would probably have finished them off. But they got very nice presents that year.'

'Good for you.' Silas sounds abstracted. 'This is amazing.' Tenderly, he lifts up his squirrel to show us. The squirrel doesn't look dead at all, merely surprised (as well it might). 'Not a mark on it, and it must have been knocked down. I shall enjoy doing this.'

'Is busking legal?' Eric asks.

'I'm not sure now. I'll phone the police and find out.'

Ten minutes later, after an interesting telephone conversation with someone official at the police station, I have discovered that busking comes under the Vagrancy Act of 1824.

'Very old-fashioned. Like being hanged for sheep-stealing,' I tell Eric (Silas is still preoccupied with his squirrel).

'Does that mean you can't do it?'

'Apparently I might get by on the grounds of providing "street entertainment".'

'Does that mean you have to have an audition?'

'Heavens, no. But I might be inspected by someone from the Town Centre Management Team, whatever that is. I could take Mr. Darcy with me, if you'll let me. People might be able to resist me, but they'll melt when Mr. Darcy does that reproachful thing with his eyebrows.'

'Are you fit to hang around street corners with your violin?'

'Perfectly fit,' I assure him. 'It'll do me good.'

'And the baby?'

'It'll do him good, too. It's never too early to start enjoying music.'

And while I've no idea whether the seahorse/rabbit has developed anything in the way of ears yet, I'm sure that I'm right. Bring on the council official and the generous, music-loving punters. I can't wait to begin.

CHAPTER SEVEN

But before I can commence my busking career, there are medical matters to attend to.

Now I have to admit that I had entirely forgotten that pregnancy is regarded not so much as a natural event as a medical condition fraught with hazards, and that a variety of investigations is required to ensure that nothing awful is happening either to me or to the baby. It was Silas who pointed this out, and Silas who took me down to his GP in his muddy Land Rover. All was apparently well, as far as the GP could tell, but I am apparently due for my twelve-week scan.

'Yes. It's important to check up on things after the first trimester,' says Silas, who has been looking things up in his book.

'Trimester?' I ask him.

'Three months. It comes from the Latin,' he informs me kindly. 'Pregnancy is divided into three trimesters, and each one —'

'Yes. Thank you, Silas, I think I get the message. And the doctor gave me this booklet. I can read up all about it.'

'My book has diagrams.'

'So has the booklet.' I pat his hand. 'Don't worry. From now on, I promise to keep myself fully informed.'

I have never had a scan before, and envisage myself being posted into one of those long dark tubes for a lonely and claustrophobic half-hour or so, but apparently this scan is quite a simple procedure, and I will be able to see what's going on. Now I come to think of it, I have seen friends coming hot foot from their scans, proudly sporting grainy and (to me) completely unrecognisable photos of their unborn offspring. Hitherto, I haven't paid much attention to scans, but now that it's time for mine, I'm rather looking forward to it.

So, it would seem, are my uncles.

'I think I should go with her,' Silas says.

'What, you mean come in and watch?' I'm not at all sure about this.

'Why not? I believe people are allowed to bring their partners, and you don't seem to have one, so I can come instead. To support you,' he adds, although even I can see that he is desperate to see what goes on (Silas is a terrible hypochondriac, and has a hypochondriac's fascination for all things medical).

'What about me?' Eric says. 'I think I should come too.'

'Of course you can come too,' Silas says. 'We'll all go. And we can go to the pub for lunch afterwards.'

'Hang on a minute,' I say, with the uncomfortable feeling that my life is being taken over. 'This is my scan. I think I should be the one to decide.'

'You need us to drive you there,' Silas reminds me.

'That's not fair!'

'No. Of course it's not. All right then. We'll take you and wait in the car while you have it.'

'With nothing to do,' says Eric.

'And these things always take hours.'

They both look at me, their expressions so ridiculously alike that I can't help laughing.

'Okay. You can both come. But don't blame me if you're not allowed in. And please don't do anything embarrassing.'

'Would we!'

'I don't know, but I have a feeling you might.'

But while it has occurred to me that one or other of my uncles might well do or say something inappropriate, I never considered the affect that two identical elderly men would have on a waiting-room full of pregnant women and their partners. There are the double-takes, the whispers, the covert and then not-so-covert glances, and the outright stares. I wish with all my heart that Eric and Silas could have worn different clothes, or brushed their hair in different ways, or at the very least, sat at opposite ends of the room. But no. Here they sit, side by side, reading old copies of *Woman's Own* and pausing occasionally to beam at their audience.

'Do you have to do this?' I whisper to Eric, who is sitting beside me.

'Do what?'

'Play to the gallery.'

'I can't think what you mean.' He turns to the problem page ("Is my partner two-timing me?" screams one of the by-lines. More than likely, I think sourly).

'You know exactly what I mean.'

'My dear Ruth, if you're born with a handicap, you might as well make the most of it.'

'It's not a handicap!'

'No, but it might as well be, the way people behave.'

'I believe you're enjoying this.'

'And why not? You must admit, it's quite fun.'

'I would have thought you'd have tired of this kind of fun by now.'

'That's what our mother used to say. But you don't have to sit next to us if you don't want to.'

'You're behaving like children!'

'She said that, too.'

Fortunately, at this stage a white-coated young woman calls out my name.

'Miss Robinson? Come this way, please.'

Eric and Silas put down their magazines and get up to follow me (more stares and whispers. Maybe everyone thinks I have twin sugar daddies).

'Are you coming with her?' The young woman looks dubious. 'Both of you?'

'We'll explain when we get inside,' says Silas. 'You see,' he continues, once the door is closed behind us, 'we're her next of kin.'

'What, both of you?' she says again.

'Oh yes. Can't you see the family likeness?' (There is no family likeness.)

'Well, maybe just one of you, if that's all right with Miss Robinson.'

I open my mouth to say something, but Eric gets in first.

'It's a bit delicate,' he says. 'You see, until six months ago, we were conjoined twins. Up until then, obviously we'd never been apart at all. And we — well, we still find it hard.' I swear I can see tears in his eyes.

'You were operated on that recently? Surely it would have been in the papers. That sort of thing is always on the news.' Apparently my white-coated friend isn't as gullible as Eric had hoped. She looks them both up and down, as though searching for a missing leg or the remains of a shared arm.

'Oh, no newspapers.' Eric looks shocked. 'Patient confidentiality,' he says, tapping the side of his nose. 'We managed to keep it out of the papers. We still walk with a limp,' he adds.

The technician is obviously baffled. As for me, I'm furious. They have obviously done this before. This routine is well-rehearsed, and they've got it off so pat and their delivery is so convincing that in the end they are both given permission to stay. Eric winks at me, but I ignore him. They may be able to get round officialdom, but it's going to take a lot more to get round me. I consider sending them both out, but I feel suddenly vulnerable, and would appreciate their company even if I haven't yet forgiven them.

But all our differences — if that's what they were — are forgotten when the scan begins and we see the monitor.

'Look.' The technician points to the screen. 'There's its heart beating, and there's an arm ... and another. See there. It's kicking.'

'Oh. *Oh.*' Silas appears lost for words. He and Eric exclaim and coo over this tiny apparition as though they alone are responsible for its existence, while I am totally bemused. True, there is something swimming about on the screen, bobbing gently in its warm watery world, and I can just about see a beating heart and something which might be a limb. But they are the heart and the limb of a seahorse/rabbit, not anything which resembles a human being, and I feel cheated and disappointed. It is like showing people round one's own haunted house, and being the only one who can't see the ghost.

'Oh, Ruth! You are *so* clever! Look what you've made!' Eric says, and this time there are real tears in his eyes. 'I don't think I've ever seen anything so wonderful.'

'Is it all right? There's nothing wrong with it, is there?' Silas asks.

'Everything looks fine, although of course she'll have another scan at twenty weeks.'

'Excuse me,' I hear myself say, 'but this is my baby.'

'Of course.' The technician smiles at me. 'I'm so sorry. But your friends —'

'Uncles,' says Silas.

'Uncles, then. Well they like to talk, don't they?'

'They certainly do,' I say with feeling. But of course, now that I have her attention, I can't think of anything else to say.

'Boy or girl?' Silas ventures.

'Boy of course,' Eric says.

'Would you both please shut up,' I say, and turn back to the technician. 'Can you tell the sex yet?'

'Blossom's never wrong —'

'*Please*, Eric. Can you tell?'

'Too early, I'm afraid. But of course your Blossom has a fifty percent chance of being right.'

'She wouldn't like to hear you say that,' mutters Silas.

Just for a moment, lying on this couch with my tummy exposed and these two mad people having their discussions across my body, I think of Amos; big, generous Amos, with his beard and his smile and his kind brown eyes, and for a moment, wish that he was sitting here beside me, holding my hand. But he doesn't even know about the baby. What kind of a father would he have made? I wish I had been able to tell him about it, for now I know that we really have managed to create a new life, even if to me at least it bears little resemblance to a human being, I feel as though I have stolen something from him, albeit unwittingly. His genes, his input, are alive and apparently well inside my body. All those weeks ago, I exercised my "right to choose" when I decided to go ahead with my pregnancy, but Amos was never given any choice at all.

In the pub over a ploughman's and best bitter (Eric and Silas) and a cheese and tomato sandwich and orange juice (me) my uncles get out their grainy photos (they managed to persuade the technician to give them one each) and coo over them together, pointing out to each other features which even I know to be invisible at this early stage. But they apologise to me very charmingly for their behaviour in the hospital, and of course, I forgive them.

For quite apart from anything else, where on earth would I be without them?

PART II: AUTUMN

By the end of the second trimester, the foetus weighs between one and a half and two pounds. The skin has thickened, the lungs are developing well and hearing and taste have developed. Eyebrows and eyelashes are present, although the eyes themselves may still be closed. A pattern of sleeping and waking may be detected, and there are periods of intense activity. At this stage, the baby has an 85% chance of survival outside the womb.

CHAPTER EIGHT

It is decided that my day for busking should be Wednesday.

Wednesday is the day for the farmers' market in town, and Eric and Silas have a small stall. They sell goats' milk, eggs, honey and rich Jersey cream, plus such vegetables as have managed to fight their way to maturity through the forests of weeds (there are always many more than I would have thought possible, but Eric and Silas claim to have green fingers). I am quite sure that the cream and the milk are illegal, since the sale of such things is controlled by a raft of agricultural legislation, but Eric and Silas have little regard for rules and regulations, and they have loyal customers who can be depended upon to keep their mouths shut. Their 'dairy produce' is kept, literally, under the counter, the surface of which is spread with respectably legitimate vegetables and flowers. Legal considerations apart, their stall is always popular, although I suspect that this owes as much to the novelty of their twinned state as the quality of their produce.

Wednesday, say Eric and Silas, is the best day for me to start as they can give me a lift, and also keep an eye on me. I think this seems a very sensible idea. Blossom, however, does not.

'What do you need looking after for? Big girl like you.' This is a long sentence by Blossom's standards and I detect more than a hint of jealousy.

'Well, I think it's very kind of them,' I tell her.

'No better than begging,' she sniffs, wielding her broom as it ploughs its familiar route through the week's clutter to the bottom of the staircase.

'I'm not begging, Blossom. I'm earning money. I'm playing for people. And if they like it, they'll pay. If not, they don't have to. It's perfectly straightforward.'

'My Kaz wouldn't.' Kaz is the errant daughter.

'Well, Kaz probably can't play the violin.'

'Wouldn't want to. Nasty scratchy thing.' Blossom takes a swipe at a spider's web.

'Well, thanks, Blossom.'

Blossom's bony backside quivers with disapproval as she stops to pick up some piece of debris.

'Don't you like music, Blossom?' I ask her.

'Nope.' She drops her findings into her dustpan.

'None at all?'

'Nope.'

'Would you like some coffee?'

'Make me own.' She squashes a spider and sweeps up the remains.

'You do that.'

Trying to talk to Blossom when she's in this kind of mood is pretty well impossible, but I refuse to let her dampen my spirits. I feel cheerful, and for the first time in three months, I feel well. Gone is the nausea and the exhaustion, and my tummy is still relatively flat, even if there is someone living inside it. Besides, I am looking forward to playing to an audience again, even if it's only an audience of short-tempered shoppers, and I have my music planned. There will be some Bach, for the more discerning, and some jolly Irish pieces I once played with a dance band, and a virtuoso little number by Paganini (almost impossible, but will anyone notice the mistakes?).

It is the day before my street début, and I am playing through my programme in the kitchen, where Eric is measuring out the plans for the Ark on huge sheets of graph paper, and Silas is finishing off his squirrel. The squirrel, once so squirrel-looking, now looks very dead and rather shapeless, and its tail refuses to stand up in the usual perky squirrel way.

'That sounds great,' says Silas, half-way through a piece, but I can tell he's not listening properly. He whistles through his teeth as he withdraws the stuffing from the squirrel's tail (wire wrapped in some kind of cotton) and unravels it. 'I shall have to start again,' he says. 'And squirrels are supposed to be easy.'

I decide not to say anything. I have never understood the point of taxidermy; of killing a perfect, beautiful animal and then taking hours and hours trying to make it look perfect and beautiful (and alive) again. Admittedly Silas doesn't do any killing — most of his specimens are found by the roadside, and only a minority of those are suitable, the remainder being squashed beyond recognition — but it still seems a pointless occupation. No doubt in the hands of an experienced taxidermist, the finished article might be considered very fine, but nothing dead, however well stuffed, can look as beautiful as it did when it was a living breathing creature.

And it's all such a palaver. There are the tools and the chemicals and the stuffing materials, not to mention the copious notes which Silas has made on his several visits to Nigel, the local expert, and which are now strewn around the kitchen. Silas's manual tells him that he should be able to do a squirrel from start to finish in a couple of days; Nigel, being kinder, says give it a week. So far, it's taken him nearly ten days, and all this work to produce something which looks like a cross between a guinea pig and a monkey.

I put down my violin.

'It looks very — fat,' I say, eyeing Silas's hapless victim.

The squirrel squints defiantly back at me through its new shiny glass eyes, its empty tail hanging limply at its side.

'Do you think so?' Silas pauses. 'It doesn't really look like a squirrel any more, does it?' he adds forlornly.

'Well...'

'It's a good effort,' Eric says, but even to me, his tone is ever so slightly patronising.

'Oh dear. Nigel said to beware of over-stuffing. He said that was the commonest beginner's mistake. But I thought a squirrel ought to be nice and plump. Bugger.' Silas runs his hands through his hair, and the nice plump squirrel/guinea pig/monkey topples over onto its side. 'Perhaps I should concentrate on the badger.'

Eric and I agree that this is an excellent idea, not least because the hide of the said badger has spent the last two days floating in a mixture of noxious chemicals in the only bathtub. Both Eric and I are longing to be able to use the bath (although I suspect that like me, Eric's not sure about using a receptacle which has recently played host to such a grisly occupant).

'The badger might be easier,' Silas says, cheering up a bit. 'A bit more to get hold of. The squirrel was very fiddly.'

'Very fiddly,' Eric and I agree.

'What shall I do with this?' Silas holds up his squirrel.

'Finish the tail, put it down to experience and give it to Blossom,' I suggest. Blossom has been quite complimentary about the squirrel and it's her birthday next week.

'Good idea.' Silas looks relieved. 'I could tie a ribbon round its neck and it might look quite festive.'

'Very festive.' I hesitate for a moment. 'If I play through the rest of my programme again, could you tell me what you think?'

'Sorry, Ruth. Yes, of course.' Silas puts aside his squirrel and sits down, folding his hands in his lap. 'Play on. I'm listening.'

This time, they both listen attentively, and as usual, applaud enthusiastically when I've finished. I'm not sure that my uncles are the most discerning of audiences, but no-one could say they aren't encouraging.

'Very good. Very good indeed,' Silas says. 'Isn't it amazing that a few pieces of cat gut and some horse hairs can make a sound like that.'

I can see that he's still in taxidermy mode, but he does have a point. I wonder, not for the first time who first decided to try this particular combination — wood, gut, horse hair — for music-making, and pay silent tribute to them. Whoever it was must have been a genius.

We all stop what we are doing, and start to get ready for market day tomorrow. Eric and Silas have to prepare the produce for their stall, and I must look out something suitable to wear. I'm not sure what the dress code is for street musicians, but respectable poverty seems safe and easy, so I settle for a pair of old but clean jeans and a Save the Dolphins tee shirt (after all, everyone loves dolphins, don't they?).

On Wednesday morning, I feel quite excited. At last I can take a bath (the badger is drying out in the kitchen; Eric kindly let me have the first go, but not before he'd scrubbed the bath thoroughly with disinfectant, muttering darkly about badgers and TB). Do I wear make-up? I decide not, but I have washed my hair and I tie it back in a neat ponytail. Mr. Darcy, who has settled himself comfortably in his usual place by the Aga, is not pleased to be disturbed, and has to be dragged out to the Land Rover, growling and complaining. It's a bit of a squeeze, what with the sacks of vegetables, the pots and jars of dairy produce and several buckets of early chrysanthemums, and I sit squashed between my uncles with my violin on my lap and Mr. Darcy lying across my feet. But physical discomfort apart, it's a beautiful morning, the sun is shining, and there should be plenty of punters. It seems a promising start.

When we arrive at our destination, Eric and Silas park me outside Boots, and go off to sort out their stall. I set out my music and tune my violin, placing its empty case invitingly open for any contributions. Mr. Darcy lies beside me looking appealing. He has that doggy knack of resting his chin on his front paws and raising his eyebrows one at a time, rolling his eyes tragically at passers-by. If my playing doesn't do the trick then Mr. Darcy's theatricals can hardly fail.

But I have forgotten how hard busking can be. It's not just the lack of eye contact or even the being ignored, but the way people take a kind of detour round the busker, leaving an arc of empty pavement in a relatively crowded street, as though it's contained by an invisible fence.

'You need some change.' Eric has returned to see how I'm getting on. 'Here.' He empties the contents of his pockets into the violin case, leaving a respectable collection of coins, some keys and a grubby handkerchief. He retrieves the handkerchief and the keys, and shakes the money about a bit. 'See if this'll do the trick.'

I thank him, and play on. Sure enough, the coins begin to arrive, among them some pounds and even one five-pound note, and my confidence grows. I smile as I play (I remember this used to help in my student days) and gradually I begin to enjoy myself. One or two people even stop to talk, to ask about the music and make a fuss of Mr. Darcy and generally pass the time of day. A man from the greengrocer's offers Mr. Darcy a bowl of water and an elderly woman buys me a sandwich in a plastic wrapper and says something about homelessness being a disgrace (do I look homeless?). The church clock strikes one o'clock, and I decide to take a break.

And it is then that I see Amos.

At first, I think it's just someone who resembles him, but this is unlikely. Amos is huge; six feet five and broad-shouldered, with a particular loping walk. He has his back to me, and must be twenty yards away, but when he turns, it is Amos's face, Amos's beard, Amos's familiar furrowed brow distantly reflected in a shop window. I feel a swell of joy and of longing, for while I haven't given a lot of thought to Amos over the past weeks, suddenly I know that of all my friends he is the one I most want to see. I want to see him and feel him and talk to him, and most of all, I want to tell him about the baby. He may not be pleased — in fact I'm pretty sure he won't be — but I've decided that he has a right to know and to choose whether or not he wants anything to do with his child.

Amos begins to move away again, and I am faced with a dilemma. He is walking fast, and I know that I'll never catch him up carrying a violin case and leading a reluctant dog. On the other hand, I can't leave them unattended. The violin is my most precious possession, and Mr. Darcy can't be depended upon not to go walkabout if I leave him. For a moment, I hesitate, and in that moment, Amos quite simply disappears. One minute he is striding away up the street, and the next, he has vanished. I decide to abandon my patch and go after him. Clutching my violin and dragging Mr. Darcy on his lead, I hurry up the street, peering into shops and down alleyways, vainly calling Amos's name, and attracting some very odd glances in the process. But to no avail. My mission is hopeless; Amos could be anywhere.

I lean against a wall to get my breath back, and tears roll down my cheeks; tears of disappointment and frustration and, yes, tears of longing. Because something lost acquires many times the value it had before, and it would seem that I have just succeeding in losing Amos. Of course, it's quite ridiculous to get so upset. When I awoke this morning, nothing could have been further from my mind than Amos, but now that I have seen him — so nearly missed him — it seems unbearable that I've been unable to speak to him.

And it was such a coincidence. What is Amos doing in this little market town? I believe that he has an aunt in Wiltshire, so he could be visiting her, but even then it's amazing that our paths should so nearly have crossed. I could look the aunt up, but of course I don't know her name. I could phone Amos, but he's recently changed his mobile number, and I don't even know where he's living at the moment, or where his parents live.

Suddenly the day has lost its shine. Even the fact that I have managed to earn nineteen pounds and forty-six pence (not at all bad for a morning's work) fails to lift my spirits. As I return to my post and share my sandwich with Mr. Darcy (who perks up considerably), I ponder my situation. And by the time the church clock strikes two, I have made a decision.

Somehow, I am going to find Amos.

CHAPTER NINE

Amos and I go back a long way, and our relationship has always been one of comfortable familiarity rather than of intimacy. We were at music college together, where we did all the usual student things; rag weeks, beer-drinking contests in The Bell, wild parties and giggling trials of a range of 'illegal substances'. When I think back to my student days, I wonder why anyone put up with us at all, but then maybe they too had enjoyed their years of reckless irresponsibility.

And of course, we played our music. The one thing we were all passionate about was our music, and we spent long hours in cramped practice rooms playing our scales and studies. Amos's preferred practice room was adjacent to mine, and to this day I believe that one of the reasons I have tended to play too loudly is all those hours trying to drown out the sound of the trombone. Once, only once, I knocked on his door and asked whether he could tone it down a bit.

'Tone it down?' Amos roared, appearing in the doorway like Moses delivering the ten commandments. '*Tone it down?* What do you think this is?' He waved his instrument at me. 'A bloody harmonica? You get back to your scraping and I'll do my blowing, and may the best man win.'

I never complained again, and soon afterwards we became friends.

We laughed at each other's jokes (Amos could be very funny) and cried on each other's shoulders. We advised each other on matters of the opposite sex and commiserated when things went wrong (which they frequently did). Amos weaned me off what he called 'silly drinks' (Bacardi and coke, snowballs and

Avocaat) and introduced me to the delights of Merrydown cider and best bitter, and we even briefly shared a flat. Free from the complications and pitfalls of sexual attraction (we had long since agreed that we were not each other's type), our friendship lasted happily throughout our student days, and while there have been times when we have had little contact with each other, we have always kept in touch.

Amos is far more gifted than I, and I envied him his musicianship, which he seemed to take for granted. While I had to work hard to pass my exams (college examinations were a far cry from the ones I had taken at school), Amos seemed to sail effortlessly through his. While I panicked and lost sleep, Amos remained calm and optimistic.

'It's just an exam,' he used to tell me. 'Just a silly little exam.' And he would clock up yet another distinction.

But the world outside college was tough and competitive, and when we left, Amos struggled as much as I did to find work. He did some jazz, and some teaching, and even spent a season playing in a dance band on a cruise liner, while I spent three years playing in a string quartet, which eventually folded through lack of funds (and, I suspect, talent), taught on the peripatetic circuit, and did a few more run of the mill jobs while 'resting' between musical engagements. My parents tempered their disappointment with quiet triumph. Hadn't they always said that my chosen career was a perilous one? I did my best to ignore them. In the meantime, Amos and I drifted apart.

It was the orchestra which brought us together again.

New, young and enthusiastic, for a while the orchestra did fairly well under its prize-winning youthful conductor (another colleague from college days). We worked hard, travelled long distances, and accepted pitiful salaries to make it work, but in an age when even the best orchestras struggle for money, it was doomed. After a difficult two years, our conductor reluctantly decided to down-size from full symphony orchestra to chamber group, and since there is no room in such an ensemble for second-rate violinists or even first-rate trombonists, Amos and I found ourselves out of a job.

At about the same time, Amos and his wife of eighteen months decided to divorce. I had always had my doubts about Annabelle (so, he told me afterwards, had Amos), but had never voiced them. Annabelle was willowy, glamorous and fiercely intelligent, but utterly unmusical. Having done everything she could to mould Amos into the kind of husband she wanted (if she didn't like beards, trombones, or beer, why on earth had she married him?), she found herself a sleekly pin-striped financial wizard and settled cosily with him into the gleaming chrome and glass and leather of his riverside flat. This didn't prevent her from trying to take Amos for everything she could get (he had practically nothing, so her efforts were fruitless), and the experience left Amos disillusioned and miserable.

'It's not that I still love her,' he confided to me in the pub, on that last evening together. 'It's just that everything's turned so *nasty*. She doesn't want me. I don't want her. Period. Why can't we leave it at that? What's wrong with "irretrievable breakdown"? Few things could be as irretrievably broken down as our marriage. But no. She wants to cite "unreasonable behaviour".'

'Hers or yours?'

'Mine of course.'

'What unreasonable behaviour?' I asked him.

'Good question.' Amos sipped his pint. 'Something about noisy practising and chicken curry and socks —'

'*Socks?*'

'I like brightly-coloured socks and she hates them. Hardly grounds for divorce.'

'Couldn't you have worn more subdued ones?' I ventured.

'Ruth, you're missing the point.'

'Which is?'

'The woman is totally unreasonable. Another beer?'

'Please.'

Amos pushed our empty glasses across the bar and nodded to the barman.

'No mention of her adultery, of course,' he continued. 'Now that *is* grounds for divorce. But, oh dear me, no. I'm not allowed to drag her precious "private life" through the divorce courts. So it's back to me and my curries and my socks.' He sighed. 'I never asked for all this unpleasantness, but it seems that it goes with the territory. I just want to get the whole thing sorted as painlessly as possible. Not a lot to ask, really.'

I agreed that it wasn't.

'Thank God we didn't have a kid.'

'Did she want one?'

'No. Annabelle's career means far too much to her.'

'And you? Did you want children?'

Amos gazed into this beer glass, as though searching for an answer.

'Yes. Yes, I think I did. Well, I did once, anyway. But marriage to Annabelle soon put paid to that.'

'But with the right person?' I persisted.

'Ah. The right person.' Amos grinned. 'With the right person it might be quite a different story. Yes. I think with the right person kids would be fun.'

How ironical that only a couple of hours after this conversation took place we were destined to make our own baby.

Of course, the baby would never have happened if Amos hadn't invited me back to his flat for coffee.

'You're too tipsy to go home yet,' he said, steering me out of the pub and down the road (I had driven up to see him). 'You need coffee, and plenty of it.'

But the coffee failed to make much impression, so Amos suggested that I should stay the night.

'You can have my bed and I'll sleep on the sofa,' he said.

His words hung in the air like something unfinished, as though waiting for one of us to deal with them. I looked at the sofa. It seemed about half the length of Amos; it was even too short for me. Amos caught my glance and smiled at me. I smiled back. I noticed for the first time that he had very sexy eyes (how come it had taken me so long?) and Amos obviously found something he rather liked about me. He took my hand.

'On the other hand...' he said.

'On the other hand,' I replied.

We both laughed, and suddenly, we were in each other's arms, tearing at each other's clothes like a pair of teenagers. Within minutes, the floor was littered with shirts, jeans, socks (including fluorescent green ones) and underwear, and we were hot-footing it to the bedroom.

Amos was a good lover; gentle and considerate as well as passionate; and despite the effects of several pints of beer (usually death to my libido) I found myself responding in a most satisfactory manner. Afterwards, I lay with my head on his chest thinking fondly of the importance of old friends and wondering why on earth we had never done this before.

'We make a good team, don't we?' Amos said, stroking my hair as we drifted towards sleep.

'Mm.'

'Shall we do this again some time?'

I laughed.

'Why not?'

I could feel him smiling in the darkness.

'Why not indeed.'

But when we parted company the next morning, we made no plans for a repeat performance. Amos had his divorce to worry about, together with the question of where the next pay cheque was coming from, and I had my gap year. But we promised to keep in touch, and meet up again "some time".

'I'll send you a postcard,' I told him as we kissed each other goodbye.

'Send me lots,' Amos said, 'One from every destination.'

'I'll do that,' I promised.

But we had both forgotten that Amos was having to move out of his flat and didn't yet know where he would be living, and neither of us could have known that the piece of paper upon which I'd written down his new mobile number had already been left behind, mislaid in a tumble of bedclothes.

By the time I reached my car that morning, I had already lost Amos.

CHAPTER TEN

For a few days following my near-encounter with Amos I feel low and dispirited. I am troubled by disturbing dreams, in one of which my poor little seahorse/rabbit (in my thoughts and dreams, it is still a seahorse/rabbit; never the grainy grey foetus of my scan) is weeping inconsolably. 'I want my daddy, I want my daddy,' it cries. I pick it up and try to hold it, but it slithers from my grasp and disappears, and when I awake, I too am weeping. In another dream it has packed up its belongings and is leaving.

'Where? Where are you going?' I cry.

'To find my father,' it tells me, bundling up its possessions in one of those red spotted handkerchiefs you read about in fairy stories. 'You are not enough.'

You are not enough. And of course, it is right. When I come to think about it, I have never been enough; not a good enough daughter, not a good enough violinist, and now apparently not a good enough mother, even though my baby is not yet born.

Is Amos the answer? Quite probably not, since however good a father he might prove to be, he wouldn't make up for my own shortcomings as a mother. And supposing he were to turn out to be a better parent than me; how would I cope with that? What would it be like to bear and give birth to a child, and then have someone else come along and cope better than I could? But even I know that parenthood is not a competition — rather, a team effort — and as Amos said all those months ago, he and I make a good team. I decide to put all thoughts of the baby on hold for the time being. After all, I have over five months before I have to meet my problems head on, as it were. Anything can happen in five months.

Fortunately, my broodings are interrupted by the activities of Sarah, that paragon of motherhood, for the following week she gives triumphant birth to her family of piglets.

This takes place in her shed, with Blossom in attendance and the rest of us admiring from a distance. Apparently Blossom is the only person Sarah will allow to come near her when she is farrowing, opening an evil piggy eye and giving a warning grunt when anyone else threatens to approach, and Blossom is in her element. As each slippery pink piglet arrives, Blossom wipes it with a handful of straw and hands it to its mother for approval, announcing the sex and condition as she goes.

'Male. Nice weight. Another male. Good. Little female. Bit weak.' And so on.

And they keep on coming. Nine, ten, eleven. The atmosphere in the shed becomes tense, for how will Blossom react if she has been wrong, and there are more or fewer than thirteen? Blossom hates being wrong (it does occasionally happen),and has been known to sulk for a week.

But no. On this occasion we are safe, for after the thirteenth piglet, Sarah gives a sigh and opens both eyes, and we all applaud. Thirteen it is. Once again, Blossom is vindicated.

To my surprise, there is no further talk of drowning and stuffing excess piglets, but there is one tiny runt, and Silas decides to rear it himself.

'Won't work,' says Blossom. 'Be dead by morning.'

The piglet is dead by morning. Poor Silas has stayed up with it all night, feeding it and rubbing its tiny body to try to keep it warm, but to no avail. When I come downstairs for breakfast, I find him in tears.

'Oh, Silas! Whatever's the matter?'

'My piglet. It died.'

'I'm so sorry.' I make him tea and give him a hug. 'Perhaps it was for the best.'

'Perhaps.' Silas blows his nose on an enormous handkerchief.

'And this sort of thing must have happened before.'

'Lots of times. But you never get used to it.'

'And — you can stuff it?'

'There is that.' He pauses. 'Except that it would be a bit like stuffing a friend.'

A friend? A newborn piglet he's known barely twelve hours, a *friend*? One of the many things about my uncles which never fails to amaze me is their emotional involvement with animals which are largely bred to be eaten. In the short time I have lived with them, they have personally despatched several chickens and ducks, and sent a pig and a beautiful billy kid to slaughter, and on every occasion Silas has shed tears. Once, when I asked him about it, he replied that it was 'the least he could do', but I think the real answer is that he simply can't help it. Eric's approach is more pragmatic, but he too hates killing things, although once the animals have been butchered into neat little meaty packages, both brothers are perfectly happy to eat them. I decide that if it is ever my misfortune to come back as a farm animal, I would like to belong to Eric and Silas. Their animals may end up in the pot, but they live happy lives and are much loved.

'Told you,' says Blossom, when she turns up after breakfast to check on her patients and Silas tells her his news.

'Careful what you say,' I whisper. 'He's really upset.'

'Silly old fool,' says Blossom cheerfully, disregarding the fact that the silly old fool has been extremely good to her, and moreover that Eric and Silas are probably the only people in the world who would employ her. 'Soon get over it.'

Meanwhile, Sarah and her brood are doing nicely. When I pay her a visit, I marvel at her serenity and at the neat little row of babies suckling from her recumbent form.

'How do they each find a teat like that?' I ask Blossom.

'Each have their own,' she says.

'And do they stick to it?'

'Course.' She eyes me pityingly. 'Don't know much about animals, do you?'

'Well, no. But I haven't had much opportunity.'

Blossom smirks.

'Not got the hands for it,' she tells me.

'What do you mean?'

'Look at them. Long white fingers.' She sniffs. 'Never make a farmer.'

I take my long white fingers — *violinist's* fingers, I console myself — and retreat to the house. I have learnt not to join battle with Blossom. She may be a woman of few words, but she has a knack of winning any argument.

The whole household seems cheered by the arrival of the piglets. Silas, having come to terms with his bereavement, is making his plans to restore his piglet to the glory it never achieved in its brief lifetime, and Eric has made progress on his ark.

'Noah's ark isn't just impossible, it's totally ridiculous,' he tells me. 'Even if you only have a few dozen species it quite simply wouldn't work. All that fodder. All that prey.'

'*Prey*?'

'Of course. Mice and rats for the foxes and things, small deer for the big cats. That sort of thing. Of course, mice and rats wouldn't be too much of a problem. I could breed those pretty fast.'

'You?'

'Well, Noah, then. But other bigger mammals have quite long gestation periods, and only produce one baby at a time. So there would need to be a lot of those, just to keep everything fed.'

'Couldn't you just breed thousands of mice?'

'I thought of that, but there still wouldn't be enough. So as I was saying, instead of simply disproving the Ark as measured in Noah's cubits, I've decided to prove how big it would really have to be, instead. At the moment, with the figures I've got, it would need to be about the size of the Isle of Wight.'

I picture the Isle of Wight as a neat lozenge off the south coast, but have no idea how big it is.

'As for the number of people needed to build it, not to mention the wood and the time it would take, I'm not even going to go into that.'

'Is all this effort really worth it?' I ask, amazed that a simple argument with my father can have given rise to all this industry. 'After all, you admit yourself it's only theory.'

'Never dismiss theory, Ruth. It can be quite fascinating.'

'He loves a project,' Silas tells me. 'With a bit of luck, this'll keep him amused for years.'

I look at Eric, bent over his graph paper.

'Perhaps you should have been an academic,' I tell him.

'I would love to have gone to university,' he agrees.

'Then why didn't you?'

My uncles exchange glances.

'It was me,' Silas says. 'I failed my exams. I spent some time in hospital with rheumatic fever, and never really caught up with my school work. I tried to make Eric go without me, but he wouldn't.'

'Do you regret it?'

But even before he replies, I know the answer. Quite apart from their mutual dependence, Eric and Silas are not the kind to waste time on regrets.

That afternoon, Mikey pays us an impromptu visit on his way down to the West Country. Mikey and I have been keeping in regular touch, and I am delighted to see him.

'I couldn't go past without calling in to see how you are,' he says, giving me a hug.

'You the father?' Blossom, who never bothers with introductions, is hovering with her empty dustpan.

'No. I'm gay. Can't you tell?' Mikey grins at her.

'Can't say as I can.'

'Ah well. Can't win 'em all.' He follows me through to the kitchen. 'What's up with her?' he asks me.

'Blossom? She doesn't like visitors. She barely tolerates me.'

Mikey laughs.

'And how's my godchild?'

'Fine. Everything's fine.'

'And the identical twin uncles? How are they?'

'Come and meet them.'

Eric and Silas take to Mikey immediately, and he to them, and after we've been out to visit Sarah and her family, we spend a companionable hour drinking gooseberry wine (apple juice for me), and chatting, while Blossom clatters mutinously up and down the hallway, eavesdropping. Mikey admires Silas's badger (which is nearly finished and stands in the corner of the kitchen looking like an ageing Master of Ceremonies), listens carefully to Eric's plans for his Ark without showing any signs of surprise, and generally makes himself agreeable. I had forgotten what delightful company Mikey can be.

'What's happened to your gap year?' I ask, as I see him out. This is something which still preys on my conscience.

'I've shelved it for the time being. Besides, I've — met someone.'

'Oh, Mikey! How exciting!'

'Yes. It's a bit soon to get excited, but I'm very happy.' He takes my hands in his. 'And you? What about you, Ruth? Are you happy?'

I hesitate.

'Yes. Yes, I am on the whole.'

'But?'

'But — well, I suppose I'd like someone, too.'

'Anyone in mind?'

'Well...'

'The baby's father perhaps?'

'Perhaps.'

'But you don't want to talk about him.'

'I do and I don't.' I sigh. 'It's — complicated.'

'Isn't it always?'

'I suppose so. But I've never had a baby with anyone before, so this is a first for me.'

'Do you — I mean, how do you feel about him?'

'I honestly don't know. We've been friends — good friends — for years, but the sex was a one-off. We've never had that kind of relationship. It was always straightforward.'

'And now it's not.'

'Now it's not even a relationship, because I have no idea where he is.'

'Oh dear.'

'Yes. So I haven't any chance of finding out how I feel about him, if that doesn't sound too weird.'

'Not weird at all.' Mikey pauses. 'But you'd like to find him?'

'Yes. Yes, I would. For a while, I wasn't sure, but now I really want to at least get in touch. To tell him about the baby.'

'Someone must know where he is,' Mikey says. 'Nowadays, it's very hard to just disappear.'

'You'd think so, wouldn't you? But Amos has a thing about technology and the internet. He has the most basic mobile, and hates computers. He never does social media. So he's not traceable the way most people are. Besides, he has a vengeful ex-wife who's after his assets, and he's trying to hide from her. He was never going to be easy to find.'

After Mikey has gone, I go up to my room and sit on my bed, gazing out of the window at the view of ramshackle sheds and untamed vegetation. Speaking to Mikey, I have finally put into words what I've been feeling for a while, especially since that fleeting glimpse in town: whatever it takes, I'm going to try to find Amos.

I reach for up my address book and start leafing through the pages. Someone somewhere must know where he is.

CHAPTER ELEVEN

In the course of the next two days, I manage to contact several people, none of whom have any idea where Amos might be. He has apparently mentioned another cruise ship, in which case he could be anywhere in the world, and also "taking time out", which could mean much the same.

But before I have time to be seriously disappointed at what is essentially non-news, something happens to turn our household completely upside-down, and take our minds off anything but the matter in question.

It is all Blossom's fault.

Perhaps I should first explain that Blossom is a fully paid-up rosary-carrying Roman Catholic. Not for Blossom the twice-yearly trip to the confessional; she apparently goes to both Mass and confession every week.

When Silas first told me I was completely stunned. 'Blossom in confession! I wonder what she says?'

'So do we.'

'Probably not a lot as she never admits she's in the wrong,' I say, rather unkindly.

'There is that.'

'But still.'

'As you say. But still.'

To be fair, Blossom doesn't talk about her faith much, but it does go some way to explain her attitude to my condition and to the behaviour of Kaz. I'm not at all sure what it is that Kaz does to incur her mother's disapproval, but knowing Catholics — and I know quite a few — it's almost certain to have something to do with sex. I have often thought that the

Catholic church would be much happier if there were no such thing as sex; if instead of having babies, people simply divided in two, like those micro-organisms we studied in biology at school. Clean, simple and straightforward, with no messy relationships or the 'impure' thoughts and deeds to which my Catholic friends felt obliged to confess.

I wonder why it is that Blossom's religion has apparently failed to make her a nicer person, but as Silas and Eric point out, she might be a lot worse without it. Silas, ever charitable, says she could well be trying very hard, and have found that this is as far as she can get on her spiritual journey, but I remain convinced that Blossom is a deeply unpleasant person, and that not much can be done to change her.

Be that as it may, it is a very different Blossom from the one we know (if not love) who bursts into the kitchen on a wet Monday morning after feeding the hens.

'Dear Lord! Oh, dear Lord!' she collapses into a chair.

'What? What's happened?' Eric asks her. 'Are you hurt?'

'Dear Lord. Oh, Holy Mother of God.' There are actual tears in Blossom's eyes.

Eric gives her a little shake.

'Come on, Blossom It can't be that bad.'

'Bad? Oh, not at all. Not bad. It's a miracle. A miracle in this house. Praise the Lord!'

'Miracle? What miracle?' Silas joins in.

'The blessed Virgin Mary. In the hen house.'

'You mean — you mean you've had a vision of some sort?' says Eric carefully. 'Is that it?'

'No, no. It's still there. Oh, praise the Lord!'

'Are you saying that the — the Blessed Virgin is in the hen house?'

'No. Yes. Well, sort of.'

'Tell us, Blossom. Take your time.'

'Oh, Holy Mother! Bless us all.' Blossom crosses herself. We all wait.

'She's there. She's right there on the wall. I saw her clear as I'm sitting here.'

'On the wall.' Silas repeats the words thoughtfully. 'Where — where exactly on the wall?'

'It's not her herself, of course —' well, there's a relief — 'but her image. With stars.'

'With stars. My goodness,' says Eric.

'Come. Come and see!' Blossom leaps to her feet and pulls at Silas's hand. 'All of you. Come and see.' She scurries out of the back door and leads the way along the muddy path to the hen house.

The hen house is the oldest of the outbuildings, having been made many years ago by my grandfather. Rather unusually, it is constructed from oak, since, as Eric explained to me, that was the only wood which was to hand at the time. Everyone has always agreed that a lovely piece of oak like that is wasted on the hens, but it has stood the test of time and of many generations of birds, and Eric and Silas are very attached to it. They used to hide in it as boys, and my poor mother once spent a terrifying afternoon in it when her brothers locked her in. It is, in short, a part of family history.

When we catch up with Blossom, her eyes are fixed on the side of the hen house and she appears to be in some kind of trance. I follow her gaze, but can see nothing unusual. I wonder whether you have to be a Catholic to see these things (after all, they always seem to appear to Catholics). Agnostics like myself probably don't stand a chance.

'There. There she is.' Blossom rouses herself and points. 'There. The Blessed Mother herself. And — stars.'

We all look. After a minute, Eric and Silas move closer.

'Well — I think I can see something,' Silas says, but he sounds a bit doubtful. He fishes in his pocket for his glasses, and peers more closely.

'What? What can you see?' Blossom cries.

'It could be — yes, it looks a bit like a figure.'

'Yes! Yes! Oh, thanks be to God!' Blossom clasps her hands and lifts her gaze heavenwards.

'Hang on a minute, Blossom. Maybe we need to calm down a bit.' Silas says. 'We mustn't jump to conclusions.'

'Can I have a look?' I ask.

Eric and Silas move back, and I join Blossom.

'There! There she is,' Blossom says, pointing a grubby finger.

Sure enough, in the grain of the wood it is possible to make out a vague figure; tall, wearing a kind of long garment, with what could be outstretched arms.

'I see what you mean,' I say.

'And stars? Can you see the stars?'

There is a circle of speckles round the head of the figure. Certainly, with a bit of imagination, they could be taken for stars.

'I think I can.'

'There! Told you! Even Ruth can see her.'

Even Ruth. Thank you, Blossom.

Eric and Silas carry out another inspection, and agree that there certainly is something that looks a bit like a figure.

'But even if it is a person, how can you tell who it is?' Eric asks.

Blossom looks at him pityingly.

'The Blessed Virgin likes to appear. That's what she *does*.'

This seems true enough. I have read of Virgins appearing, variously, on hillsides, in skyscapes and even on pieces of toast. Why not on the side of our hen house?

It is a strange phenomenon that once you see a figure or an object in a piece of wood (or in anything else, come to that) it becomes impossible not to see it. I myself have found the head of a fox and a lop-sided dragonfly in the knotted wood of the bathroom floor, and there are lots of faces in the floral material of the curtains in my old bedroom at home. Thus the curtains are no longer flowery, but peopled with little pink and white strangers, and whichever way I look at them, I can't turn them back into flowers.

So it is with Blossom's Virgin. Now that I have seen her, I can't *not* see her. She is there. And the more I look, the more Virgin-like she becomes. I fancy I see features, hair, even a veil. The outstretched arms bless, the tiny stars twinkle. I am almost convinced. I try looking away, and then looking back again, but she is still there. I can almost imagine that the garment she is wearing is blue. Whatever happens, from now on every time I look at the hen house, I too will see the Virgin Mary.

'I'll phone Father Vincent. That's what I'll do,' Blossom says.

'What can he do?' Eric asks.

'Father Vincent will *know*.'

Father Vincent doesn't know. When summoned to inspect Blossom's miracle, he seems far more concerned about the mud on the route to the hen house and the lively and unwelcome attentions of Mr. Darcy than the possibility of any miraculous manifestation.

'Hm.' He stands at the side of the hen house, looking thoughtful.

'Well? Well, Father?' Blossom is almost skipping up and down in her excitement. I am amazed, not only at Blossom's unusually high spirits and the sudden loosening of her tongue, but also by her demeanour. I have never seen Blossom showing respect for anyone before, but she is almost grovelling in her behaviour towards Father Vincent.

Father Vincent puts on his spectacles and leans down, rubbing his chin thoughtfully.

'Hm,' he says again.

We all wait. It would appear that without Father Vincent's imprimatur, Blossom's miracle isn't a miracle at all, so a lot hangs on his verdict.

'You can see her, can't you, Father? There she is, bless her, with all those little stars.'

'Well...'

'Yes? Yes, Father?'

'I suppose it could be. Just could be. But it's very hard to tell.'

'Perhaps we should pray, Father? Shall we pray?' Blossom makes as though to kneel down in the mud.

'No need to kneel,' Father Vincent says hastily. 'We can pray standing here quietly.'

Father Vincent and Blossom stand for several minutes with their eyes closed, and once again, we all wait. When they open their eyes, I find that I'm holding my breath, as though their verdict is of great importance.

'It is the Blessed Virgin, isn't it, Father? Please say it's her!' Blossom says.

'It's not for me to say whether or not this is the Blessed Virgin.' Discreetly, Father Vincent wipes his shoes on a clump of grass.

'Who then?' I ask, unable to contain my curiosity. 'Who decides what's real and what isn't?'

'We need a miracle or two,' says Father Vincent. 'Yes. That's what we need. A miracle.'

'What sort of miracle?'

'A healing, perhaps. Yes. A healing would certainly help.'

I cast about in my mind for someone who needs healing.

'Sarah has a touch of mastitis,' Eric suggests.

'Sarah?' Father Vincent turns to him.

'Our sow.'

'Oh, no. Not a sow. That would not be appropriate.' Father Vincent sighs. I feel that he is not really entering into the spirit of the occasion. 'I'll need to talk to the bishop.'

Even I know that people like bishops are busy and take a long time to answer things, and as we all troop back into the house for a cup of tea, I feel quite sorry for Blossom. After all, does it really matter whether her Virgin is real or not? If it makes Blossom happy (and it would seem that it does) then where's the harm?

But despite her disappointment, Blossom seems strangely cheery, stirring Father Vincent's tea for him and getting out chocolate biscuits and even cracking a little joke or two. I have the distinct feeling that Blossom is up to something, and I wonder what it can be.

In the event, I don't have long to wait.

CHAPTER TWELVE

Two days later, Blossom turns up with two strange men who, she says, wish to pay their respects to the Virgin. She will escort them herself, she tells us. She knows how busy we all are (Does she? Blossom never seems to have any idea what anyone else is doing, and cares even less, but we let it pass).

But on Friday, we find out who Blossom's friends were.

MIR-*EGG*-LE OF THE HEN HOUSE! screams the headline in the local paper, together with what appears to be a craftily airbrushed photograph of Blossom's Virgin and a half-page article about Blossom herself:

'*Local farmer, Blossom Edgar, has discovered what is believed to be a manifestation of the Blessed Virgin Mary ingrained in the wood of her hen house*', it begins.

Blossom a *farmer*? *Blossom's* hen house? Even Eric and Silas are indignant.

'Well, really, Blossom. This is a bit much. You could at least have asked us,' Eric says.

'You'd have said no.' Blossom is unrepentant.

'Yes. We almost certainly would have.'

'There you are, then.'

'But Blossom, this is our house and our hen house. We should be the ones to decide whether we want to be invaded by the press.'

'Should be pleased.' It would seem that Blossom has returned to monosyllabic mode.

'Well, we're not.'

'Too late,' says Blossom with a hint of triumph.

'Well, yes. In this case, it is too late. But please don't let anything like this happen again.'

'Oh well. I suppose there's no harm done,' Silas says later when Blossom has gone home. 'And she's had her moment of glory.'

But the following week, the first pilgrims arrive.

'Where is she? Where's the Blessed Virgin?' The two women who appear at the front door are breathless with excitement.

'I'm afraid this is private property,' I tell them. 'And in any case, the — the manifestation has to be verified. It may take some time.'

'Oh, we don't mind about that,' one of them assures me. 'We can make up our own minds.'

'But this is still private property. I'm afraid I can't invite you in. It's not my land. And the owners are out.' Eric and Silas have gone to the feed merchant in town.

'If it is the Blessed Virgin, then you have no right to keep her to yourself. This kind of thing belongs to everyone.' She turns to her companion. 'I'm right, aren't I?'

'Well...' The other woman looks uncertain.

'Of course I am,' she continues. 'It'll be round the back. We don't need to trouble you, and we won't be any bother. Just ignore us.'

And before I have time to think of a reply, she has taken her companion's arm and led her round the back of the house towards the outbuildings. They look harmless enough, and as it's pouring with rain, I decide to leave them to it, although I keep a watchful eye from the kitchen window.

When Eric and Silas return, I tell them about our visitors.

'Probably just a one-off,' says Silas. 'I don't expect we'll be bothered again.'

But how wrong can you be. The next day, there are two small parties, and the day after that, four. Blossom, who has had two days off, is delighted when we tell her what's been happening.

'A shrine,' she says ecstatically. 'A shrine in our own garden!'

'No, in *our* garden, Blossom,' Eric says. 'We've already told you, this is our garden, not yours. And the hen house is ours too. You have no right to invite all these strangers round as though you own the place. It really is too much!'

I have never seen either of my uncles angry before, but obviously the very real threat posed to their privacy is having its effect.

'Didn't invite them,' says Blossom mutinously. 'Just came.'

'Yes, because of that stupid article in the paper. Blossom, you knew this would happen, didn't you?'

'Might have.'

'Of course you did. I have a good mind to take the hen house to pieces and destroy that panel. I can always make another.'

'Can't do that. It's holy. It's a *shrine*.'

'Just you watch me.'

'Your dad's hen house? Turn in his grave.'

'He'd get over it.'

Eric and Blossom glare at each other for a moment, then Blossom appears to change tack.

'I'll sort it out. See to the visitors. Won't know they're there.'

'I don't know.' Eric looks doubtful, as well he might. 'They'll disturb the animals. And then there's the security risk, too.'

'Leave it to me,' says Blossom.

'I still don't think it's a good idea. What do you think?' He turns to his brother.

'Let's give it a few more days, and see what happens,' says Silas, whose mind is on other things. He has found a particularly pleasing specimen by the roadside on the way home and is obviously longing to deal with it. 'This may all die down.'

But the pilgrims keep on coming. They arrive in cars and on foot, and they traipse up and down the garden, creating a mud bath as they go. To be fair, they are on the whole respectful and apologetic, they don't make much noise and they come and go quite quickly, but they are there. And someone has to be around to oversee the proceedings.

A week later, when an entire minibus full of pilgrims has made its way up the track, my uncles are at their wits' end.

'The trouble is, they'll come whether we let them or not,' says Silas. 'And the idea of people creeping round the house in the middle of the night to pay homage to our hen house, and disturb the hens, is not a pleasant one.'

'Creosote,' says Silas. 'We'll creosote the whole hen house, and that will be that.'

'We can't. Creosote's illegal. Cancer risk or some such nonsense,' Eric tells him.

'Paint, then. We'll paint it.'

'Seems a pity. It won't fit in with the other outbuildings.'

I open my mouth to suggest that nothing other than total squalor would fit in to the chaos of tumbledown sheds which comprise my uncles' domain, but then I close it again.

'Wood preservative, then,' says Eric.

'Won't it show through?' I ask.

'Shouldn't do. And it could do with a spot of weatherproofing, anyway. This way, we'll kill two birds with one stone.'

'Or chickens.'

'This isn't funny, Ruth. We have a real problem here.'

'Sorry.'

'You can help. It shouldn't take long.'

The following day, Eric drives into town and returns with several large tins of very dark wood preservative, and by the evening, we have the whole job done. The hen house looks very smart, standing out among the other more ramshackle outbuildings, but more to the point, there is no sign of the Virgin. Several disappointed visitors have had to be turned away, and there is now a large sign on the gate to the effect that the Virgin Mary has "disappeared".

'Which is true enough,' says Silas, 'even if she needed a little help. After all, if these manifestations can appear, then presumably they can disappear. I'm going back to my fox.'

Neither Eric nor I are going to argue with him. The fox in question has been with us now for two days, and is beginning to smell.

'What do you think Blossom will say?' I ask Eric, as he and I mix feed for the pigs.

'She'll be furious. Apart from anything else, she hates not having her own way.'

'We did do the right, thing, didn't we?'

'Of course we did.' Eric laughs. 'You're not turning Catholic on us are you? It's a bit late for that.'

'No. But you must admit, it was odd. It really did look like — well, like *something*. A bit more than a few knots in the wood, anyway.'

'I reckon Blossom's Father Vincent will be relieved,' Eric says. 'He didn't seem at all keen on the idea of a shrine on his patch, and I can't say I blame him.' He slops pig feed into a trough. 'It seems to me that miracles are a lot more trouble than they're worth.'

But if Eric thinks miracles are trouble, they are nothing compared to Blossom's reaction when she comes to work the next day and finds out what we've done. Shocked silence gives way to hysteria, followed by a torrent of vituperation. What we have done is apparently worse than blasphemy, worse than the blackest of mortal sins. Not only have we looked a spiritual gift horse in the mouth, we have outraged God Himself with our behaviour. We are worse than heathens and idolaters, and are, all three of us, condemned to eternal hell fire.

'Goodness!' says Silas, when Blossom has slammed out of the back door to have another look at our handiwork. 'I didn't know Blossom even knew half those words. She's a dark horse, and no mistake.'

'Why do you let her talk to you like that?' I ask them, more surprised at my uncles' reaction than by Blossom's behaviour, which was more or less what I had expected (Blossom's vocabulary is all there when she chooses to use it, as I've discovered to my cost).

'We don't "let" Blossom do anything. She's a law unto herself.' The plans for Eric's Ark are spread all over the table, and he's engrossed in designing an enclosure for some of his reptiles. He doodles with his pencil and rubs his chin. 'Do crocodiles eat snakes?'

'I've no idea.'

'Ring the zoo and ask, Ruth. There's a pet.'

CHAPTER THIRTEEN

Within a week, the drama of the hen house and its apparition has died down. One or two visitors still knock on the door to enquire about the whereabouts of the Virgin, but most people appear to have accepted her disappearance, and life returns to normal. Blossom's attitude remains unforgiving, but as Eric remarks, we can live with that. She never was a little ray of sunshine, so the fact that she's sulking is barely noticeable, and if her efforts with the duster and the vacuum cleaner are even less effective than before, her devotion to the animals remains intact. Even Blossom can't blame the animals.

Meanwhile, my own attention returns to my burgeoning pregnancy. With all the recent goings-on, not to mention my preoccupation with finding Amos, I have given scant thought to the development of the baby, but it would seem that my attention is not required for it to flourish quite satisfactorily. It continues to grow steadily, and of course I continue to grow with it.

My feelings towards it are ambivalent. While I am happy to acknowledge the miraculous nature of pregnancy and childbirth, I am not quite so happy about the way I am being taken over. Accustomed to having my body to myself, I find that there are times when I resent having to share it with someone else; someone who will grow and stretch, making me grow and stretch too; someone who plans to requisition my breasts for feeding purposes, and to that end is already causing them to balloon out of all proportion to the rest of me (I have always been rather proud of my small, neat boobs). And it's not just my body that I have to share. Presumably I have to share my nutrition as well, and common sense tells me that the baby will get first pick of everything — food that *I* have eaten, for *me* — leaving me with such organic leftovers as are not required for its further development. Add to all this the tiredness and the mood swings, and the fact that neither the baby nor I are allowed to mitigate them with a soothing glass or two of wine, and there are times when I feel more than a little hard done by.

None of this is helped by the involvement of my uncles. Ever since the scan, they have taken a proprietorial interest in my condition, volunteering to take me into town for my check-ups and on occasion entertaining perfect strangers with accounts of my progress. The grainy photographs still play a part in all this, one of them currently occupying the mantelpiece (together with a handful of baler twine, the latest electricity bill and several empty rifle cartridges), but I find that my own enthusiasm for my condition diminishes in inverse relation to that of my uncles. It is as though the baby has become their property rather than mine, and while I know that it needs all the friends it can get, I find myself resenting this. I am tired of being asked how I am feeling (tired), whether I have felt the baby moving (no) and whether I'm feeling excited about it (no, no, *no*!).

And then there is Silas's particular interest in all things medical.

In my experience, there are two kinds of hypochondriac. There is the anxious, neurotic am-I-going-to-die-of-this kind, and the interested, isn't-this-fascinating kind. Silas's hypochondria is of the second variety. Hence, while he anticipates — seems almost to want — investigations and operations, he appears unafraid either of them or of the possible outcomes. Not for Silas the gloomy contemplation of death and disease; more the dispassionate absorption of the scientist. Silas is deeply interested in the workings of his body, and sees illness, real or imagined, as a challenge; a problem to be solved rather than an unpleasant experience to be endured. I personally feel that it is no coincidence that Silas has taken to taxidermy. When he has no preoccupations with his own body, he can concentrate on trying to restore those of his hapless subjects. In many way, Silas would have made a very good doctor.

The *Book of Family Medicine*, his favoured bedside reading, is a well-thumbed volume to which he has frequent recourse. Its fragile pages are worn, many of its paragraphs underscored, with comments in the margins in Silas's spidery handwriting, and he is happy to dispense its advice to anyone who might require it. He also possesses an ancient stethoscope, courtesy of a medical friend (although I think it unlikely that he has any idea what he's listening for) and a DIY blood pressure machine. Since I joined the household Silas has self-diagnosed, variously, a brain tumour, appendicitis and a duodenal ulcer. These have all subsided within a few hours — before medical help could be sought — but have been as real to Silas as the genuine article. In many ways it's a good thing he doesn't have access to the internet, which can be a rich source of medical misinformation (and misleading suggestions) to people like Silas.

Silas's hypochondria extends to the rest of the household — a kind of hypochondria by proxy — and this can be tiresome. His book has a large section on Pregnancy and its Complications, and I find him reading it covertly when he thinks I'm not looking.

'How's the blood pressure, Ruth?' he asks me this morning. We are in the kitchen together, where Silas is putting the finishing touches to his fox.

'Fine.'

'How do you know?'

'Well, it was last time.'

'Should I — would you like me to check it for you?'

'No, thanks.'

'It'll only take a minute.'

'*No*, thanks.'

'Just to set your mind at rest?'

'My mind is at rest. Or it would be, if people would just leave me alone.'

'I'm sorry, Ruth.'

'No, *I'm* sorry.' I feel suddenly ashamed. 'I know I'm being ungracious and horrible. But Silas, I just want to forget about the baby. I've got ages yet before I have to think about it properly, and I want to enjoy the time I've got.'

'Don't you want the baby?' Silas says, after a moment.

'I don't know. I really don't know. At first, I didn't. Then I did. And now I'm not sure.'

'What's not to be sure about? You're young, you're healthy, even if you won't let me take your blood pressure. You seem to have made your decision. But Ruth — you seem to be ignoring the baby. You won't talk about it, plan anything. You're just — drifting.'

All this is true. After my vision — hallucination, dream, whatever it was — at the abortion clinic, I knew I wanted the baby. Or at least, I didn't want to do away with it. I would have the baby; decision made. But I never really thought beyond that point, especially since my failed attempts to find Amos. It's as though there is a wall in front of me, and I can't think about what lies beyond it. For the time being, life is comfortable; I'm with people I love and who care about me; I have plenty to keep me busy. I daren't even try to look beyond that wall for fear of what I might see.

'You could have it adopted,' Silas says. 'Plenty of people do.'

'Do they?' In my experience, people no longer have their babies adopted. It seems that everyone, from penniless teenagers who are seeking to give meaning to their lives to wealthy celebrities (who are probably doing the same) is having babies out of wedlock. It's the cool thing to do. Having your baby adopted is uncool. It is also, strangely, something I have barely considered.

I try to imagine myself handing over the seahorse/rabbit to a pair of delighted and grateful strangers. I think of the freedom I would regain and the glow of a good deed (selflessly?) done. My parents would be freed from their impending disgrace, I would be able to go on my gap year, and if Mikey would be minus a godchild, I'm sure he could live with that. After all, this isn't about Mikey, it's about me, not to mention that delighted and grateful couple, who even now could be out there somewhere grieving over their childless state.

Then I examine the other side of the adoption coin; the guilt, the emptiness, the now pointless stretch marks and other scars of childbirth, and the milky breasts waiting for someone to feed. And then the years of wondering and imagining, and eventually the waiting for that knock on the door, when a grown-up and reproachful teenager may well accost me to ask why I didn't want him; why I *gave him away.*

And Amos. Okay, so he doesn't know about the baby — may well never find out about it — but supposing he does ('You gave away a baby? *Our baby*? Oh, Ruth! How *could* you!')? What on earth would I tell him? Having stolen half a baby from him (albeit unwittingly), do I have the right simply to give it away?

'Well?' Silas is still looking at me. 'It's a possibility, isn't it? But you need to make up your mind, Ruth.'

'No.' I sigh. 'No adoption.'

'You're sure?'

'Quite sure.'

'Well, then.'

'Well then what?'

'Ruth, you know we're happy to have you here for as long as you like. We love having you around, and the baby will be welcome, too. But it's not much of a life for a young woman, stuck out here in the sticks with two old men. Or for a child, come to that. You need to make — plans.'

'I've rather liked not making plans. Apart from my job, I've never really been a planning sort of person. I've tended to — well, to let things happen.'

'So I gather.'

'But I suppose you're right. I ought to plan *something*.' I gaze out of the window. In the lemony light of a late-summer sunset, Eric is leaning on the three remaining bars of what used to be a five-barred gate admiring the livestock; Mr. Darcy is rolling in a patch of what could just be mud, but is probably something worse; one of the cats is carefully peeling a pigeon on the lawn. None of them appears to have — or need — plans. 'What would *you* do, Silas?'

'What would I do?' Silas stands back to admire his fox (really quite fox-looking). 'I think I might start by making my peace with my parents.'

'But I never wanted to fall out with them in the first place!'

'I know that.' Silas tweaks a foxy ear. 'But I also know your mother is pretty miserable about this situation. It wouldn't take much to talk her round.'

'Do you think?'

'I know.'

'How do you know?'

'We talk. From time to time. You forget; she's our sister.'

'I did try phoning Mum. I rang her last week.'

'And?'

'She sounded a bit strained. Not herself. But I think Dad was probably there too, and she never says anything that would upset him. I didn't dare mention the baby. One step at a time, I guess.'

'Well, maybe the next step is to go and see her. It's always better, face to face.'

'You're right. I'll do that. I'll go next week.'

'Good girl. You can borrow the Land Rover.' Silas regards his fox thoughtfully. 'You know, this fox reminds me of someone.'

'I know — Blossom!' When I come to think about it, the fox does bear a startling resemblance to Blossom.

'You're right.' Silas grins. 'Better not tell her.'

'Mum's the word.'

'And talking of mums —'

'Okay, okay. I'll go and see her. I've already said I will.'

But in the event, it turns out that my visit is not necessary after all.

CHAPTER FOURTEEN

The knock at the front door is timid; almost apologetic.

'Was that the door?' Eric asks.

'I'll go and see,' I tell him.

'It's probably the man about the llamas,' Eric calls after me (this is a very long story, and I won't go into it now). 'Tell him next week. Definitely next week.'

But it's not the man about the llamas.

'Mum!' My mother is standing on the doorstep holding a small suitcase and a collection of bags. 'What are you —'

'Can I come in?' Mum pecks me on the cheek. She looks tired and drained.

'Of course. Of course you can come in. Here, let me take your bags.' I usher her into the hallway. 'Eric! Silas! It's Mum!'

'Rosie! How lovely to see you! This is a nice surprise.' Silas gives her a hug. 'What brings you here?'

I'd forgotten that my uncles call Mum Rosie (my father always uses her full name), but looking at her now, small and vulnerable beside her big — in every sense — brothers, I can see that she could be a Rosie.

'I need — I need to speak to Ruth. Is that all right? For a few minutes.' She turns and then starts as she catches sight of Silas's fox. 'Gracious! What's that?'

'Oh, don't mind him.' Silas drapes a tea towel over the fox's head. 'There. Now he can't see you.'

'Is he — is he —?'

'Dead?' Silas laughs. 'Oh yes. Very.' He turns to Eric. 'We'll make ourselves scarce, shall we?'

When they've left the room, I make coffee, and Mum and I sit together at the kitchen table. She seems ill at ease, twisting a flowery handkerchief in her fingers, her eyes darting round the room as though expecting more foxes to creep out of the woodwork.

'How — how are you, Ruth?'

'Fine. I'm fine.'

'And — the baby?'

'Fine too, as far as I know.'

'You look well.'

'Yes. Thank you.'

There is a pause in which Mum stirs sugar into her coffee (she doesn't normally take sugar).

'This is difficult,' she begins. 'I've got something to tell you. Not good news, I'm afraid.'

'Dad? Is it Dad?' I feel a frisson of fear.

'No. Well, yes. In a way. Oh, Ruth —' she turns to me, and there's a kind of desperation in her eyes — ' I've left him. I've left your father.'

'You've *left* him?'

'Yes.'

'When did this happen?'

'This morning. Well, things have been difficult for a while. They came to a head last night, and we had a row. We've never had a row before. Not a real one.' Mum looks as though she still finds is hard to believe. 'I couldn't get through to him how I felt. He just wouldn't listen. So after I'd washed up the breakfast things, I — I left.'

'But why? How did all this start? You two have always seemed such a — *couple*.'

'It's — complicated.'

'Tell me. You have to tell me, Mum. If I'm to understand.'

'Yes.'

'Come on.' I reach across and take her hand. 'Just tell me. It can't be that difficult.'

'Oh, Ruth! I can't — I couldn't —' And she bursts into tears.

I let her cry for a few minutes, awkwardly patting her shoulder, wondering how best I can help her.

'It was — it was about you.' She blows her nose. 'Oh, Ruth — I couldn't bear it. Not knowing how you were, not having anything to do with the — with the baby. I just couldn't bear it.'

'But you know I'd have come home any time. You only had to say.'

Mum shakes her head.

'Your father.'

'Dad.' Of course. My father has never been one to go back on a decision, particularly one involving matters of morals (or, as in my case, the lack of them). I was brought up to believe that the man was the head of the family, and therefore Always Right (my father is a fervent follower of the teachings of St. Paul), and it took the outside world and a good dose of common sense to teach me that this was by no means always the case. It could be that my mother is at last beginning to see the light.

'He didn't want you to come home. He didn't even want me to see you. Well not yet, anyway. He loves you, Ruth, in his own way. He really does. But —'

'On his terms?'

'I suppose so. Yes. And he really didn't know how to deal with this — with this situation.'

'No. I can see that.' I drink my coffee, which is cooling rapidly. 'What's he doing now?'

'Painting the fence.'

'Painting the fence?'

'He thinks I'll be home to cook his dinner. But I won't, Ruth. I won't. I can't take it anymore. I've had enough.'

'Do you — do you love him?' I ask, after a moment.

'I did. I certainly did once. But I don't know any more. Being married to him was a habit. Our life together is a habit. I care about him. Of course I do. And I'd never wish him harm. But I want more than that. Before it's too late. I know what I've done is wrong — leaving him like this — but you're my daughter. My only child. This — baby could be my only grandchild. I may not get another chance.'

'And God? What about God?' I know this is cruel, but I genuinely want to know. I feel that all my life I've come second to God, as far as my parents are concerned. Is my mother really willing to compromise her beliefs for me?

'God. Yes.' Mum fiddles with her teaspoon. 'I think there's room for Him, too. Somewhere. But maybe my God isn't the same as your father's any more. Can you understand that?'

I have always thought of my father's God as the God of the Old Testament; a God who often seemed to me more concerned with battles and sacrifice and punishment than forgiveness and love.

'Yes. Yes, I can.' I stand up and look out of the window, where I can see Eric and Silas hovering at a tactful distance, pretending to be busy. 'So what are you going to do?'

'That's the other problem. And you may not like this either, Ruth. But I thought I might ask if — well ask whether I could stay here. Just for a while. Until I've got myself sorted.'

'Oh.' Of course I don't like it. I don't like it at all. I was more or less compelled to come here, and at the time I didn't really want to. Now, it would appear that my mother wants to gatecrash my comfortable new life and join in. 'Well...'

'I knew you wouldn't be pleased, Ruth. And I can understand how you must feel, after what — well, after what your father and I have done. But I've nowhere else to go.' She spreads her fingers in a little lost gesture, and I feel sorry that I ever made her feel unwelcome. Poor Mum. Trapped in a life where she is bound to my father and God (probably in that order), she has never had time to make a life of her own. She hasn't had a job since I was born, and such friends as she has are from the church or the voluntary organisations to which she belongs. They are all nice enough, but I think it unlikely that any of them would stand by her in this crisis.

'Of course I don't mind. It would be good to have you here, though it's not exactly what you're used to.'

'I know that. Silas and Eric have always lived in a bit of a muddle, but they're family. My family. We used to be — well, we were very close before I got married, but — but —'

'Dad didn't really approve of them?'

'Something like that. I think he likes them. Well, he hasn't anything against them, anyway. But he doesn't understand them. Their way of life, the fact that they've never really had proper jobs, the way they've turned their back on God.'

'I think if Dad took the trouble to get to know them better, he'd be surprised. They're good people, which is what really matters, and they've been wonderful to me.'

'I knew they would be.' For the first time, Mum smiles, looking almost pretty. I've never thought of my mother as pretty, but when I come to think of it, I haven't often seen her smile. 'I knew we could trust them to look after you.'

Of course, when she asks them, Eric and Silas both say they are delighted to have Mum for as long as she likes. She can have the room she slept in as a child. It will need a bit of a tidy (this, I happen to know, is an understatement), but they're sure she'll be comfortable.

'We thought it might come to this, one day,' Silas tell me some time later, when a large pile of assorted junk has been moved from Mum's room and she's has taken her things upstairs. 'I probably shouldn't say this to you, Ruth, but we never thought the marriage was — quite right for her. Not that we have anything against your father,' he adds, glancing at his brother, 'but they seemed so — unsuited somehow.'

'How, unsuited?' I ask him.

'Well, your mum was quite a girl when she was young. She had lots of boyfriends and she liked a good time. Your father...'

'Wasn't so much one for a good time?' I suggest.

'I suppose you could say that. But he was serious and steady, and maybe that's what your mum needed. And after all, it seems to have worked so far, doesn't it? And may well do again.'

'Do you think she'll go back to him?' I ask him.

'I've no idea. Perhaps she needs a bit of time to — well, to find herself. Sort herself out. But there's no hurry. We're happy to have her.'

When Mum comes downstairs some time later, she has changed and freshened up, and looks more in control.

'Would you like a guided tour?' I ask her.

'Yes. That might be a good idea,' she says. 'Then at least I can be of some use.'

I find her a pair of old wellingtons and we walk round the garden and outhouses. I introduce Mum to Sarah and her fast-growing family, and she admires some new fluffy chicks and a beautiful Jersey calf. She makes no comments about the state of the place, and I'm grateful; for seeing things as it were through her eyes, I can't believe that Silas and Eric have managed to function so well for so long in all this chaos. I refrain from telling her about the Virgin of the hen house; it's too soon for anything quite so outré. My parents see Roman Catholics as idolaters; unworthy to be called Christians, and under no circumstances to be trusted. Visions of the Virgin are most certainly to be avoided at all costs.

'Well, that's it,' I say, as we end up back at the house. 'What would you like to do now?'

'I think,' says Mum, 'I'd better phone your father. To tell him he'll have to cook for himself this evening.'

CHAPTER FIFTEEN

'Who's this, then?' Blossom demands, when she comes in the next morning.

'This is my mother. Mum, this is Blossom.'

'How do you do?' says Mum.

'Humph.' Blossom, ignores my mother's outstretched hand (I'd forgotten to warn Mum about Blossom). 'How long you staying?'

'Well, I'm not sure...'

'Where you sleeping?'

'She's sleeping in her old room,' I say, for the pleasure of seeing Blossom's reaction.

'What old room?'

'The little one on the top landing.'

'I slept in it as a child,' Mum adds.

'Relation then, are you?'

'I'm Eric's and Silas's sister. Ruth's mother, as she said.'

Blossom regards her stonily for a moment, and then hauls the vacuum cleaner out from the cupboard under the stairs, and plugs it in.

'Can't stand here chatting,' she says. 'Work to do.'

'We weren't chatting, Blossom. I was introducing you to my mother.' Just this once, I've been unwise enough to let Blossom's rudeness get to me.

'Can't hear you,' yells Blossom above the roaring of machinery. Something rattles up the tubing, and Blossom switches it off and stoops to investigate.

'I said that I was just trying to introduce you to my mother,' I repeat.

'Well, met her now, haven't I?' Blossom pokes about in the vacuum cleaner's innards and retrieves half an old toothbrush (an item much favoured by Mr. Darcy as a toy) and stows it away in her apron pocket, then switches on again. I can see we're not going to get anything more out of Blossom, and Mum and I retire to the kitchen.

'What an — odd person,' says Mum.

'Oh, she's odd all right. Goodness knows why Eric and Silas put up with her. But she'll be okay now she's met you. Just ignore her. She's upset because she likes to feel she's in charge of this place, and she hates surprises.'

But Blossom has only just started. She follows poor Mum round the house, ensuring that whatever job she is about to do, Mum's in the way. She skins a freshly-killed rabbit under Mum's nose (quite unnecessarily, as Silas usually does that sort of thing) and she flatly refuses to spring clean Mum's room, although Eric asks her very nicely.

'No time,' she says.

'You've got another two hours yet,' says Eric reasonably. 'It shouldn't take that long.'

'Take more'n that.'

'No it won't. Not if you start now.'

Blossom eyes Eric beadily.

'Bad back,' she says. 'Done enough cleaning for today. Do the pigs.'

'What bad back?' asks Silas, the medical expert.

'Personal,' says Blossom going out and slamming the back door behind her.

'How can a bad back be personal?' asks Mum, puzzled.

'Blossom's bad back can be anything she likes,' says Eric wearily. 'If she's got one. Which I very much doubt.'

'Why doesn't she like me?' Mum asks.

'I suspect you're a threat,' Eric says. 'Ruth was bad enough — another woman around the house, and all that — but now there are two of you, she probably sees it as two against one.'

Poor Mum. Her visit has not got off to a good start, and there is more to come, for the next day, Mikey pays me another visit. He says he is 'just passing' again, but I suspect there's more to it than that, for he seems strangely excited.

Mum hasn't met Mikey, and as far as I know has never met any gay person. She's not so much homophobic as homo-ignorant (if there is such a thing), and given Mikey's exuberant lack of tact, I anticipate trouble.

At first, things go well enough. Mikey greets Mum very nicely, doesn't ask embarrassing questions as to the whys and wherefores of her visit, and there is a safely general discussion round the kitchen table when he joins us all for lunch. But I can see that he is bursting to say something, and after half an hour, he can contain himself no longer.

'Oh, Ruth! I've been dying to tell you. You know that new partner I was telling you about? We're in love!' he tells me (and of course, everyone else).

'That's great, Mikey.' I try making warning signals, but Mikey is oblivious.

'Yes. It all happened so quickly. We're going on holiday together.'

At this stage, I try to reach Mikey's foot with mine to give him a kick under the table, but he's too far away. I look despairingly at my uncles, but neither of them seems to have noticed the impending danger.

'How lovely for you,' Mum beams. 'What's her name?'

'Gavin. *Gavin.*' The word rolls off Mikey's lips as only a lover's name can; smoothly, adoringly, and (to most people) indisputably male.

'What an unusual name for a girl!' cries my mother, still completely in the dark.

I make one last, desperate attempt to reach either Mikey's love-glazed eyes or his foot, but it's too late.

'Oh, Gavin isn't a girl; he's a man,' Mikey tells her. 'Can't you tell? I'm —'

At last my foot reaches its target and administers a sharp blow to Mikey's ankle, and he finally shuts up. But of course, the damage is done. I have never seen anyone blush the way Mum does when she realises what Mikey's saying; what Mikey *is*. Even the tips of her ears seem to go puce. She looks at me despairingly, and I realise that of course she has no idea what to do. She has no rules for this kind of situation, and Mum lives her life by rules. My father isn't there to give her guidance, and she hasn't the confidence to trust any reaction of her own. She is almost certainly torn between politeness, horror and a deep and unspeakable embarrassment, and I feel desperately sorry for her.

'Mum, why don't you go and put your feet up?' I suggest. 'You must be tired. I know you didn't have a very good night.'

She gives me a grateful look and practically scampers from the room. A few minutes later, Eric and Silas wander off to inspect a leaky roof, and Mikey and I are left on our own.

'Oh, *Mikey*! How could you!' I am furious with him.

'How could I what?'

'My mother's never come across a gay person before. She didn't know where to put herself!'

'Perhaps it was time she did.'

'Did what?'

'Meet a gay person.'

'Oh, don't be so ridiculous.' I begin collecting up the lunch things. 'Mikey, my mother is a complete innocent. She lives under the thumb of my father and thinks and believes what he thinks and believes. In my father's book, gay people are beyond the pale.'

'How sweet,' Mikey murmurs.

'No. Not sweet. Just ignorant. But they are basically good people, and they are *my parents*.'

'Am I supposed to be sorry?'

'It would be a start.'

'Okay. I'm sorry.'

'Not good enough.'

'I really am sorry, Ruth.' He kisses my cheek. 'Will that do? But I'm so happy, and I wanted you to be happy for me.'

'Of course I'm happy for you. I'm delighted for you. But next time you have a piece of news like this, please spare my mother. She's having a hard time at the moment, and she can do without you and your love life.'

'Okay. Understood.'

'That's all right, then.'

'So can I tell you about Gavin now? Please, Ruth. Just five minutes.'

Mikey spends the next half-hour telling me about Gavin while we do the washing up together, and I listen, because Mikey is a good friend and I really am happy for him.

'So,' he finishes. 'Now tell me about you.'

'There's not much to tell, really. I'm fine, and the baby's fine. But the bad news is that my mother seems to have left my father.'

'Goodness!'

'Yes. I'm sure it's not permanent, but still, it's all a bit messy.'

'And you're caught in the middle.'

'Well not really, because my father hasn't been in touch. Mum only arrived yesterday.'

'And she's now trespassing on your patch.'

'Well, I'm glad she feels she can come here, of course I am.'

'But you were comfortable as you were. The three of you, and that ghastly Blossom.'

'Yes. Does that sound awful?'

'Not awful at all. It's perfectly natural. You've settled in so happily here — it all seems so *right* — and of course your mum being around is bound to make a difference.

'It does a bit.'

'And still no man?' he asks me.

'I'm hardly likely to find one round here, am I?'

'No. I suppose not. But what about the baby's father, Ruth? Is there no chance of your making a go of it with him?'

'I don't even know where he is.'

'Mm. That could be problematic.' Mikey stacks plates neatly away in a cupboard. 'Are you ready to talk about him yet?'

'Oh, why not?'

So I put away my tea towel, and tell Mikey about Amos. I tell him about our long friendship, Amos's divorce and the night we spent together. I tell him about the comforting familiar *hugeness* of Amos, his sense of humour, his warmth and his kindness.

'And — I miss him,' I end lamely. 'I never thought I would, and if it weren't for the baby, I probably wouldn't be giving him a thought, but I really, really miss him.'

'Anyone would think you were in love with the guy,' Mikey remarks after a moment.

'Can one fall in love with someone when they're not there?'

'I don't see why not. After all, you seem to know him pretty well. And I'm sure having a baby with someone must make a difference.'

'Yes. Yes, it does. And of course, that's another thing. The baby.'

'What about the baby?'

'I've done nothing about it. I can't think about it or make plans for it or anything. I'm just — stuck. Eric and Silas say I should start making decisions about the future, but I can't *see* a future. Not with a baby. I know I decided to keep it, and I've no regrets about that, but it doesn't seem real, somehow. I just see myself living here for ever with my bump, milking goats and arguing with Blossom and playing my fiddle to bored shoppers.'

'You could give the baby to me. I'd love to have your baby.'

'That's a thought.' For a moment, I have a vision of the seahorse/rabbit being carried off into the sunset by Mikey (and probably Gavin as well. Why not?). It would be loved and cared for by someone I know, and I could have visiting rights. The perfect solution all round.

But while Mikey is undoubtedly half-serious, the baby wouldn't have a mother, and I'd like it to have a mother. Besides, now that my own mother is joining in I am no longer the only person involved. Mum is clearly preparing for — even looking forward to — her role as a grandmother, so I can hardly give her grandchild away. It seems that the Woman's Right to Choose ends once the pregnancy is under way; after that, other people enter the equation, with their own hopes and expectations, and it's hard to ignore them.

'You'd make a lovely dad, Mikey, and it's tempting. But I have to go ahead with this. I'll manage somehow.'

'Then at least find Amos.'

'I've done everything I can think of. He just seems to have vanished.'

'People can't do that. Not with the internet, and mobiles, and CCTV.'

'Amos can. He hates the internet, and likes people not knowing where he is. It's a kind of pride thing with him, being invisible. Plus, he's hiding from his ex.'

'I could still try to Google him for you.'

'Other friends have tried, but no luck so far. But I'd love you to have a go, if you don't mind.'

'Of course I will. There can't be that many trombone-playing Amoses. He should be pretty easy to find.'

'Even Amos Jones?'

'Especially Amos Jones.'

'You're a star.' I give him a hug.

'And still a godfather?'

'Certainly still a godfather,' I assure him. 'I can't think of a better one.'

CHAPTER SIXTEEN

All things considered, my mother has settled into the household surprisingly well. She appears unfazed by the chaos, seems to enjoy the animals, and is obviously deeply fond of Eric and Silas. It's as though the three of them have picked from where they were when they were children, and it's lovely to see Mum laughing once more.

Of course, not everything delights her, and she finds Silas's taxidermy hard to understand.

'I wouldn't mind so much if they looked the way they're meant to,' she confesses to me. 'But they all look so — odd. Not at all the way they must have when they were alive. That badger looks more like a small bear on its way to a fancy dress party than a real badger.'

'Silas over-stuffs them,' I tell her. 'He can't help himself. He gets an animal just right, and then he can't resist adding a little bit more stuffing, and ruins the effect. He also puts in the wrong eyes.'

'The *wrong eyes*?'

'Yes. He has to send away for the eyes. He got a batch of dogs' eyes by mistake, and he can't bear to waste them.' Which of course explains the reproachful doggy gaze of several ill-matched animal faces. 'Mr. Darcy can't stand it. He doesn't like the taxidermy thing any more than we do, but it's the eyes that really get to him. I think he takes it personally.'

And then there's Eric and his researches. Poor Mum is torn between curiosity and her long-held fundamentalist beliefs. I can see that she is longing to look at Eric's plans (which have now had to be moved into what is optimistically known as the study because they've outgrown the kitchen table), but has misgivings because of her loyalty to Dad and her church.

'Oh, go on, Mum. What harm can it do?' I ask her. 'You can carry on believing what you've always believed, and still have a look at Eric's Ark. It's really very interesting.'

So Mum spends an hour on her hands and knees with Eric poring over his plans, while he explains at length about carnivores and herbivores, which animals can co-habit and which must be kept apart, and the amount of excrement they will all produce in a day (which, Eric explains cheerily, can all be chucked into the sea, because if there's one thing Noah has plenty of, it's sea).

'I thought you didn't believe in Noah,' Mum says, perhaps glimpsing a tiny opportunity for Eric's salvation.

'I don't. This is all theory.' Eric rolls up his plans and stows them carefully away in an old chest out of Blossom's way (Blossom has no time for Eric's researches, and given half a chance is more than capable of hoovering up all his hard work). 'Don't worry, Rosie.' He pinches her cheek. 'I'll be okay. You don't need to believe in a great boat full of animals in order to be saved.'

Every evening, my father phones, and Mum speaks to him for about five minutes. She is reluctant to tell us what he says, but he is apparently coping well.

'The church are all praying for us,' she tells me.

'I bet they are,' mutters Silas, mixing chemicals in the sink.

'But he keeps asking when I'm coming home. I don't know what to do, Ruth. I've never been in this situation before. What do — what do people do?'

'I've no idea. But you're doing okay, Mum. And at least you're able to think things through without anyone putting pressure on you.'

'I suppose so.'

'Do you miss him?' I ask her.

'I don't know.' Mum rolls out pastry for a pie she's making (she's "earning her keep" as she puts it by doing much of the cooking). 'I ought to miss him, oughtn't I? After nearly forty years. I certainly ought to feel — well, something more than this.'

'I don't think oughts count when it comes to feelings. After all, you can't help what you feel, can you? It's what you do that counts.'

'And what I'm doing is wrong. I made vows, Ruth. Important vows. I believed — believe in them. And now look at me.'

Poor Mum. I don't think there are any divorced or separated couples among her sheltered acquaintance, so this is unknown territory for her. I often wonder how people like my parents survive the mores of our post-modern world. They behave like lost time-travellers from a bygone age, expecting everything to be as it used to be — as it ought to be — unable to accept or understand change. I'm sure my father is more worldly-wise than my mother, and that he has succeeded in protecting her from the more shocking aspects of the twenty-first century. They rarely watch television, and newspapers are carefully rationed. They have what Dad calls the "wireless" (who still uses that word?), listening to the news and the occasional church service, and such books as they read are all about the Bible or the joyous "witness" of those who have seen the light. There are a few children's books left over from my childhood (*Peter Rabbit*, *Barbar the Elephant*, *What Katy Did*, *Little Women*; safe, clean stories with happy endings), but that's about it. Matters sexual were never discussed, and such information as I had was gleaned from the rather clinical sex education lessons at school, and ill-informed friends (you can't get pregnant if you have sex standing up; that kind of thing. My friend Molly Wilkins put this theory to the test, and soundly disproved it).

'But I'm not going back. Not yet,' Mum says now. 'I'm not ready.'

I think it's the first time I've heard Mum say what *she* wants to do. It occurs to me that she's spent her whole life doing things for other people or because other people have told her to do them. Things are certainly changing.

The next day's post brings news from Mikey. He has Googled Amos, and come up with some interesting, if ancient, snippets, under the following headings:

'Young trombonist wins prestigious prize' (*The Times*, May 1990). Typical.

'Student leads demonstration against regime in Zimbabwe' (*Daily Mail*, February 1994). Also typical.

'Gifted jazz-player survives window fall' (*Daily Telegraph,* April 1999). Ditto. Amos is accident-prone. He puts it down to his height, but actually he's incredibly clumsy.

' "His playing made our holiday," wrote Enid Horton, who enjoyed one of our musical cruises last year' (Cruise brochure, Summer 2000).

There are various other bits and bobs; extracts from local newspapers, concert reviews, a mountaineering accident and, strangely, a brief appearance on a TV cookery programme, but nothing which can be of any use in actually tracking Amos down. The last mention is two years ago, and since that, nothing. It would appear that Amos hasn't just disappeared from the face of the earth; he's vanished from cyberspace, too.

Mikey is sympathetic in his accompanying note, and says he's "sure Amos will turn up sooner or later". It's the sort of banality lovers delight in; the world they inhabit is so blissful (if in the long run, so removed from reality) that they feel it incumbent upon themselves to spread the bliss around by trying to convince the rest of us that our worlds, too, will reach this pinnacle of perfection, if only we wait long enough.

I am more disappointed by Mikey's letter than I would have expected. I have faith in Mikey, and I had really hoped that he would come up with something more concrete. Each Amos-related disappointment is harder to deal with than the last, and this time, I find myself close to tears.

I wander outside to find someone to talk to. Mum and I are getting on pretty well, considering our different predicaments, but I don't think either of us is ready yet for an Amos conversation.

I run Silas to ground in the greenhouse, where an amazing array of plants is managing to flourish among the broken flower pots and the weeds which have managed to negotiate the spaces left by several broken panes.

'It smells wonderful,' I tell him, as I am hit by a blanket of warm moist air, redolent of sun and soil and tomatoes.

'Mm. Doesn't it.' Silas straightens up and smiles at me. 'What's up, then?'

'How do you know there's anything up?'

Silas taps his nose. 'I can always tell. Baby okay?'

'As far as I know.'

'Made any decisions yet?'

'I've been trying to find its father.'

'Good for you! Any luck?'

I shake my head. 'Not yet. Mikey's been on the case, but Amos seems to have disappeared.'

'Amos. You never told us he was called Amos. Well, that's certainly a good name for anyone's father.'

'Yes. Even Dad would — might approve.'

'So what next?' Silas ties up a drooping frond of something with a piece of string.

'I don't know.'

'Have you talked to your mum yet?'

'Not yet. I guess she's got enough problems of her own at the moment.'

'It might take her mind off them. Give her a chance, Ruth. I think she really does want to help, but doesn't know where to begin.'

'Has she said so?'

'She doesn't have to.' He puts away his string and wipes his hands on the seat of his trousers. 'You forget. We've known her a lot longer than you have. People don't change that much.'

'I will talk to her. Soon.'

'That's good.'

I'm grateful for the way my uncles lead but never coerce me. Their advice is often good, but they never either assume I'll take it or put pressure on me to do so. It's just there; an offering, nothing more. And because of the generous undemanding spirit of the offer, as often as not, I accept it. I remember all the times my father gave me "advice", and how I frequently refused to take it on principle, although it wasn't all bad. It might not have been given in the way Silas's is, and was often couched in the terms of a command or a criticism, but perhaps I should have given him some credit. He was probably only doing what he thought was right.

I pick a tiny bright red tomato and put it in my mouth.

'Would you have liked children, Silas?'

'Yes and no.' Silas seems unsurprised by my question. 'Yes, because it's one of the most wonderful things anyone can do, and no, because it's such a huge responsibility. And I never met the right person to have them with.'

'Did you — have you — I mean —'

'Have I ever had a girlfriend? On yes. When we were younger, Eric and I had quite a few. But the twin thing got in the way, and in any case, none of them worked out. In the end we settled for what we have, which is more than many people manage.'

Later, we make our way back to the house together carrying baskets filled with bright red tomatoes and yellow peppers and glossy aubergines the colour of bruises. They look almost too beautiful to eat, and certainly much too good to part with, but they have to go, for tomorrow is market day.

I must go and practise my violin.

CHAPTER SEVENTEEN

A few days later, just when life seems to be settling down a bit, there is another major interruption in the form of the reappearance of the Virgin of the hen house.

'She — it — can't be back!' Eric says in disbelief, when a triumphant Blossom announces these unwelcome tidings.

'See for yourself.'

'You must have done something, Blossom. This is certainly your doing.'

'Rain did it.'

'It couldn't have. That was perfectly good wood preservative. It's guaranteed waterproof.'

'Suit yourself.'

Eric and Blossom glare at each other.

'I will suit myself. And I'm certainly not going out in the rain to look at all this nonsense,' Eric says.

'Shall I go and look?' My curiosity is aroused.

'Fine, Ruth.' He lowers his voice. 'But please don't encourage her.'

I put on wellingtons and an old raincoat and trudge down the garden behind Blossom.

'There!' she says, when we reach the hen house. 'Told you.'

Sure enough, Blossom's miraculous image appears to have made a come-back. There it (she?) is, outstretched arms, little stars and all. If anything, the image is even more lifelike than it was before.

'How...?' I am astonished.

'Rain,' Blossom says again. And she's right. I don't know what substance it was that we used to paint the hen house, but it has completely washed away, leaving the oak pale and pristine, if a little wet, and Blossom's Virgin as good as new.

Blossom crosses herself, and risks a rare smile.

'Can't keep *her* away,' she tells me. 'If she wants to appear, she'll appear. No stopping her.'

Mystified but oddly fascinated, I make my way back to the house. There's no sign of Eric or Silas, but Mum has just returned from taking Mr. Darcy for a walk (Mr. Darcy neither likes nor needs walks, but it's all part of Mum's idea of being useful). They are both soaked to the skin.

'What's going on?' she asks me. 'Eric won't say, but something's happened, hasn't it?'

'Sort of.' How do I tell my fervently anti-papist mother that there's a religious apparition on the premises?

'Well?' Mum takes off Mr. Darcy's lead (an unreliable structure concocted from baler twine) and dries him with an old towel.

'It's like this.' Very carefully, trying as much as possible to spare Mum's feelings, I explain about Blossom's faith and Blossom's apparition.

'It's idolatry,' says Mum, after a shocked silence. 'That's what it is. Idol-worship. I wonder Eric and Silas put up with it.'

'They don't. They've done their best to get rid of it. But when you come to think about it, it's pretty harmless.'

'Harmless? You call this *harmless*? Ruth, what can you be thinking of?'

'Mum, you don't have to have anything to do with it. It's between Eric and Silas and Blossom. It's their hen house and her apparition. And look at it this way. If this is actually going to put a smile on Blossom's face, isn't it worth it?'

Mum still looks unhappy.

'I don't like it,' she says. 'This — kind of thing. It's not right. It's evil.'

And try as I might, I can't persuade my mother that Blossom's Virgin need have nothing to do with her. Mum's now part of the household, albeit temporarily, and apparently she feels that she will be in some way contaminated by its presence.

'What would your father say?' she keeps repeating

'Don't worry. Eric and Silas will probably paint over it again, and we can forget all about it,' I tell her. 'Would you like to see it?'

'No. Oh, no. Certainly not. I wouldn't — couldn't look at it. That wouldn't do at all.'

Meanwhile Blossom, sensing the strength of Mum's feelings, does her best to make things worse by praising the Lord and crossing herself, and telling us all how good the Holy Mother is to visit us again like this, when we have gone out of our way to get rid of her.

'It can't stay,' Eric tells her, when he's been out to have a look for himself. 'That stuff they gave us was useless. We'll have to get something stronger. We're not going through all that miracle business again.'

'Can't get rid of her,' Blossom says. 'Not twice.'

'Three times if necessary,' says Eric. 'Blossom, let me make this absolutely clear. These are our grounds, and they are home to our animals. We are not having strangers tramping about visiting our hen house. It's quite out of the question.'

'It does look quite — well, quite real,' I venture. 'Have you looked at it properly? You have to admit, Eric. It's more than just a bit of wood grain and a few scratches.'

'Whose side are you on?' he asks me (Eric is not in a good mood today).

'Well, yours, of course. But all the same...'

'No, Ruth. Absolutely no. It's got to go, and there's an end to it.'

Blossom sulks and curses and bangs about the house until Silas tells her to take the rest of the morning off and go home.

'Can't. You'll do something to her.' Blossom gets out a mop and bucket and starts sloshing soapy water round the kitchen floor.

'So what are you going to do? Stand guard by the hen house?'

'Might do.'

'Blossom, I'm not asking you. I'm not even telling you. I'm *ordering* you to go home and cool down. Come back tomorrow and we'll talk about it. We can't do anything about it before tomorrow, anyway, and we certainly can't have a sensible conversation when you're in this kind of mood.'

After Blossom has clattered off on her ancient bicycle, leaving the kitchen floor awash with suds and her mop lying across the hallway, Mum asks Silas what he's thinking of.

'Why do you let her speak to you like that?' she asks him. 'You should get rid of her. You can't just hang on to her because you're sorry for her.'

'Sorry for her? Sorry for Blossom?' Silas roars with laughter. 'No-one needs to be sorry for Blossom, I can promise you. And there's no need for us to get rid of her. That's just Blossom's way. She'll calm down soon enough.'

'You're too soft. Both of you. That's always been your trouble.'

'Maybe. But Blossom suits us.'

'You mean, you suit Blossom. No-one else would employ her.'

'Probably not.'

'You two are impossible.'

'That's what you love about us.' Silas pats her on the head. 'Now, I'm going to ring up the hardware shop and complain about that preservative. There must have been some mistake.'

The following morning, Blossom turns up early. Her mood has clearly improved, and she is almost polite to Eric and Silas.

'Got an idea,' she tells them, as she washes up the breakfast things without being asked (Blossom never does the washing-up).

'Oh, yes?' Eric says.

'Move the hen house into the back field.'

'Move the hen house? Who's got time to move the hen house, even if we wanted it moved?'

'Our Lazzo.'

'Oh yes?' Lazzo (short for Lazarus, so called because he nearly died as a baby) is Blossom's son. She rarely mentions him, and appears to have as little time for him as she has for Kaz, but apparently he has his uses. 'Well, even if he would, why should anyone move the hen house? It's perfectly all right where it is.'

'Visitors,' explains Blossom.

'Ah. Visitors. But there won't be any visitors because there won't be anything for them to see once we've painted over it.'

I wait for Blossom to explode, but she has obviously changed her tactics.

'Shame,' says Blossom. 'Should be pleased. It's a sign.'

'Yes. A sign that that dratted hardware place sold us the wrong stuff. And as you know, we're *not* pleased. Not at all pleased. We just want to be left in peace to get on with our lives.'

But Blossom's not going to let Eric and Silas get away quite so lightly. She has it all worked out, she tells them. If the hen house is moved to the back field (which is more thicket than field), together with its occupants, then a separate track can be made which will bypass the house and garden, and any visitors can come and go without disturbing anyone.

'What about the hens?' Silas asks.

'Be fine. Leave them to me.'

'And how do we control the number of visitors?'

Blossom wheels out her trump card.

'Tickets.'

'Tickets?'

'S'right.'

'And do you imagine that we're all going to take it in turns selling tickets so that people can view our hen house? Do you think we've got the *time*?' Silas is becoming seriously angry.

'Church,' says Blossom. 'Church'll do it.'

'Oh, will they!'

'I've asked.'

'You had no right!'

'No harm in asking.' Blossom breathes on a glass she's drying and polishes it. 'He said yes.'

'Who said yes?'

'Father Vincent.'

'Oh, him.'

Blossom goes on to explain that Father Vincent is quite happy for the parish secretary to distribute tickets. Not for money, of course; that wouldn't be right. But it would limit numbers, and there would be strict visiting times.

'You've given this a lot of thought, haven't you?' Silas asks wearily.

'Yep.' Blossom polishes another glass, and holds it up to the light.

'Why, Blossom? Why are you doing this?'

'For Our Lady,' says Blossom piously.

Eric and Silas look at each other.

'I suppose we could look into it,' Eric says. 'Just look into it, mind. No promises.' Eric is currently preoccupied with the dietary habits of snakes, and is anxious to defuse the situation so that he can return to his researches. 'And of course, we'll have to speak to Father Vincent.'

'If — *if* we decided to go ahead with all this, how much would your Lazzo charge for his — relocation activities?' Silas asks.

'Wouldn't charge,' says Blossom.

'What, nothing at all?'

'S'right. Do it instead of penance.'

I know a bit about Catholics and their penances. With a bit of luck, Lazzo might even get time off purgatory, as well. If he's anything like his mother, he could probably do with it.

'We'll need to phone Father Vincent,' Silas says.

'You do that.' Blossom puts away the last of the crockery. 'Going to do the pigs.' She goes out of the back door, closing it quietly behind her.

'Goodness!' says Silas. 'If that's what Blossom's Virgin does for her, it's almost worth it.'

'Hmm. I want to know what Father Vincent has to say,' Eric tells him 'I have a feeling we haven't heard the whole story.'

After a lengthy telephone conversation, Eric informs us that we've been seriously misled.

'Reading between the lines, I suspect that Father Vincent agreed to Blossom's suggestion in order to get her off his back. It was late last night, and he says he'd "had a little drink or two". He did admit he'd said yes to something, but he can't remember what. Most unwise.'

'Did you explain?' Silas asks.

'Yes. To be honest, I don't think Father Vincent's too bothered about Blossom and her Virgin. I get the feeling he'd probably agree to anything. But apparently, he has a very accommodating secretary, and he says that she'd probably agree to give out tickets. Provided it doesn't take up too much of her time.'

Listening to this exchange, I build up a picture of an idle parish priest, fond of a tipple, and a poor overworked secretary, who'll probably be less than enthusiastic about all this. I may of course be wrong.

'What's happening?' Poor Mum, who is also listening, is looking more panic-stricken by the minute.

'Nothing. Yet.' Silas smiles at her. 'And certainly nothing for you to worry about.'

'People aren't going to worship this — this *thing*, are they?' she asks.

'Of course not,' says Eric, who I'm sure has no idea what they're going to do. 'And nothing's been decided yet, in any case.'

'I could help,' I say, after Mum's left the room, for I've been thinking. 'I could oversee things; make sure no-one steps out of line.'

'Oh, not you too, Ruth. I thought you of all people would understand!' says Silas.

'Of course I understand. It's just that I have a feeling you're going to give in anyway, so we might as well do the thing properly.'

'And that includes the church and tickets?'

'It could do. But not every day, of course. If we restrict visitors to certain times, then surely there's no harm in it. And if things don't work out, or people become a nuisance, we can always paint over it again.'

The truth is, despite the fact that I'm enjoying my new life, I still have time on my hands. I do my bit to help, and there's my weekly busking, but Blossom's Virgin offers new possibilities, and it would be something else to take my mind off the future.

'Are you prepared to do this? Because we certainly haven't got time.'

'Yes. It might be fun.'

'Don't let Blossom hear you say that.'

'I think Blossom will agree to anything, if you let her keep her Virgin.'

'I'm not sure I want Lazzo around the place,' says Eric. 'Can he be trusted?'

'I've no idea.' I know even less about Lazzo than my uncles do. 'But you could say you'd like to meet him first.'

'I suppose we could.'

Lazzo turns up later in the afternoon. He's not at all what I expected, for while he's not especially tall, he's built like an army truck, with a wide moon of a face, short thick legs and hands like shovels. Taken all together, his appearance would be terrifying if it were not for the mild, almost childlike expression in his eyes, which are so pale as to be almost colourless. It's hard to believe that Lazzo ever issued from the womb of anyone as tiny as Blossom, but this must have been the case (and of course, he was premature. Perhaps Blossom's body, as uncompromising as Blossom herself, expelled him as soon as he'd outstayed his welcome). On reflection, I'm grateful that I shall never have to meet Lazzo's father.

'Come to help,' says Lazzo, leaning his (Blossom's) bike against the wall. It would appear that he has inherited his mother's way with words.

We invite him indoors and ply him with tea (strong, four sugars) and biscuits (seven custard creams) after which we all repair to the hen house to see what would need to be done.

Lazzo inspects the hen house and its possible destination, strokes the hens (he must have his mother's way with animals, because the hens would normally run a mile rather than be stroked), and gives his stubbled chin a thoughtful rub.

'Okay,' he says.

'You'll — you would do it, then?' Silas asks him.

'No prob.'

'And the run?'

'Yeah.'

'You'll need help.'

'Do it on me own.'

'It's very heavy.'

'Take roof off. And nesting boxes. Be fine.'

'And you'll be careful? It's very old, and we're — fond of it.'

'Yeah.'

'If you're sure, then.'

'Sure. Do a path, too.' Lazzo gives us a surprisingly sweet smile.

'And what about pay?' Eric asks him.

'Nope. Mum says not.'

'Are you sure?'

'Yeah.'

'Do you always do what your mum says?' Silas is obviously as curious as I am.

'Better that way.' Lazzo laughs, and we join in. I'm beginning to warm to Lazzo. 'Start tomorrow?'

Eric and Silas exchange glances.

'Start tomorrow,' they agree.

It would seem that Lazzo has got the job, and Blossom has clocked up an important victory. The Virgin of the hen house is here to stay.

CHAPTER EIGHTEEN

Blossom is in triumphant mode. She practically dances round the house with her duster, and even comes in on her days off. She also smiles.

Surprisingly, this is neither a pretty nor a welcome sight. Blossom smiling is not like other people smiling. There is none of the open friendliness one might expect from a normal person; none of the acknowledgement by one well-intentioned human being of the common humanity and good will of another. Blossom's smile has something sinister about it; a touch of the I-know-something-you-don't (or perhaps in this instance, I'm-up-to-something-you're-not-going-to-like).

'I wish Blossom would stop smiling,' my poor mother says. 'I don't like it.'

I know she feels threatened by Blossom and that her feelings are compounded by this new and terrifying smile, but there's not a lot we can do about it. We can hardly tell Blossom to stop. As for my uncles, they have other preoccupations than the newly-smiling Blossom. Eric has just arrived at the knotty problem of insects ('they're small, of course, but there are so *many* of them'), and Silas has found a dead whippet.

'I've phoned the police, and no-one knows anything about it,' he says wistfully. 'I'll never get another chance like this. I need to get started on it soon.'

'What did the police say?' I ask him.

'They said I'd better wait, but I can't. They don't understand. It's beginning to smell. And Eric won't let me to put it in the freezer.'

'Is it like when you find money?' I ask him.

'How do you mean?'

'If it's not claimed within a certain period, then you can keep it.'

'Probably, though I don't suppose they get many people wanting to keep other people's dead dogs.'

'The owners might be quite grateful,' I suggest. After all, a stuffed whippet has got to be better than a corpse. 'You could stuff it, and then if someone claims it, drive the car over it so that it looks run over again, and let them have it back. They mightn't notice the difference.'

'Do you think?' His face is so boyishly hopeful that I can't help laughing.

'Oh, why not?'

'I'll get started, then?'

'I would. No time like the present.'

Meanwhile, Lazzo is labouring away at the task of moving the hen house. He appears to be incredibly strong, and a very hard worker once he gets going. His triceps bulge and the veins in his neck stand out as he lifts huge sections of timber, and if glimpses of buttocks and an expanse of hairy stomach are less than attractive, then we can always look the other way. I trot to and fro with mugs of strong tea and doorsteps of bread and cheese (Lazzo's size is matched only by his enormous appetite) and Mr. Darcy watches adoringly from the sidelines. He brings Lazzo his ball and his old rubber bone, and the tattered bedsock he sleeps with at night, and even the treasured half-toothbrush. He lays them all at Lazzo's feet, then lies down in the long grass, his chin on his paws, following Lazzo's every move with soulful brown eyes. I'd give a lot to be adored the way Mr. Darcy adores Lazzo.

Blossom's attitude towards her son is to ignore him.

'Best left,' is her only comment, when I mention his presence.

'You must be proud of him,' I venture. 'He's an amazing worker.'

'Humph.' Blossom shrugs.

'Who does he work for normally?'

'Doesn't work.'

'Why not?'

'On benefit.'

'Why?'

'Special needs.' Blossom turns on the vacuum cleaner, her chosen way of terminating a conversation, and I am left to ponder the special needs of Lazzo.

If you discount tea and sandwiches, Lazzo's needs seem to be few, and certainly not particularly special. Is there something about Lazzo we ought to know, I wonder? Or is he — or more likely, his mother — pulling a fast one? And if so, how does Blossom reconcile that with her faith? The next time I bring Lazzo his tea, I scrutinise his face for clues, but can find none. I would have thought that someone like Lazzo would be eminently employable.

'Do you have — another job, Lazzo?' I ask him as he leans against a tree trunk drinking his tea.

'Nope.'

'Why not? You seem — very capable.'

'Not allowed.'

'Why not?'

'Born premature,' explains Lazzo, posting a fist-sized sandwich into his enormous mouth.

'But wasn't that rather a long time ago?' For few people must resemble a premature baby less than Lazzo does.

'Yeah.' Lazzo grins. 'But Mum says I've got special needs.'

'And have you?'

'Used to have fits,' he says, swallowing a huge piece of sandwich. I watch in fascination as it makes its journey down a neck so thick that it could be an extension of his head. It's a bit like watching a snake swallowing an antelope (I saw this once on a television programme).

'And do you still — have fits?' I know I'm being impertinent, but Lazzo intrigues me.

'Nah. Well, little ones.'

'What kind of fits?'

In reply, Lazzo rolls his eyes and slobbers a bit, shaking his massive frame like a tree in a gale. I try to stand my ground.

'Epileptic, then?' I suggest, after a moment. I have an epileptic friend who manages to hold down a very high-powered job with no apparent difficulty.

Lazzo nods, and loads his mouth up with another sandwich.

'Can't you have tablets?'

'Forget to take 'em.' As he speaks, I can see clumps of bread revolving in his mouth like cement in a mixer.

'What about your mother? Couldn't she remind you?'

'She'd be cross. Thinks I take 'em.'

'So what do you do with them?'

'Sell 'em.'

'*Sell* them?'

'Yeah. Got a mate gets high on my tablets.' Lazzo laughs. 'Do him more good than me.'

'And — the benefit people. Won't they catch up with you?'

'Haven't yet. Do a little fit for 'em when they come round. Soon gets rid of 'em. People don't like fits.'

'I can imagine.' If I were a benefit person, I'd soon make myself scarce if I had the misfortune to witness Lazzo doing his special needs act.

'So you just — stay at home?'

'S'right.'

'How do you get on with your mother?' I've been dying to ask him this.

Lazzo laughs. 'No-one gets on with Mum.'

So it's not just us, then. Well, I suppose that's something.

'That must be difficult. How do you manage?'

'Just take no notice.'

'And — Kaz?'

'She's all right. Never in, though. Pole dancer.'

'Really?' I've never met anyone who's related to a pole dancer. Though I'm not sure why Blossom disapproves of her daughter. After all, pole dancing is perfectly above board, isn't it?

'Good money,' Lazzo explains, picking his teeth with a piece of straw.

'I'll bet.'

Lazzo looks me up and down appraisingly. 'Should give it a go,' he suggests with a grin.

I make a mental note to try not to become over-familiar with Lazzo. He has a certain charm even though he may be a little odd, but no doubt he's equipped with the usual complement of hormones and urges, and if there were to be any sort of struggle (perish the thought) there's no doubt as to who would — literally — come out on top.

As though to drive the point home, half an hour after this conversation, the baby takes the opportunity to remind me of my responsibilities by delivering its first unmistakeable kick. I've been told to expect 'flutterings' or feelings I might mistake for indigestion, but this is a proper kick; faint, to be sure, but almost certainly delivered by a tiny foetal foot. It may be that there have been other movements, and in my state of semi-denial I have failed to notice them. I shall never know. Whatever may or may not have happened, I now have unequivocal proof that the baby is, quite literally, alive and kicking.

CHAPTER NINETEEN

'I can go with her. I'd like to go with her. And she said after last time she didn't want us both again, so only one of us can go.'

'What about me? It was my idea.'

'But I know more about this sort of thing than you do. I promise I'll bring back a full report.'

'Anyone can bring back a full report. Ruth can do that.'

'True. But it makes sense for it to be me. I've read all the books, and I know what questions to ask.'

'Lend me the books, and I'll know what to ask, too. Anyway, the hospital staff are the people in the know. *We* don't have to know anything at all. And I'm sure they'll be delighted to explain.'

I listen in fascination as Eric and Silas argue over the lunch table as to which of them is to accompany me to my twenty-week scan. I've never heard them argue before, and while this is a relatively amicable discussion, there is an undertone of stiff-necked determination on both sides.

'May I say something?' I ask at last.

'Of course. Go ahead, Ruth,' Eric says.

'This is my scan, right?'

'Of course.'

'And I'm insured to drive the Land Rover now?'

'You know you are.'

'Then I can go to the scan on my own. And I can bring back — how did you put it? — *a full report* myself. That way, no-one needs to feel left out, and you can both stop this silly argument.'

Their faces fall into identical expressions of surprise and disappointment, and I can't help laughing.

'I'm sorry, Ruth,' Eric says, after a moment. 'I suppose we just forgot, well, forgot...'

'That I was here?'

'Something like that.'

'Well, it's a good thing I am here. And presumably I have the casting vote.'

'But it seems such a waste,' mourns Silas. 'It's so interesting, and you're allowed to take someone. I'll never get an opportunity like this again.' He makes it sound like a wasted theatre ticket.

'Yes. But I can hardly choose between the two of you, can I? So it's fairer to have neither of you. No-one will be pleased, but no-one will be disappointed.'

'We could toss up for it,' Silas suggests.

'I don't think so.'

'Ruth?' I'd forgotten my mother was there.

'Yes, Mum?'

'I'd love — I'd really love to come with you. If you'll let me.'

'Oh, Mum! Of course I'll let you. I'd love to have you with me. You're the obvious person. And we can go for lunch afterwards.'

Eric and Silas stand down gracefully (after all, they can hardly take issue with my mother accompanying me to the hospital), and after extracting promises of photos and answers to the list of questions Silas has compiled, they go out to do something unpleasant to a goat.

'Did they really both go with you to your last scan?' asks Mum over the washing-up.

'Yes. They were an absolute pain.'

'I'm sure they were. But Ruth — was it appropriate for them to, well to see you like that?'

'Like what?'

'With no clothes — *down there.*'

'It was a knickers-on affair; all perfectly dignified,' I assure her. '*Down there* was all covered up, and just the tummy showing. But in any case, I don't think I'd want them again, and certainly not both together. They were very sweet, but they wouldn't let me get a word in edgeways. And they did their double act in the waiting room and made an exhibition of all of us. I'm not going through that again.'

'They used to do that as little boys.'

'Well, it's probably all very sweet with little boys, but with elderly men, it's excruciating.'

'I can imagine.' Mum folds her tea towel and hangs it up. 'Ruth?'

'Yes?'

'I'm — I'm so glad I came. Not glad about leaving Dad, of course, but glad I'm here now, seeing you like this. Being — well, being with you.'

'I'm glad too.'

'But I'm worried about your father.'

'Why? He's okay, isn't he?'

'Up to a point.' She sighs, twisting her wedding ring round on her finger. 'But he's not used to looking after himself, and — well, it is my job. I know that's an unfashionable view, but it's all I've ever done since we married. Looked after the house and Dad, and you of course, when you were at home. Dad worked hard before he retired, and I saw it as my role to support him. I still do.'

'Did you enjoy it?'

'Enjoy what?'

'Being — well, a housewife, I suppose.'

'Yes. On the whole, I did. But that's another thing. I'd like to do something else as well; I'd like to be *good* at something else. Something different. Before it's too late. Does that sound odd?'

'Not odd at all. Isn't that what most of us want? To do something really well? That's certainly how I feel about my violin, and although I'll never be as good as I'd like to be, at least I've given it my best shot. What sort of thing would you like to do?'

'I don't know. I'm not creative, or musical, or anything like that, but there must be something I could do. Something new. Something *different*.' Mum sits down at the table, and rests her chin in her hand. 'I may have been quite a good wife, but I wasn't really a very good mother, was I?' she says after a moment.

'Well, you looked after me beautifully. I had a — good childhood,' I say carefully.

'But I never tried to understand you. I thought I did, but now, when I see you with Eric and Silas, so relaxed, so *easy* — I feel I must have got something wrong. And the violin.' She sighs, and pulls at a strand of her neatly permed hair. 'I knew it meant a lot to you, but I didn't understand why. When I hear you playing now, and see how much Eric and Silas enjoy it, and the encouragement they give you...' her voice tails away. 'I should have been the one to encourage you, even if I don't know much about music. It was as much a part of my job as looking after you. But I didn't know. I never really understood. And now I suppose it's too late.'

'I don't think it's ever too late in relationships,' I tell her. 'Provided both people want things to change. I don't think I'm really the daughter you wanted, am I? And it's not your fault

I'm the way I am. Take the music. In some ways, I'd prefer not to want to be a musician. It leads to so much heartache and disappointment. Life would have been so much easier if I'd wanted to be — a chartered accountant, for instance. A nice safe profession, with far less scope for failure and a good income. And Dad would have been thrilled.'

'He would, wouldn't he?' We both laugh.

And of course, all this is true, provided that in the fullness of time Dad was able to walk me down the aisle in my white frock and hand me and my virginity over to a suitable young man (maybe another chartered accountant. Why not?), after which I would "settle down" and keep house for him and any offspring we might have. And the whole cycle would begin again. A little dull and predictable, but safe, and oh, so respectable.

'And I'm to blame, too,' I say now. 'Instead of ranting and slamming doors, I could have sat down with you and explained things properly. I could have tried to understand you, as well as the other way around.'

'You did get pretty angry,' Mum says. 'But we were the adults.'

'Well, now I'm an adult too, and we — well, you and I, anyway — can start to understand each other.'

'Don't make the same mistakes with — with your baby,' Mum says now. 'You've got the chance to make a better job of it than I did, and a clean slate, even though you've got no — there's no —'

'Father?'

'Yes.' She hesitates. 'Who was he, Ruth? What was he like?'

I recognise that she's been working up to this question, and I admire her courage, for it can't have been easy. Mum and I have never really confided in each other, and this is uncharted territory.

'Well, he's nice,' I begin lamely. 'A musician. A very good one. Much better than I'll ever be.'

'And — oh, Ruth, I really need to ask you this. Is he — is he married?'

I shake my head. 'He was, but his wife found someone else and he's now divorced.'

I note the little intake of breath at the D word, but Mum doesn't comment.

'Do you still see him?' she asks me.

'No. We've lost touch.'

'That's a shame.'

'Yes. Yes, it is. It's funny, really. We've never played a big part in each other's lives, and yet now I really miss him. I haven't even had the chance to tell him about the baby, and he ought at least to know that. Then it would be up to him what he did about it. If anything. And before you ask —' for I can see the question trembling on Mum's lips, almost begging to be let out — 'I might even marry him, if he'd have me. Not just because of the baby, but because he's a good man, we've lots in common, and I think we'd be good together. But we'd have to see about that.'

'He can't have just — disappeared.'

'That's what I thought. But it seems that he has. Disappearing is what he does. He'll probably turn up sooner or later, but we could be talking months or even years. I've tried to track him down, but I think he must be abroad.'

'Does he have a steady job?'

'I've no idea.' I laugh at Mum's expression. 'Musicians and steady jobs don't necessarily go together. As you and Dad kept telling me, it's risky business.'

And for the time being, we leave it at that. I realise afterwards that Mum and I have covered more ground in the last hour than we have in the past ten years, and I'm grateful to her for initiating the conversation. If it had been left to me, would we ever have talked like this? I doubt it. My mother has the courage that I lack, and I feel new respect for her. In many ways, she is a much better human being than I can ever hope to be, and while I disagree with many of her principles, she has certainly lived by them. It is to my shame that this could never be said of me.

The scan takes place the next day, and while the baby certainly appears to be more baby-like than it was last time, and Mum 'oohs' and 'aahs' over tiny fingers and toes, a waving arm, a 'dear little face' ('I believe it's got your nose, Ruth.' Has it? How on earth can she tell?), I still fail to experience any of the wonder and delight I'm supposed to feel.

'Aren't you at all excited, Ruth?' Mum whispers, when the technician disappears for a moment to fetch something. 'I'd no idea it would be as amazing as this. We never had this sort of thing when I was expecting you.' She seems to have forgotten the unfortunate provenance of her foetal grandchild in her wonderment at the combined miracles of nature and modern technology.

'Of course I'm excited,' I tell her (what else can I say?).

'Do you want to know the sex of your baby?' The technician has returned.

'No — yes — I don't know.'

'Silas does,' Mum reminds me.

'Well, it's not his baby,' I snap, and am instantly sorry. I give her hand a squeeze. 'Yes, okay. Why not?'

'A boy,' we're told. 'Were you hoping for a boy?'

'I — don't mind. But Blossom will be pleased.'

'What's Blossom got to do with it?' Mum asks.

'Blossom reckons she can always tell. She told me weeks ago that it was a boy.' It would have been nice to be able to confound Blossom, but now it seems that even that small victory is denied me.

We go through Silas's list of questions, and receive patient (and on the whole, satisfactory) answers. No, the baby doesn't appear to have any congenital defects or chromosomal abnormalities, although there are no absolute guarantees. Yes, it is the right size for its gestation, has all the right bits and pieces in the appropriate places and the degree of its activity is normal. It probably weighs about a pound (only a pound? That's less than half a bag of sugar. I try to imagine a pound of baby, and fail) and its various measurements are to scale.

As we emerge later on into pale autumn sunshine, I feel an overwhelming sense of loneliness, and suddenly I ache for the big, comforting presence of Amos; for the feeling of his arms around me, his clean man-smell, his comfortable chest, even the tickle of his beard against my cheek. I imagine him seeing in our baby all the things I don't yet seem able to see, and telling me what a clever girl I am (isn't that what new fathers are supposed to say?). We would walk hand-in-hand across the road to the pub for lunch, and he would have his usual pint of bitter (in a jug with a handle) and I would sip my tomato juice, and we'd get out our new photos of the baby, and admire them together. Best of all, we would be a *couple*; a couple sharing *our* baby.

Mum has been better company than I could have hoped for (or deserved), but it's Amos that I want with me now. I imagine his delight at the prospect of a son, his dreams of taking him to football matches (Amos loves football. Who will take the seahorse/rabbit to watch football if it hasn't got a father? Every child deserves at least one parent who understands the off-side rule), helping with maths homework, running in fathers' races on school sports days, and in the fullness of time, teaching it to drive. How will I manage to do all these things on my own? How do single parents *cope*?

'Are you all right, Ruth?' Mum asks me.

'Something in my eye,' I tell her, fumbling in my bag for a tissue.

Despite our new improved relationship, I'm still not ready to tell Mum how much I long to find Amos.

CHAPTER TWENTY

It has taken Lazzo nearly a week to complete his labours with the hen house, and the project is almost finished. A large patch has been cleared in the back field, with a rough path leading to it from the main track, and the hens are comfortably installed in their new surroundings. The Virgin side of the hen house is exposed, with the rest — including the nesting boxes — fenced off by the run, so that the hens are spared the worshipful activities of their visitors. As Silas says, whatever the hens may or may not be, they are certainly not Roman Catholics. As it happens, they seem to have suffered very little from the upheaval, and I put this down to Lazzo. He has a quite extraordinary way with animals, reminding me of Dickon in *The Secret Garden*. Cows come up to him to be stroked; Sarah, who normally eschews any physical contact, allows him to tickle her tummy; the cats — usually so haughtily independent — fawn all over him; and poor Mr. Darcy is completely besotted.

'How do you do it?' I ask, as Lazzo and I sit together on a log contemplating his handiwork. Lazzo is holding a chicken on his lap, gently ruffling its feathers with a very dirty thumb, while Mr. Darcy lies adoringly at his feet.

Lazzo looks down at the chicken.

'Dunno,' he says.

'Have you always been good with animals?'

'S'pose. Had a hamster when I was five,' he offers, as though this is some kind of explanation.

'And?'

'Cat got it.'

'Oh.' I don't seem to be getting anywhere. 'Have you ever thought of working with animals?'

'Never thought of working.'

We both laugh. I have grown fond of Lazzo. Apart from his appraising glances and the occasional suggestive wink, he has been on the whole civil, sensible, and fun. He has a good sense of humour, and his company is undemanding. He appears to be perfectly self-sufficient, comfortable in his own skin, and content. While Blossom may have been a pretty awful mother, she must have got something right.

'What do you want to do? In the future?' I ask him. 'There must be something you'd really like to do.'

'London Zoo,' says Lazzo promptly.

'What, work there?'

'Just go.'

'Have you never been?'

'Never been to London.'

'Then I'll take you,' I promise him. 'One day, I'll take you to London Zoo.' I bend down to pull Mr. Darcy's ears. 'But what else? You must have some kind of — ambition?'

'Nope.'

'Would you like to — get married?' I venture, realising that this is possibly a tactless question.

'Mum says no-one'd have me.'

'She can't be sure.' I feel a surge of indignation on Lazzo's behalf. How dare Blossom pass judgement in this way? How can she possibly know?

'Says I'm too lazy. Got a point.' Lazzo grins, and pats my shoulder. 'Fine as I am.'

And he's probably right. It's so easy to attribute to other people one's own hopes and aspirations; to decide that they can't be happy because their lot isn't what one would want for oneself. In a way, I envy Lazzo. He appears to have everything he wants, plus his childlike ability to live in the present. A doorstep of bread and cheese, a can of beer, a sunny day, the rough lick of a cat's tongue on his hand — Lazzo appears to get his pleasures from simple things. I can't imagine him agonising over past mistakes or future plans; wanting things he can't have or worrying about what people think of him. Lazzo is what he is, take it or leave it. One could learn a lot from Lazzo.

Now that the business of relocation has been dealt with, the small matter of the Virgin has to be addressed, together with the imminent advent of her admirers. But when I mention the subject to Blossom, it would seem that everything's in hand.

'All sorted,' she tells me, her beady eyes challenging me to interfere with her plans.

'What about the tickets?' I ask her. 'You said it would be a tickets-only affair.'

'Done,' says Blossom.

'What do you mean, done?'

'Church.'

Blossom's minimalist means of communication can be absolutely maddening. Sometimes I want to take her by her shoulders and shake the syllables out of her until there are enough of them to constitute a proper sentence.

'What about the church?'

'All in hand.' Blossom reaches for the switch on the vacuum cleaner, but I turn it off at the wall.

'Blossom, we need to know. We need to know who's coming, when they're coming, and how many. You can't just make all the decisions off your own bat.' Eric and Silas are out, and Mum is washing her hair. Blossom and I are on our own.

After a lot of cajoling I manage to acquire a few basic facts. A small committee from the Catholic church has apparently visited the hen house (how come we didn't notice? It's not as though small committees are a normal part of the landscape) and have given their seal of approval. Someone has volunteered to print tickets on their computer, and Father Vincent has given his blessing (I'll bet he has. I suspect Father Vincent will do anything for a quiet life). Visitors will be admitted on two afternoons a week. A large notice has been made for the gate (we now have a separate path leading to the hen house), giving the days and times when the Virgin is receiving visitors, and Father Vincent is donating a padlock out of the church petty cash.

'You could at least have checked with Eric and Silas,' I tell her.

'Did. Weren't listening,' Blossom tells me. 'Eric on the phone; Silas stuffing something. Often don't listen,' she adds. 'Not my fault.'

I know very well whose fault it is. Blossom has a habit of raising awkward subjects when she knows they are least likely to be heard, and then interpreting silence as agreement. Whatever may be said about Blossom, she's not stupid.

'Oh, well. I suppose that's okay,' I concede. 'Two afternoons should be manageable. How will people know about it?'

'Parish magazine. Told them start next week.'

It would appear that Blossom has thought of everything.

When Eric and Silas return, they agree that we should be able to accommodate visitors on two afternoons a week, although, as I suspected, they were unaware that they had already agreed to the arrangement.

'So long as you take charge, Ruth. You said you would,' Silas reminds me.

'If Blossom lets me, I'm happy to be in charge.'

'She'll have to do as she's told,' Eric says.

'Blossom,' I remind him, 'never does what she's told.'

'Well the two of you will have to work things out together. Silas and I haven't the time.'

Working with Blossom proves to be easier than I had anticipated, largely I suspect because she is so keen for the project to work and knows that as Eric's and Silas's representative, I have the power of veto. After the first week, Eric and Silas agree that the project has given rise to very little trouble. Visitors arrive at the appointed times, bearing their tickets, and on the whole they behave nicely. They come in twos and threes, reverent and respectful, murmuring in low voices, sometimes praying, and Blossom, Lazzo and I take it in turns to oversee things.

The Virgin herself looks if anything more lifelike than she did before she was moved. Her outline is sharp and well-defined, her robe flowing, the stars — and they really do look like stars — form a halo round her head. I find myself wondering whether Blossom might have touched her up a bit when we weren't looking, but everything is true to the original grain of the wood. Even Blossom can't interfere with nature. Blossom herself maintains a small vase of flowers beneath the apparition, and while these are regularly consumed by Sarah and her brood, they add to the hen house a touch of the roadside shrine which reminds me of a long-ago Austrian holiday.

Do I believe in the Virgin of the hen house? Once I would have said categorically that I did not, but now, I'm not so sure. I've never been the kind of person who looks for (or wants) signs or miracles, but I have to admit that this is, if not miraculous, then certainly a rare kind of curiosity. Mum watches me anxiously, and I know she harbours a secret fear that I shall "go over to Rome" (I heard her confiding as much to Silas), but I certainly have no intention of doing that. Not for me the trips to the confessional, the collection of indulgences and the weekly attendance at Mass; I had far too much religion when I was a child to be tempted back into any kind of church. But I have a growing respect for our pilgrims; for their apparently unquestioning faith and their readiness to accept proof of the existence of God, while having no actual need of any such proof. And I envy them. It must be wonderful to be able to place oneself in the hands of a deity, and trust that everything will be taken care of.

Eric and Silas take little interest in the Virgin. Now that they know that their chickens are safe and that Blossom is being kept sweet, they apparently feel they can get on with their lives. Silas is still working on his whippet ('I think it's my best yet, Ruth. I do hope no-one wants it back.' Since it no longer bears any resemblance whatever to a dog, never mind a whippet, I think he can rest assured that this is unlikely to happen). And Eric's researches are becoming increasingly complicated.

'Take the bettong,' he says at breakfast.

'What's a bettong?' Mum asks.

'A small Australian marsupial.'

'How interesting.' Mum reaches for the marmalade.

'And the possum,' Eric continues. 'And the wallaby, and of course the kangaroo. And all the other marsupials. I'd no idea there were so many of them. Would Noah have taken two of all of them, do you suppose?'

'You don't believe in Noah,' I remind him.

'That's not the point, Ruth.'

'No. Of course not. Sorry.' I have a vivid mental image of kangaroos (and bettongs) leaping over the side of the ark into the boiling waves. 'Can kangaroos swim?'

'Why?' Eric looks at me suspiciously.

'It doesn't matter. No. I'm sure Noah would have taken just two kinds of marsupials. A big one and a small one.'

'Ah.' Eric looks relieved. 'It's just that all the working out takes *so much time*. I've given up with all the insects. I'm keeping those to a minimum. Not that they take up much room, but there are literally millions of them.'

'I know.' I have the flea bites (courtesy of the cats) to prove it.

'Sad about the marsupials, though. I liked the sound of the bettong.'

'Something would probably have eaten it.'

'Ruth, I wish you wouldn't persist in treating this whole thing as a joke.'

Mum excuses herself and gets up from the table. Ark conversations always make her uncomfortable.

'And bees,' Eric continues (he loves it when we pay attention to his research).

'What about them?'

'Big problem, bees. Did you know that without bees, life on earth would die out in two years?'

'Then you'd better take more than two.'

Eric looks at me in exasperation.

'Of course there'd have to be more than two. But how would they survive, without flowers?'

'Don't they hibernate in the winter?'

'Yes. But the flood didn't subside until the 'tenth day of the tenth month'. It would be difficult to persuade a hive — or even several hives — of bees to sleep for ten months.'

'Pot plants? You could take lots of pot plants.'

'Now you really are being silly.'

'Yes. I doubt whether the Noah family would have the time to look after pot plants as well as everything else.' I myself have never managed to keep even one pot plant alive, and I don't have an Ark full of animals to take care of. 'So without the bees, the whole thing falls apart?' I ask him.

'You're missing the point, Ruth. What I'm trying to do is not so much prove that Noah *didn't* build his Ark, as showing exactly how big and how much of everything there would have to be, and therefore he *couldn't* have done it. I'm designing an Ark which could take everything, but showing that it would have to be far too big to be remotely possible. So we have to have bees, even if it means an even bigger Ark.'

'Bigger than the Isle of Wight?'

'Quite possibly.'

'Ah.' I start clearing away the breakfast things. 'I think I ought to get going,' I tell him. 'And it seems clear that you've got a few more calculations to do.'

CHAPTER TWENTY-ONE

Meanwhile, Mum is still fretting about Dad.

'How does he seem when you speak to him?' I ask her.

'Not too bad. But he keeps asking me when I'm coming home. He doesn't seem to understand that I can't. Not yet, anyway.'

'And you've told him that?'

'Yes.' She hesitates. 'Ruth?'

'Mm?'

'Would you do me a favour?'

'Of course.'

'Would *you* go and see him? Just to make sure he's looking after himself?'

'Mum, of course he's looking after himself. The reason he's usually no good in the house is that you do everything for him. He's perfectly capable if he's got no-one else to wait on him. Why don't you go and see for yourself? You don't have to stay.' But even as I speak, I know that my mother can't do as I suggest. I know as well as she does that if she goes back, she'll stay there. My father has such a hold over her that she would never be able to, as it were, leave him twice. It's a miracle that she's managed to do it at all.

'Okay,' I tell her. 'I'll go. Just this once, mind.' I'm still smarting from Dad's treatment of me. 'I'm not making a habit of it.'

'Thank you. And I won't ask you again, I promise.'

I set off the following morning in Mum's car, feeling like Little Red Riding Hood, with my basket of eggs and cream (courtesy of Eric and Silas) and a casserole and a cake from

Mum. Silas is desperate for me to take his whippet ('see if he thinks it's real, Ruth. I haven't tried it on anyone new') but whatever I feel about Dad, I wouldn't go so far as to subject him to that.

There are long delays on the motorway and a diversion, and the journey takes me twice as long as it normally would. When I arrive at my parents' house, I am not in the best of humours.

Neither is my father.

'Your mother said you'd be here in time for lunch,' he says, without preamble, as he whisks me through the front door (presumably so that prying neighbours are spared a glimpse of my shameful new shape). 'Lunch is at one o'clock in this house, as you well know.' There seems to be a lot of smoke, and a strong smell of burning. The smoke alarm is ringing merrily in the background.

'Sorry. The roads were horrendous.' I wipe my feet carefully on the doormat and make as though to kiss him, but he backs away as though fearing an attack, covertly eyeing my bump.

'Well, the lunch is ruined now.' He leads the way into the kitchen, and I resist the temptation to tell him that a delayed meal doesn't have to be a burnt one.

The kitchen table is laid for two, and on the side is a baking tray containing four sad little black smoking bundles.

'What is — was it?' I ask.

'Sausages.'

'Anything else?'

'Mashed potato.' He lifts the lid off a saucepan, revealing a grey viscous mass which could once have been potato. I also notice a recipe book opened at "Braised Sausages with Onion Gravy". I decide that it would be pushing my luck to enquire about the gravy.

'We could go to the pub?' I suggest. 'My treat.'

Dad looks shocked.

'You know my feelings about pubs, Ruth,' he says. 'Anyway, this food is perfectly edible. Waste not, want not.' (This is one of his favourite mantras.)

'We wouldn't have to waste it. I could take it back with me for the pigs. They'd love it.'

This is not the right thing to say, and I am given a short lecture on my lack of gratitude and my shortcomings as a guest.

It is one of those meals where you have to concentrate all your energies on forcing the food down while trying hard to think of something else. As I swallow crunchy morsels of sausage (my father has contrived to burn them so thoroughly that there is barely any sausage at all remaining inside the crisp carbon shell) I try to imagine that they are pork scratchings, potato crisps, peanut brittle — anything crisp and delicious. Anything but burnt sausage. There is no alcohol to anaesthetise the taste buds, and the potato is if anything worse than the sausages. Mercifully, there is ketchup, and I smother my food with that.

'I thought you didn't like ketchup.' Dad says.

'Craving,' I explain, patting my bump. 'With some, it's coal. With me, it's ketchup.' In a way it's a pity I don't crave coal, since burnt sausages might well be the next best thing.

'No pudding, I'm afraid,' Dad says, when we've finished. 'I'm not much good at that sort of thing. But I've got some fruit.' He produces a bowl with three freckled bananas and a rather tired bunch of grapes. There's a fly sitting on the grapes (will there be flies on Eric's Ark?). Dad shoos it away.

'No thanks. I'm fine.'

'Coffee, then?'

'Coffee would be great.'

As Dad fusses over cups and percolator, we make small talk: Dad's allotment, the people at church, the weather.

'And — your mother?' he asks eventually. 'How's she?'

'Fine, She's fine.'

'She should be here, you know. With me. That's where she should be.'

'Do you miss her?'

'Miss her?' Dad looks puzzled. 'Well, yes. Of course I do. But it's more than that. People — talk.'

Ah yes. How could I forget? People talk.

'I expect they'll get over it.'

'First — you, and now your mother,' Dad continues, as though Mum and I have been playing a game of tug-of-war with his reputation. 'It's very difficult.'

'It's been difficult for all of us,' I say evenly.

'Has it? Has it really? You and your mother seem to be having a wonderful time cavorting about in the country.'

'Actually, we're working very hard.'

'So you've got her working, have you? Looking after all of you? I bet you have. I should think Eric and Silas are delighted to have your mother running around after them.'

'She's not running around after anyone. She's just doing her bit.' I spoon sugar into my coffee. 'We both are.'

'So when's she coming back?'

'You'll have to ask her that.'

'Well, I'm asking you.'

'Dad, I don't know when she's coming back. Mum's a grown woman. She makes her own decisions.'

'But she sent you here, didn't she?'

'She wanted to make sure you were okay.'

'And what will you tell her?'

'That you seem to be coping pretty well.'

For I have a feeling that all is not as it seems. When I went to fetch milk from the fridge, I noticed half a shepherd's pie neatly covered with cling film, a whole cooked chicken and what looked like a compote of dried fruit (so much for there being no pudding). Either Dad is a better cook than he lets on, in which case the burnt sausages were some kind of ruse, or he's being fed by someone else.

'You had a visitor,' Dad says now.

'A visitor? When?'

'It must have been a couple of weeks ago. A man came looking for you.'

'What sort of man?'

'Big bearded chap. Looked a bit like a tramp. He said he was a friend of yours.' Dad pours more coffee. 'Carrying some kind of instrument. A trumpet or something.'

'A trombone?'

'Could be. It was in a case.'

Amos! Dad has found Amos! Or rather, Amos has found Dad. I don't have any other big bearded friends, and Amos never goes anywhere without his trombone. I remember that I once gave him my parents' address, and he's obviously kept it.

'Oh Dad, that's wonderful! What did he say? What did you tell him?' I can hardly contain my excitement. 'How did he seem? Was he well?'

'I've no idea. I didn't ask him. He appeared to be well enough. He was only here for a few minutes. Seemed to think you were abroad — a gap year, I think he said — and asked if we'd heard from you.'

'You told him where I was, of course?'

'I did no such thing. Chap looked most unsuitable.'

'Someone came looking for me, *and you didn't tell him where I was?*'

'No. I just told him you'd gone away.'

'So he could still think I'm abroad?'

'Quite possibly.'

'Dad, you had no right! You had no right to send him away without telling me!'

'It's not my responsibility to put you in touch with strangers who turn up on our doorstep. He could have been anyone.'

I am so angry, I'm shaking. How could he? How could Dad have taken it upon himself to send Amos away like this?

'You might at least have phoned me to let me know, then I could have decided what I wanted to do. Have you any idea what you've done?'

'The responsible thing, I should hope.'

'You've sent away the father of my child. That's what you've done. I've been looking for him for weeks, and you've sent him away without even telling me!'

'Well, I'm telling you now.'

'But it's *too late*! How am I supposed to find him now? Did he leave an address?'

'He said something about going abroad. Yes, I'm sure that was what it was. He said he was going on a cruise. It's all right for some,' he adds sourly, which is rich coming from Dad, who doesn't approve of holidays, and certainly wouldn't dream of going on a cruise himself. 'Going on a cruise, when he has — responsibilities.'

'He won't be *going* on a cruise. He'll be *working* on a cruise. He's a musician. He has a living to earn. As for the responsibilities, he can hardly be accused of neglecting them if he doesn't know anything about them, can he?'

'You mean — you mean he doesn't know about — about your condition?'

'That's exactly what I mean. And now he may never know, thanks to you.'

'If you go around behaving like an alley cat, then you have only yourself to blame,' Dad tells me. 'Don't you start blaming me.'

'How dare you!'

'The truth hurts, doesn't it?'

'I can't believe you're saying this! And you call yourself a Christian!'

'It's *because* I'm a Christian —'

'*No.* No, Dad. You're not a Christian. Christianity is about love and forgiveness and tolerance, and —'

'If you're such an expert, how did you manage to get yourself into this mess, Ruth? You tell me that.'

'This is not a mess!' I yell at him. *'It's a baby!* My baby. And it's your grandchild too. Like it or not. Nothing I say or do can change that. And if I'm trying to do the right thing by finding Amos and making some kind of life with him, then you should be with me, not against me.'

'I think you should go, Ruth. Before you say something you regret.' Dad gets up from his chair, and prepares to see me out. He is calm and unruffled, glowing with churchy self-righteousness, and at this moment, I really hate him. I can't believe that a couple of hours ago I actually felt sorry for this lonely man and his burnt sausages; that I was touched by the promise (albeit unfulfilled) of onion gravy. Now, I can't wait to be on my way.

'Don't bother to see me out,' I tell him. 'I know the way.'

'That's all right, then.' He gives me the pitying look of one who is looking down on a sinner from the cosy perspective of the moral high ground. 'Give my regards to your mother.'

'You can give her your — *regards* — yourself.' Regards? After forty years of marriage? No wonder poor Mum's had enough. 'And it might just help if you were to do the phoning from time to time, instead of leaving it all to her. *If you want her back.*'

As a parting shot this is unworthy of me, and I experience a brief moment of shame. After all, Dad is on his own; he has no-one to complain to or take his side, for he's got far too much pride to confide in anyone outside the family. On the other hand, he's scuppered what I currently see as my one chance of happiness, for as far as Amos is concerned, I too could be anywhere. We could chase one another round the world until kingdom come, and never find each other. And since Amos was merely trying to look me up, probably on the off chance, and is unaware of the urgency of the situation, from now on, any real effort is going to have to come from me. By now, he has probably forgotten all about me, and is happily bobbing about on the ocean waves playing smoochy dance music to rich, over-fed tourists.

On my return journey, a lorry driver winks at me as we stop alongside each other at traffic lights. He has a beard and a kindly face, and his big, capable-looking hands rest lightly on the steering wheel. He reminds me of Amos.

I cry all the rest of the way back to Applegarth.

CHAPTER TWENTY-TWO

When I arrive back, tired and disillusioned (I had set out willing to bury hatchets and offer at least one small olive branch), Mum is naturally anxious to know how things went.

I am closely questioned as to the cleanliness of the house (not bad at all), the welfare of my father (ditto) and whether he is eating properly. I answer to the best of my ability, while trying to keep my tone positive.

'I'm not sure about his cooking skills,' I tell her, 'but he's certainly getting food from somewhere.'

'You make him sound like a stray cat.'

'Same kind of thing.' I am entertained by the idea of Dad eating saucers of scraps left out on people's doorsteps.

'Really, Ruth!'

'Sorry. But he's missing you, and sends his love.'

'Are you sure? Are you sure that's what he said?'

'Certain.' After all, I can hardly pass on the chilly "regards" Dad wanted me to relay, and my little lie is unlikely to be discovered.

Mum looks pleased.

'Perhaps he's coming round after all.'

'Well, you were the one who left,' I remind her.

'Yes. But I meant coming round to the idea of you. And the baby.'

'Well, I suppose he might be. But I wouldn't count on it. Not yet, anyway.' It would be unkind to raise her hopes. 'You know Dad and his principles. It takes a lot to make him change his mind.'

Mum sighs. 'Well, I suppose there's no hurry. Provided Eric and Silas don't mind putting up with me.'

'You know they love having you,' I tell her. 'So do I,' I add, and find to my surprise that it's true. It's been good having Mum around, and while we're not yet exactly confidantes, we're becoming increasingly comfortable with each other.

The following afternoon is a hen house afternoon, but there is no sign of Lazzo, whose turn it is to do hen house duty. Eric and Silas are out seeing a man about a pig and I was hoping to have a few uninterrupted hours of violin practice (Mum, needless to say, is having nothing to do with Virgins or hen houses). It is a warm for late October, and I am sitting in the garden rehearsing all the things I'd like to say to Dad (I'm still smarting from the Amos incident), when the phone rings. I run indoors to answer it. It is Blossom.

Blossom on the telephone is something else. At least when you have her face to face, you can fill in some of the gaps by trying to interpret her expression, but listening to her disembodied voice is like trying to unscramble a foreign language.

'Laz fitting,' she says, without preamble.

'*What?*'

'Our Laz. Fitting.'

'Fitting? Fitting what?' Carpets? Soft furnishings? What is Blossom talking about?

'*Fitting*. Like he does. You know.'

'Oh. You mean Lazzo's having fits?'

'What I said, isn't it?'

'Is he okay?'

'Course.' Pause. 'Won't be coming in.'

'Can you come then, Blossom? We've got a lot on.'

'Can't. Busy.'

'Oh dear.'

'Kaz coming instead.'

'That's kind of her.'

'Not kind. Told her to.'

'Oh. Right.' I spare a thought for Kaz. Supervising pilgrimages is hardly compatible with Kaz's professional calling and I open my mouth to say something appreciative, but Blossom has already rung off.

Fifteen minutes later, Kaz arrives.

I'm not quite sure what I was expecting, but whatever it might have been, Kaz isn't it. She is amazingly like Blossom, and yet totally different, for while following her mother's template, Kaz manages to be beautiful. It is as though someone had taken Blossom and airbrushed out her age and her imperfections, to make, literally, a new woman of her. The eyes which appear black and beady in Blossom, are dark and luminous in Kaz. Blossom's small bony body becomes toned and celebrity slim in Kaz, and Blossom's sharp features and pointed chin give an elfin, Peter Pan look to her daughter.

That Kaz contrives to be beautiful is all the more astonishing since she appears to have gone out of her way to deface the gifts with which nature has endowed her. Her dyed-blonde hair is scraped back in an untidy ponytail, and a variety of studs and rings pierce her eyebrows, ears and lips, while two tiny snakes are tattooed around her wrists. All this is set off with knee-length laced leather boots, a skimpy top and a faded denim skirt which just about covers her bottom. The effect is electric.

'Sorry I'm late,' Kaz says, giving me a radiant smile. 'Bloody bike had a puncture. Laz was supposed to fix it, but he forgot. He's a lazy bugger.'

'Oh, that's okay,' I say weakly, trying to imagine how anyone can ride a bike in a skirt that short.

'I'm Kaz,' she says, unnecessarily.

'Hi. Good to meet you.'

'You must be Ruth.'

'Yes. Yes, I am.'

'Expecting, I see,' remarks Kaz, patting my bump. 'I was expecting once,' she adds.

'Oh. What hap— I mean, what did you do?'

'The usual.' Kaz sighs. 'I couldn't keep it. I hadn't any money. Besides, Mum said she'd kill me if I had a baby. I was only fourteen.'

'I thought Catholics were against abortion?'

'They're against murder, too, but that wouldn't have stopped Mum from killing me. She's what you might call a pick and choose Catholic. And she didn't pick my baby.'

'How did you feel about that?'

'A bit sad, I suppose, but I was only a kid. And in our house, we do what our mum says. It makes life easier.'

'I can imagine.'

Kaz grins. 'You don't like Mum much, do you?'

'Well ... she's very good with the animals.'

'Don't worry. I don't like her much, either.'

'Then why do you live at home?'

'I guess I'm too lazy to move out.'

We both laugh. I'm warming to Kaz. She's bright and funny, and unlike her mother and brother, she actually speaks in whole sentences.

'Did she tell you about my work?' Kaz asks.

'Lazzo did mention something about it.'

'Well, for the record, I'm not what you probably think. Mum thinks pole dancing is the same as lap dancing.'

'Isn't it?' I know nothing about either.

'Not at all. We don't touch the clients, and they're not allowed to touch us. Sex is strictly off limits. But I'm in demand, and I get good tips.'

'I'll bet you do.' I would imagine that most men would give a great deal to spend an evening watching Kaz. 'How — I mean, what do you actually do?'

Kaz slips off her shoes, and grasping the edge of the door, shimmies effortlessly up and down it.

'Bit like that, but with a pole,' she says. 'It doesn't really work with a door.'

'Goodness!' I'm impressed.

'What's your feller do?' Kaz asks, picking a splinter out of her hand.

'I don't really have a — feller,' I tell her.

'You must have once.'

'He's — disappeared.'

'Buggered off, has he? Typical.' Kaz fumbles in the top of her boot and brings out a packet of cigarettes. 'Mind if I smoke?'

'Go ahead. No, he didn't bugger off exactly. We just — lost touch.'

And I find myself telling Kaz all about Amos. She's a surprisingly good listener, and it's a luxury for me to have someone to confide in. Eric and Silas are very sweet, and Mum does her best, but Kaz is nearer my own age, and has no personal involvement in either me or my baby.

'Tricky,' she says, when I've finished.

'Yes.'

'And you really want the baby?'

'I've thought about it a lot, and while I'm certainly not desperate for a baby, I don't *not* want it.'

'And you don't fancy being a single mum.'

'Not really.'

'Me neither,' says Kaz with feeling. 'But then I don't really fancy being a mum of any kind. Not after seeing the mess Mum made of me and Laz.'

Actually, I think Blossom's children have turned out remarkably well, but maybe they have arrived where they are through their own merits rather than because of anything their mother did.

'Ok. Let's get to work.' Kaz stubs out her cigarette on the heel of her boot. 'Where's this hen house of yours?'

In the course of the afternoon, eleven people come to pay their respects to the Virgin.

'All barmy,' says Kaz, when the last of them have said their farewells and driven off into the dusk. 'Quite barmy.'

'You don't believe in any of this, then?' I ask her.

'Good lord, no. Do you?'

'Well, I'm not a Catholic.'

'And you think I am?'

'I suppose I assumed you must be a Catholic of sorts.'

'According to Mum, I'm beyond the pale. No pearly gates for me,' says Kaz cheerfully.

'Is that what *you* think?'

'I don't know.' Kaz lights up another cigarette. 'I think I believe in God, or something like God. But not this miracle stuff.'

'But you must admit it looks very convincing.'

'Not bad,' Kaz says. 'But it would have to be all-singing all-dancing and glorious technicolour to convince me.'

We walk back towards the house together.

'Cup of tea?' I ask her, as we arrive in the kitchen.

'Got anything stronger?'

'We've got nettle wine or —' I examine a smudged label — 'parsnip brandy.' These are the only bottles which are open. I hesitate to broach a new one, even for Kaz.

'Blimey.' Kaz looks impressed. 'Let's have a go at the parsnip stuff, shall we?'

'Why not?' I know I shouldn't be drinking, but surely one little glass won't hurt the baby?

The parsnip brandy nearly takes the skin off the back of my throat, and even Kaz has a brief choking fit.

'Wow!' she says, when she can speak again. 'Where did that come from?'

'I think Eric made it. He likes experimenting.'

'It's the kind of drink,' Kaz says, after a few minutes, 'where you have to have more in order to appreciate it.'

'I see what you mean,' I say, as the kitchen revolves slowly round us (I'm not used to alcohol). 'You sort of get used to it, don't you?'

'Certainly do. Bloody, hell! What's that?' Kaz has caught sight of the whippet.

'It's a stuffed whippet,' I tell her.

'Get away! What is it really?'

'It really is a stuffed whippet.'

'A stuffed whippet! Now I really have seen everything.' Kaz begins to laugh. 'A stuffed whippet!'

Kaz's laughter is so infectious that I begin to laugh too. Within a few minutes, we're both helpless.

'Stuffed Whippet ... whipped stuffit ...' By now, Kaz is crying with laughter. 'Oh my goodness!'

It is at this moment that my mother decides to put in an appearance.

'What on earth's going on?' she asks.

'Stiff whuppet,' Kaz explains.

'*What?*'

'Dog thingy.' Kaz waves a hand in the direction of the unfortunate whippet, and collapses in another fit of giggles.

'This is Kaz,' I say trying to affect an introduction through my tears. 'We've — we've had a little drink.'

'So I see.' Mum is not amused. 'And what about the baby?'

'He's had a little drink too,' says Kaz.

For a briefly sober moment, I realise that I may have made a mistake.

'I'm surprised at you, Ruth,' Mum continues. 'Look at the state of you!'

'My fault,' says Kaz cheerily. 'It was my idea.'

'But Ruth's a responsible adult. She's perfectly capable of deciding for herself.'

There is something about a completely sober person trying to be sensible when it is far too late for sense that is totally irresistible. Kaz and I howl with laughter.

'Really, Ruth! You're drunk!' says Mum.

'Lighten up, mate. It's not the end of the world.' Kaz offers her glass to Mum. 'Here. Have a little drink. Do you good.'

'I am not your mate, I don't drink, and I think it's time you were going.'

Oh dear.

'Can't ride a bike like this,' says Kaz. 'Fall off,' she explains.

'You came on a bike?'

'They all come on the bike,' I tell her.

'Not all together,' Kaz says. 'It's the family bicycle.'

Fortunately, at this point Eric and Silas return. They seem to know Kaz, and are quite unfazed by what's going on.

'I see you've been trying the parsnip brandy,' Eric says. 'What did you think of it?'

'Excellent,' says Kaz. 'Very — very tasty.'

Eric looks pleased.

'Yes. I thought it was rather good. Silas hates it. Have you tried it, Rosie?'

'No, I certainly have not.'

'Well, never mind.' He turns to Kaz. 'I'd better run you home, Kaz. The bike can go in the back of the Land Rover.'

After Kaz has gone and I have sobered up a bit (giggling isn't the same on your own), Mum asks me about Kaz.

'She's Blossom's daughter,' I explain.

'Ah.'

'What do you mean, *ah*?'

'Well that explains it, doesn't it?'

'Explains what?'

'Her behaviour.'

'Mum, Kaz is nothing like Blossom. She is nice and intelligent and kind, and she's *young*.'

'What's that supposed to mean?'

'I spend all my time here with you and Eric and Silas. And that's fine. But sometimes it's nice to talk to someone my own age.'

'She's hardly your age, Ruth.'

'Well, someone nearer my age, at any rate. My friends are all over the place, and I hardly ever get to see them. Sometimes it's nice just to let go and — be silly.'

'Well, you certainly managed that.' Mum is still in shrewish mode. 'What does she do, anyway? For a living?'

'She's a pole dancer,' I tell her.

'But that's disgusting!'

'That's what Blossom thinks, but pole dancing is perfectly respectable.' I try to remember what Kaz told me. 'They never touch the customers, and the customers aren't allowed to touch them. It's a bit like — like the ballet, really.'

'That's not what I've heard,' says Mum, who having made up her mind about Kaz seems reluctant to change it. 'I just hope she's not trying to persuade you to do anything like that.'

I think I'll stick to my busking. I know my limitations.

CHAPTER TWENTY-THREE

November is heralded by the typical cold dank conditions I always associate with this most unpleasant of months. Gone are most of the colours and the fruits of the autumn, and we tramp to and fro over ground thick with a mush of mud and fallen leaves. Most of the chickens have stopped laying, one of the goats has lost her kid ('wrong time of year,' said Silas glumly), and despite our best efforts, such vegetables as have survived are rotting faster than we can gather them in the damp conditions. I have had to give up my busking as I find standing around in the cold so tiring, and while I know it was the right decision, I resent having had to make it for reasons beyond my control.

I have always hated November, not least because I loathe fireworks. When I was about five, I was invited to a fireworks party, where a nasty little boy chased me all over his garden with bangers. That, coupled with the horrifying image of someone who looked very much like his father being incinerated on the huge bonfire, instilled in me a terror I remember to this day. I managed to unfasten the gate and run home, crossing two roads on the way, and was eventually discovered hiding in the tool shed, weeping with terror. I had nightmares for weeks afterwards. To this day, I cannot see the point of fireworks. If I want to look at something pretty, I can find it in flowers and scenery and art. If I want surprises, life provides plenty of those without any need for the artificial kind. And I do not enjoy sudden loud noises.

Neither do Eric and Silas's animals.

You would think that out here in the country, November 5th would pass virtually unnoticed. Not so. There are a couple of houses not far away, both with children, and both apparently hell-bent on commemorating Guy Fawkes and his nefarious activities. Fortunately, Eric and Silas have managed to persuade them to restrict their celebrations to the night in question (in recent years Guy Fawkes, like Christmas, has tended to spread itself over several days), so that some precautions can be taken. But with the best will in the world it's impossible to persuade a cow that unexpected bangs and bumps and showers of coloured stars aren't cause for consternation. While the neighbouring households are no doubt oohing and aahing as they fire their rockets and burn their effigies and eat their hot dogs, for us it's all hands to the pump, trying to offer consolation to the livestock.

We have locked up such animals as we can, but I suspect that for some, this merely compounds their misery. Inside the house, Mr. Darcy is beside himself with terror, the cats are hiding in Mum's bed, and Sarah, that most independent of animals, has managed to escape from her shed and get into the house, where she has taken refuge in the larder, her anxiety betrayed by the trail of terrified little turds she has left in her wake.

Fortunately, Lazzo has come round to help, and has been a tower of strength, visiting sheds and outhouses, stroking and comforting, and ending up on a kitchen chair with Mr. Darcy shivering in his arms and a can of beer in his hand.

'Noisy,' remarks Lazzo, as another shower of sparks lightens the sky outside the window.

'D'you think fireworks are getting louder?' Eric asks, of no-one in particular. 'I'm sure they never used to make so much noise.'

'It probably just seems like it.' Silas pours himself some nettle wine (we are having our own party of sorts. I, needless to say, am back on the wagon). 'It'll pass.'

'Should that pig be in the larder?' Mum is much exercised by the mess (not to mention the smell) which has accompanied Sarah's visit.

'She always spends Guy Fawkes in there,' says Eric.

'Is it — hygienic? I mean, a pig in a larder...'

'Probably not.' Eric grins at her. 'But it hasn't done us any harm yet.'

Mum moves her chair nearer the door. 'If you say so. Though I don't know what Brian would say.' (Brian is my father.)

'Then don't tell him,' Silas says.

Mum looks uncomfortable. I'm pretty sure that she still tells Dad most of the things that go on in this household, for old habits die hard, and I wonder how long she can hold out before the inevitable climb-down and return home. I know she's not happy, suspended as she is between two very different lives; torn between her loyalty to my father and her feelings for me, not to mention her hurt at the minimal effort Dad has made to retrieve her. But what can she do? Poor Mum. With the best will in the world, she'll never really fit in here. It's too far removed from everything she's used to. But having made what is — for her — a very courageous move, will she fit back into her old life again? Only time will tell.

A few days later, all of our minds are taken off our individual worries by a more serious matter.

For some time now, Silas has been researching the long-term effects of rheumatic fever, and we haven't taken a lot of notice. After all, health issues have always been a major source of fascination for Silas, and most of the time there is little for the rest of us to concern ourselves with. And if he's been a bit tired of late, perhaps a little breathless, then these things happen at seventy-four, don't they?

'Mitral stenosis,' says Silas, reading from his medical book. 'I think that must be it. I seem to have all the symptoms.' He applies his stethoscope to his chest and listens attentively. 'But I can't hear anything. Damn.'

'Do you know what you're supposed to hear?' I ask him.

'Not really.' Silas sighs. 'I've read about heart murmurs, but I've never heard one, so I don't really know what I'm looking for.'

'Perhaps you should let the doctor check you out.'

'Oh no. Well, not yet, anyway. People don't usually drop dead from mitral stenosis.'

'Are you sure?' It certainly sounds impressive enough to be fatal.

'Quite sure,' Silas assures me. 'This kind of thing can rumble on for years. And my blood pressure's fine.'

'Good.'

'And I'm not a bad colour.' He examines his reflection in the hall mirror. 'Or maybe just a little cyanosed. What do you think, Ruth?'

'What's cyanosed?'

'Blue. Pale. It's caused by lack of oxygen.'

I examine Silas's face. 'You look okay to me.'

'Mm. I'm not sure.' He examines his hands. 'It can affect the extremities, too.'

Silas's hands are so dirty I don't think it would much matter what colour they were, but if Silas reckons his fingertips are a little blue, he may be right. After all, he's lived with them for long enough.

‘Are you sure you shouldn’t go to the doctor?’ I ask him. ‘I’ll take you.’

‘Maybe eventually, but there’s plenty of time yet. This was bound to happen sooner or later.’

‘Was it?’

‘Oh yes. Rheumatic fever does this. It goes away for years, and then the effects come back to haunt you in later life.’

And he goes on to give me a detailed explanation. He uses words like haemolytic streptococcus and carditis, subcutaneous nodules and erythema marginatum, mitral regurgitation and aortic stenosis. This kind of vocabulary is meat and drink to Silas; to me, it’s double Dutch.

‘Gosh. All that,’ I say weakly, when he’s finished.

‘Yes. It’s a nuisance, but so interesting, don’t you think, Ruth?’

‘I suppose so.’

‘We are fearfully and wonderfully made,’ Silas tells me cheerfully.

‘Yes.’

‘I’m going to do the pigs now.’

‘Take care.’

A week later, Silas collapses. One minute, he is standing at the kitchen table putting the finishing touches to his latest victim (a weasel; Silas has always wanted a weasel, and has been wildly excited ever since he found it); the next, he’s lying on the floor, looking very pale and rather surprised.

‘Silas? Silas! Are you all right?’ I’m completely panic-stricken. I’ve never seen anyone pass out before, and have always been queasy when it comes to medical emergencies. I also have no idea what to do.

‘Yes. Yes, I think so.’ Silas tries to sit up.

'No. No. Stay where you are. You mustn't move.' Somewhere in that tiny section of my brain which stores my minuscule knowledge of things medical there is the strict injunction *not to move the patient.* Or is that just in the case of accidents? And what about the recovery position? What is it, and should I put Silas in it now? I have always wondered about the expression 'in a flap', but now I understand, because my hands seem to be making involuntary fluttering movements as I panic and dither, and Silas lies obediently on the floor, waiting for me to do something helpful.

'Fetch Eric,' Silas tells me.

'Yes. Yes, of course. Eric.'

'He's fixing the bedroom window.'

'Bedroom window. Yes.' I look down at Silas. 'Can I — should I —'

'Fetch Eric. Please, Ruth.'

'Yes. Yes, of course.'

I fly upstairs and fetch Eric. Together we arrive back in the kitchen, where Silas is still lying on the floor.

'Well, now.' Eric creaks down into his knees and places a hand on Silas's forehead. 'Mm. You are a bit sweaty. What exactly happened? And how are you feeling?'

'I had some kind of syncope attack —' *syncope attack?* — 'and I'm feeling a bit — woozy.' Silas takes his own pulse. 'Atrial fibrillation,' he tells us, after a moment.

'Translate,' Eric orders. 'This is no time to show off your medical knowledge, Silas. Ruth and I are worried.'

'I've fainted, and I'm having palpitations,' Silas explains. He looks calm and untroubled, and the unworthy thought occurs to me that Silas is enjoying this. He now has a real illness with real symptoms. He will be able to spend hours poring over his grisly book analysing his condition.

'Can you sit up?' Eric asks (no recovery position, then).

'I think so.' Carefully, Silas sits up. The colour immediately drains from his face. 'Better not.' He subsides onto the floor again.

Eric places a folded jacket under his head. 'Dial 999, Ruth. I think we need help,' he tells me.

Burly ambulance men arrive, cheery and reassuring. They ask Silas lots of questions before levering him onto a stretcher and into the ambulance. Eric and I follow in the Land Rover, leaving a note for Mum, who is at the hairdresser's. Eric is pale and quiet, and we don't speak, although I long to offer some kind of comfort and also to ask whether he's suffering any of Silas's symptoms. I've read about twins suffering identical pains even when they're miles apart; is Eric's pallor due to some psychic twin response, or is it simply anxiety?

At the hospital, there is a lot of waiting around. Silas is offered an injection for the pain.

'I haven't got any pain,' he objects.

'For your distress, dear,' the nurse tells him.

'I'm not distressed.'

'It'll calm you down.'

'I'm perfectly calm.' But in the end, Silas agrees to the injection because, as he says, he's always wanted to know what diamorphine ('you'll know it as heroin, Ruth. Highly addictive') feels like. And it can't do any harm, can it? Personally, I think it's Eric who could do with the injection, but no-one's asking me.

Much later, when Silas has had a variety of tests and seen at least three doctors, they tell him he has 'a little problem with a heart valve'.

'Mitral stenosis. I told you,' says Silas.

'Well, yes. It could be.' The doctor looks disappointed. Even I know that doctors don't like patients to use medical-speak. There is a strict boundary between the medical practitioner and the layman, and Silas has crossed it.

'Rheumatic fever,' Silas explains, his words still slurry from diamorphine. 'When I was, when I was...'

'Seventeen,' Eric says.

'That's right.' Silas smiles. 'Seventeen.'

'We'll have to keep you in,' the doctor tells him. 'For observation and more tests.'

'Valve replacement?' Silas asks, his face bright with anticipation.

'It's much too early to say.'

'But I might have to have one?'

'It's possible.'

'Pig or titanium?' Silas asks (what *is* he talking about?).

'That would be for the surgeons to decide. If it becomes necessary. But that's a long way off at the moment.'

'Goodness,' I say to Eric, when much later we have said our farewells and are on our way home, leaving Silas cosily tucked up in bed. 'You'd think he was enjoying it.'

'He is enjoying it.'

'How can he?'

'Silas loves to be ill. He's always been like that.'

'Yes, but this is his *heart.*'

'So much the better,' says Eric grimly.

'He must be mad!'

'He is.'

'Poor Eric. You must be awfully worried.'

Eric attempts a smile. 'Of course I am.'

'And you can't share that with Silas.' Eric and Silas usually share everything.

'Quite.'

I put my hand on Eric's knee. 'You've got us. Mum and me. I know it's not the same, but at least you're not on your own.'

'No. I know. Thanks, Ruth.'

We get home to chaos. Mum, who's been keeping in touch by phone, has been trying to cope with Blossom, who's been called in for emergency animal duties. The argument they have been having has evidently turned nasty, and Sarah has taken advantage of the situation by coming in through the open back door and helping herself to an unattended bag of groceries, while Mr. Darcy is chasing a chicken round the living room.

'She can't tell me what to do,' Blossom tells us mutinously.

'I haven't been telling her to do anything,' says Mum, who is very close to tears.

'Have.'

'No, I haven't. I just asked you — *asked* you — if you would mind seeing if there were any cabbages left.'

'Not my job.'

'But surely in an emergency that doesn't matter?'

'Don't need cabbages in emergency.'

'It's not for the emergency! It's for *dinner*!'

'Perhaps you'd better finish the animals and go home,' Eric suggests to Blossom.

'Done 'em,' says Blossom.

'Well, it doesn't look like it. Sarah's in the kitchen, for a start.'

'Not my fault. *She* left the door open.'

'I did not!' Mum cries.

'Did.'

'Enough!' Eric's patience has finally run out. 'Blossom, would you please put Sarah to bed, and catch that dratted chicken before Mr. Darcy does. Then for pity's sake, go home. We've got enough troubles without all this.'

CHAPTER TWENTY-FOUR

Silas spends several days in hospital, and is in his element. He has a whole range of tests, and talks of, among other things, unpronounceable blood tests, an echo something-or-other, and an ECG. I have just about heard of the ECG, but everything else is shrouded in mystery. We have travelled to and fro fulfilling Silas's requests for, among other things, clean pyjamas, chocolate, nettle wine and the medical bible. Eric refuses to bring in the stuffed whippet (Silas apparently promised to show it to the nurses) and has to take the wine home (no alcohol allowed), but manages to smuggle in a tiny stuffed mouse "to compensate the nurses for their disappointment".

Poor Eric is exhausted. He and Silas have rarely been apart, and he seems somehow depleted without his brother. I know he's not sleeping well, and the journeys to and from the hospital are both time- and energy-consuming, involving as they do a thirty-mile round trip plus the obligatory search for a parking place and the trek along miles of dismal hospital corridors. Mum and I take it in turns to accompany him, but he won't hear of us going without him, and I know that he is fulfilling his own needs as much as Silas's. As for his Ark, that's had to be put on hold, and I know he misses it. The Ark has become Eric's treasured hobby, fuel for his brain (not to mention his imagination), and perhaps the only thing which might have taken his mind off his worries. I too miss the Ark; I miss the curious questions and conversations to which it gives rise, and my even more curious dialogues with the people at the zoo as I assist Eric with his enquiries. I have developed quite a cosy relationship with one of the curators, who rashly invited me out on a date, although we have never met. I reluctantly declined out of loyalty to Amos and the seahorse/rabbit.

Meanwhile, the rest of us are desperately short-handed, and Lazzo and Kaz are brought in to help. Kaz is currently short of work, and Lazzo has nothing better to do, so it suits everyone (except, of course, Blossom).

The weather continues to be bleakly unpleasant, and the increase in my size is slowing me down. The only person/thing which appears to be thriving is the Virgin, whose followers are growing by the day and who I swear is getting more and more life-like. Eric I know has had more than enough of her and thinks it's time we called it a day (the hardware store has promised him a preservative which is guaranteed to cover up pretty well anything, supernatural or otherwise), but when he mentioned this to Blossom, she threatened to withdraw not only her own services, but those of her family as well, and as she very well knows, we can't do without them.

In addition to all this, Mum is beginning to pine.

'I miss him, Ruth, I really miss him,' she admits to me, as she slices vegetables for the evening meal. 'I know he's awkward, and I don't expect you to understand, but I — I'm *used* to him.'

'Then go home, Mum. Go back to him,' I tell her. 'I'll understand.'

'I can't.' She pushes her hair out of her eyes, weeping onion-tears. 'He told me I had to choose, and I've chosen you. You and the baby. I can't go back on that now. In any case, he mightn't even have me.'

'Oh, he'd certainly have you.'

'Do you think so?'

'I know so.' I crunch a piece of raw carrot. 'What does the minister say?' Mum has joined a kind of house church in the nearby town, and seems to derive some comfort from the support it offers.

'He prays with me, of course. He's been very kind, but I know he thinks I ought to go back to your father.'

'Then go back. You can still see me. It's not as though I've emigrated. And when Dad sees the baby, he may change his mind.'

'I don't think so. He's so obstinate. He always has to be *right*. He'll never climb down, even if he secretly wants to. Besides,' she says, chopping celery, 'I'm needed here. Eric and Silas are my brothers, and I'm all the family they've got. It's the least I can do, to help out in this crisis. They've always been so good to me.'

I gaze out of the window. Through the drizzle, I can make out Eric's stooping figure bent over some ancient piece of machinery, and I fight back sudden tears. Eric is miserable, Mum is unhappy and guilt-ridden, the animals, those most reliable barometers of emotional climate, are restless and jumpy, and I am suffering from backache and indigestion. And there is still no sign of Amos.

'Ruth? Are you okay?' Mum looks up from her vegetables.

'Yes. No. I don't know. Everything's suddenly — horrible.'

'I know what you mean.'

'I just wish something *nice* would happen.'

Two days later, something nice does happen in the form of another surprise visit from Mikey.

'Oh, Mikey! Am I glad to see you!' I practically leap into his arms.

'Hey! Hang on! You nearly knocked me over! What's all this about, then?' Mikey laughs as he disentangles himself and kisses me warmly on the cheek.

I sit him down and tell him about Silas and how worried we all are and how miserable life has become since his admission to hospital. I tell him about Mum, about Blossom (who is now ruling not just the roost, but the house, and just about everything else, and loving every minute of it) and about the abundance of unwanted pilgrims. I tell him that I shall be thirty-seven next year and life is passing me by, that my violin-playing has deteriorated so badly that no-one will ever want me to play for them again, and that I still haven't managed to find Amos. And I finish by bursting into tears.

'Oh dear.' Mikey pats and soothes and makes sympathetic noises.

'I know I'm wallowing,' I say, when I can get the words out, 'but just for once — for once —'

'It's good to have a wallow?'

'I suppose so. Yes.' I take the not-very-clean hanky Mikey has offered and blow my nose.

'I've brought Gavin to meet you,' Mikey says, when I've calmed down a bit. 'But maybe now's not the best time.'

'Why? Where is he?'

'In the car. I thought I'd make sure it was a good time before bringing him in. Just as well, as it happens.'

'Oh, do bring him in. Please. I'd love to meet him.'

'Are you sure?'

'Quite sure. Just give me a minute to mop up.'

Five minutes later, Mikey introduces me to Gavin.

In my time, I have come across many attractive men, but I have never met one I would describe as beautiful. Gavin is beautiful. He is tall and slim and blond, with completely even perfectly-formed features, the bluest eyes I have ever seen, and the kind of smile that bathes you in warm sunshine. For a moment, I'm completely lost for words.

'Ruth? *Ruth!*' Mikey wrenches me out of my trance. 'This is Gavin.' His pride is so transparent that I almost laugh.

Gavin smiles, and holds out a hand.

'Yes. Sorry. Hi.' I shake the hand, which (of course) is warm and firm and smooth. 'I'm so sorry you had to wait all that time in the car.'

'Not at all.'

'Ruth's my oldest friend,' Mikey says (am I? I'd no idea. The thought of being Mikey's oldest friend is ridiculously cheering).

'Any oldest friend of Mikey's has to be a pretty good friend of mine,' says Gavin, with another radiant smile.

'Tea? Coffee? Er — mulberry wine?' I ask them, examining the label on the currently open bottle.

'Tea, I think. We're sharing the driving,' says Gavin.

Sharing the driving. It sounds so cosily domestic I want to weep.

For few minutes we make small talk; the household, the animals, my violin-playing, Gavin's job as an estate agent. This seems a terrible waste, but I resist the temptation to ask him whether he's ever thought of a career on the stage or perhaps as a model, as I'm sure he's been asked this many times before. But I bet he sells a lot of houses.

The back door opens and Kaz comes in. She stops short, and takes a long, astonished but practised look at Gavin.

'Fucking hell!'

'*Kaz!*' I feel instantly ashamed, although strictly speaking, Kaz is nothing to do with me.

'Sorry. But you have to admit he's a bit of a stunner.' Kaz appears unabashed by the fact that the stunner is almost certainly within earshot. She crosses the kitchen and holds out a hand. 'Hi. I'm Kaz.'

Gavin introduces himself, and they chat for a moment or two. Gavin tries to bring Mikey into the conversation, but Kaz ignores him, for she is doing what she obviously does best. Kaz is flirting.

Now of course, I've seen people flirt, many times. I have flirted myself, and enjoyed it as much as anyone. But I have never seen a professional at work.

Kaz is a professional.

I watch in admiration the lowered eyes followed by the coy Princess-Diana peep through the lashes; the tilt of the body which reveals just enough décolletage; the pout of the lips and the little-girl voice. This is a new Kaz; one I haven't seen before. Hitherto the only men around here have been Eric and Silas, who are obviously too old for this kind of treatment. The pilgrims, Kaz has told me more than once, have their minds on other things, and aren't worth the bother. Unfortunately, she appears to be unaware that Gavin is also not worth the bother, if for an entirely different reason, but I'm unable to catch her eye.

Mikey, unintroduced and ignored, is enjoying all this hugely, and he returns my despairing glance with a wink.

Eventually, Gavin manages to affect an introduction. 'Kaz, have you met Mikey?'

Mikey and Kaz nod to each other.

'I'm Gavin's partner,' Mikey says, dropping his tiny bombshell with impressive insouciance.

Kaz pauses for a moment, then shrugs and laughs. 'Well, that was a waste of time, then, wasn't it?' she says, returning to her normal spiky self. 'Worth a try, though,' she adds with just a hint of wistfulness.

'Certainly worth a try,' says Gavin graciously. 'And I'm honoured.'

'You're welcome. Can I have some of that wine?' Kaz reaches for the bottle. 'I reckon I've earned it. I've finally got the hang of that bloody goat. Milking a goat,' she says, to no-one in particular, 'is a bit like sex. Once you get going, it's difficult to stop. It's sort of — compulsive.'

I have never felt that milking a goat is remotely like sex, and since over the past few months I've had a great deal of the one and none at all of the other, it is difficult not to feel just a little sour.

'I'll bear that in mind,' I mutter to her, 'next time I —'

'Milk a goat?' Kaz grins at me.

'Something like that.'

But generally, it's been a very pleasant visit, and culminates with a tour of the hen house. It appears that Gavin is a lapsed Catholic, and is especially intrigued by the Virgin. I have met lapsed Catholics before, and have always been puzzled at their extraordinary loyalty to a church which, by definition, has let them down in some way. At least one friend of this persuasion (or perhaps it should be dissuasion) has told me that while she doesn't attend Mass any more, she will certainly require the services of a priest on her death-bed, and most Catholics won't hear a word against the Church they have (if only temporarily) deserted.

'It's the gay thing,' Gavin tells us, as we toil up the muddy path. 'I know God doesn't mind about it. He's much too broad-minded. But the Catholic Church is terribly hung up on sex. Always has been.'

'Then join another church; one which is as broad-minded as God.'

'Oh, I couldn't do that,' Gavin tells me.

'Why ever not?'

'Because it's the One True Church,' Kaz pipes up with a wink. I imagine Kaz has long since passed the lapsed Catholic stage on her journey to her present state of cheery godlessness.

'Not exactly,' Gavin says. 'It's just that a Catholic is what I am.' He negotiates a puddle, splashing his immaculate trousers. 'You know when you have to fill in those hospital forms, and they ask you your religion?'

'Yes.'

'Well, I always put RC. I simply can't imagine putting anything else.'

'And if you're dying, you'll want a priest to come with one of those little bottles of oil?'

'Oh, definitely. Little bottles of oil are de rigeur.'

'And last confession?'

'Definitely last confession.'

'Will you have to confess to being gay?'

'God knows I'm gay. He's fine about it.' He pats me on the shoulder. 'Don't worry about it. I certainly don't.'

But lapsed or not, Gavin is impressed by the Virgin of the hen house.

'This is amazing,' he tells Mikey. 'Why didn't you tell me about it before?'

'It's just a few scratches.' Mikey is not only an atheist; he also has no imagination. 'I didn't think it was really worth mentioning.'

'Mikey, this is more than a few scratches.' Gavin squats down to examine it more closely. 'It really does look, well, it looks...'

'Virgin-like?' I suggest.

'Yes.' Gavin agrees. 'I'm not usually one for signs and miracles, but this is something else.'

'Well, the punters certainly think so. They come in their droves.'

'Any miraculous cures yet?' he asks with a grin.

'None that we know about.' I straighten Blossom's vase of flowers (hideous plastic violets from the pound shop, as Blossom has given up trying to stop the animals from eating real ones. This has not, however, deterred the goats, who have paid an illegal visit and eaten several).

'And what does the local priest say?'

'Not a lot. He has as little to do with it as possible. I think he's the drinking, delegating sort.'

I think of Father Vincent, who hasn't been near us in weeks, and once again, I wonder what he really thinks about all this. His secretary continues to churn out tickets, and the pilgrims keep on coming, but Father Vincent keeps a very low profile. Father Vincent may be lazy, but he's certainly not stupid.

Later on, as Gavin and Mikey get into their car, bickering affectionately about whose turn it is to drive, and whether they should take the bypass, the baby performs a fluttering tap dance inside me.

'Don't worry,' I tell it, as I walk back towards the house. 'Sooner or later your daddy will come and find us.'

And then perhaps I too will have someone to bicker with and argue over the map-reading. I give a sigh. Seeing Mikey and Gavin has been lovely, but I envy the cosiness of their coupled state.

I hope my turn will come soon.

CHAPTER TWENTY-FIVE

Silas is ready to come out of hospital. They have "stabilised" his condition, but apparently not cured it. Silas tells us that the only permanent cure lies in an operation, and seems disappointed that his condition's not considered serious enough to merit one for the time being. But never mind. He has a wonderful range of new tablets — heart tablets, water tablets ('not water tablets. *Diuretics*,' says Silas, who hates to be patronised) and blood-thinning tablets with a name which even Silas has trouble remembering.

Eric fetches him home.

It is only now, seeing the newly stabilised Silas, that I realise how ill he must have been. It's a long time since I confused him with his brother — in fact, now, I wonder that anyone could confuse them at all — so I have become accustomed to seeing him as an individual. And if he's been a bit paler and thinner than Eric, then I assumed that was the way it's always been. But since he's been in hospital, Silas has put on weight and his colour's improved, and he looks, literally, a new man.

We all tell him how well he looks, but his feelings about this are obviously ambivalent. While he appears to feel fitter and stronger, I know that he hankers after the attention and the drama which accompanied his admission to hospital, and we are not allowed to forget that he has been 'very ill, you know, Ruth. Very ill indeed.' Yes, Silas. We know.

Although he's anxious to get back into the swing of things, we try to prevent him from overdoing it. Light duties only, we tell him, and point him in the direction of his half-finished weasel. In this, he's more than happy to comply, and while the weasel has suffered from being abandoned at a crucial stage, Silas doesn't appear to mind. As he tells us, very few people know what a weasel looks like anyway, so if this one deviates a little from what nature intended, it's unlikely that anyone will notice. Meanwhile, Lazzo stays on to help, but we can no longer count on Kaz. She's being taken on by a new club, she tells me, and she has acquired a small car, so she no longer has to rely on buses and trains. She's happy to lend a hand when she can, but we mustn't rely on her.

'A mobile dancer is a busy dancer,' she tells me cheerfully, as she drives round to show us her new wheels. 'The manager won't pay for taxis, and I can't afford them.'

Kaz has painted her car buttercup yellow and decorated it with neat turquoise daisies.

'What do you think?' she asks me.

'Well, it'll certainly stand out,' I tell her.

'That's what I thought. You can borrow it if you like,' she adds.

'That's kind of you, but I think the Land Rover is more — me.'

'You're probably right.' Kaz climbs back into her car and winds down the window. 'Well, I'm off to see a man about a pole.'

'Good luck.'

'Who needs luck?' Kaz shouts, as she bounces off down the track.

Sometimes I wish I had Kaz's confidence.

It would appear that during the winter, my uncles' activities die down, and they enjoy a period of relative quiet. They close their market stall, selling what little produce there is to private customers, who come and collect it themselves. I have no idea what they live on, since even in the summer, their income from what they sell wouldn't even heat the house, but then this has always been a bit of a mystery. I know they have various investments from their inheritance, and Eric at least enjoys dabbling on the stock market, so I assume most of their income comes from that.

Outside home, their needs are few. They rarely travel anywhere, and as far as I can see, never take holidays. Most of their clothes are falling apart, but then as Silas says, what does it matter? Hardly anyone sees them and they certainly don't mind what they look like. They do occasionally buy new shoes and wellingtons, and they make a monthly trip to the barber's; a filthy establishment, cluttered with old newspapers and magazines, with unsightly heaps of greying hair in every corner and a ceiling stained yellow by bygone years of cigarette smoke. Here Lennie, a wizened man of indeterminate age, dispenses haircuts and gossip for a fiver a time. Eric and Silas consider this excellent value, and wouldn't dream of going anywhere else.

Mum and I both pay our way, but my savings are dwindling rapidly, so I return to my busking, but on different days now that Eric and Silas no longer have their market stall, driving myself and sometimes travelling further afield to give myself (and the punters) a change. Mr. Darcy, who has his own fan club, now loves these outings, so I still take him with me, and while I'm finding it all increasingly tiring, in my present situation, needs must. My burgeoning pregnancy attracts plenty of interest, not to mention increased revenue, and people come up to chat and give advice. I've even made one or two friends.

Mum, however, hasn't changed her views since I was a busking student, and while she sometimes lets me borrow her car, she doesn't hesitate to tell me what she thinks.

'I don't know how you can stand there in the street like that, with everyone looking at you, Ruth,' she tells me.

'But that's the whole point, Mum. I'm a performer. That's what performers do.'

'An orchestra is one thing,' she persists (that's not what she said at the time), 'but hanging round street corners collecting *money*.' She gives a delicate little shudder. 'It doesn't seem right.'

'I don't hang around anywhere, and I don't *collect* money. People pay me. I'm not pretending to be homeless or even particularly poor. And if my playing gives people pleasure, and they're prepared to pay, what's the problem?'

'I don't know what your father would say.' This, as always, means she knows exactly what Dad would say, as do I. What Dad would say in almost any circumstance is usually entirely predictable.

But the phone call we receive from him two days after this conversation isn't predictable at all. The call brings tidings of unexpected disaster, for apparently Dad has had an accident with the chip pan, and the resulting inferno has succeeded in destroying two thirds of the house.

Mum, needless to say, is beside herself.

'The house burnt down. Our home. *Burnt down*.' She is inconsolable. 'And chips! Your father's never made chips in his life. He doesn't even like chips!'

'Is he all right? Is he hurt?' I want to know.

'Oh, yes yes. He's fine. But *the house*. And *chips*. What was he doing making chips?'

I recognise the preoccupation with chips as some kind of displacement anxiety, and it's probably fulfilling its purpose, for isn't it better that Mum should worry about my father making chips than the fact that she's probably lost almost everything she possesses?

'Of course, he must come here,' says Eric at once.

'Oh, could he?' Mum says. 'He's nowhere else to stay. He's had offers from the church, of course, but I don't think he'll want to take them up. He hates to be *beholden*.'

'Of course. He's more than welcome.' This is nice of Eric, since my father has never been especially polite to my uncles, and wouldn't have relished having either of them to stay.

'I haven't mentioned it to him yet. I hope he'll agree to come,' Mum says. 'He can be so — well, he may not want to...'

'I think he'll come,' I tell her, because of course this is the perfect excuse for Dad to bring about a reconciliation without the necessity for a climb-down. In a way, for my parents' relationship (if for nothing else) it's a win-win situation.

Sure enough, Dad accepts the invitation, but typically refuses all offers of transport (both Eric and I offer to fetch him), insisting on driving himself. When he arrives a few hours later, subdued and bedraggled, I am shocked at the change in him. Gone is the confidence and the self-control; the air of pious sobriety. He looks somehow shrunken and vulnerable, like the little old man he will no doubt one day become. He is unshaven, and wearing a dirty cardigan with the buttons done up unevenly, and funnily enough it is this which I find most touching.

'Dad!' I give him a hug, and for once he barely resists. 'Are you all right?'

'A little shaken, of course. But no real harm done.'

'That's good.' I take his small suitcase, wondering what can be in it. Does he still have any clothes, or did they all go up in flames?

Mum comes into the hall to meet him. She looks shy and awkward, her hands twisting together in front of her as though involved in some private battle of their own.

'Brian.' She starts to walk towards him, and then seems to think better of it.

'Rosemary,' Dad says, but makes no move towards her.

'Tea?' I ask quickly, hoping to oil the wheels of this very awkward reunion. 'I'm sure you could do with a cup of tea, Dad.'

'Yes. Thank you. Tea would be very nice.' My father follows me into the kitchen. 'Where are Eric and Silas?' He sounds apprehensive.

'They're outside with the vet. They may be a while,' I tell him.

He looks relieved. 'Oh. Right,' he says. 'Nobody — nothing too ill, I hope?'

'Just a couple of castrations.'

Mum blushes, and I feel a wave of exasperation. She has lived here for some weeks now, in the course of which there have been a number of births and a variety of couplings, none of them particularly discreet and one or two in full view of the house. Will she never get used to the idea of sex?

'Well,' says Dad, some time later, as he sits at the table stirring his second cup of tea. 'We are very blessed.'

'How do you make that out?' I ask him.

He turns a reproachful gaze on me.

'The Lord has been good to us, Ruth. Our home is almost destroyed, and yet no-one has been hurt. Yes. The Lord has been very good.'

Mum nods her agreement, although she is still red-eyed from crying.

This is one of the things I shall never understand about my parents' faith. Their home of nearly forty years almost razed to the ground, many if not most of their possessions destroyed, and here they are, praising the Lord; the same Lord, presumably, who could have stopped the fire if he'd had a mind to. It seems to me that my parents' God cannot lose; he gets all the credit when things go well, and none of the blame when they don't. This is not the right time to raise the matter, but I would dearly like to hear how they can explain this (to me) extraordinary dichotomy.

'How much — how much is — gone?' Mum asks now.

'Well, the kitchen, obviously,' Dad says. 'And most of the rest of the ground floor. Upstairs, things are a bit better. The fire only managed to get as far as Ruth's room. The rest is more or less undamaged.'

'Is my room — completely destroyed?' I ask carefully.

'Pretty well,' says Dad, reaching for another biscuit (his spirits seem remarkably improved). 'But you didn't use it much, did you? And there was only a lot of old stuff from when you were a child. Nothing you'll miss.'

Nothing you'll miss. How typical of Dad that even now he's incapable of putting himself in anyone else's shoes; of trying to understand a situation from any viewpoint other than his own. I feel a sudden ridiculous surge of grief as I think of the room which I slept in all my life until I left home, and which is still officially mine; the room which was my refuge in times of trouble, where I nursed my teenage sulks and (oh, delicious danger!) shared my first bumbling kiss with the minister's son while, through the floorboards, we could hear the faint sounds of our parents' voices as they prayed together in the room below.

Of course, all the stuff I really need has long been removed, but there are all those other things; all those bits and pieces of my childhood. The swimming certificates and posters on the wall, and the rosette I won in my brief equestrian career (it was for fourth place, and there only were four competitors, but I carried that rosette round with me for weeks). Then there are the books; among them *Heidi*, *The Wind in the Willows*, *the Secret Garden*, and my favourite of all, *Charlotte's Webb.* The baby might have enjoyed those. There was the patchwork quilt stitched by my grandmother, the only person who I felt really understood me. She and I used to call it the "crosspatch quilt" because I could never remember the word "patchwork". I remember her arthritic fingers stitching away at that quilt while she told me about her early married life and my mother's childhood. There was a particular patchwork square — pale blue brocade roses — which I remember especially because it was a one-off, and she was sewing it the day her beloved cat was run over.

And then there were the drawers full of mementoes: my first tiny pink ballet shoes, my music certificates, old school books, letters and photos; and the usual dross of foreign coins, broken pencils, buttons, ancient pots of dried-up cosmetics, hair clips and odd earrings. Someone once said that everyone has a broken wristwatch in a drawer. I had two.

'Of course, I got in touch with the insurance people straight away.' Dad is still talking. 'They're getting back to me tomorrow. I gave them this phone number. I hope that's all right?'

'Of course,' Silas says. 'And now perhaps you'd like to get yourself settled? Will you be sleeping — I mean, where would you like to sleep?'

'Oh, with Rosemary of course.' Dad appears unfazed by the question. My mother's opinion obviously doesn't count, but she nods her acquiescence.

As I carry Dad's suitcase upstairs and find extra pillows and towels, I wonder what kind of reconciliation my parents will have (I assume they will be reconciled. It must be hard to stay separated in the same bed). Will they talk things through? Touch each other? Make love? Like most people, I find the idea of my parents' sex life hard to envisage, but there's no reason why they shouldn't still have one.

I shall probably never know.

PART III: WINTER

During the third trimester, the baby's eyes open, the bones develop fully and the lungs mature. The movements become more forceful and the baby gains several more pounds in weight in order to reach an average birth weight of between seven and eight pounds. The soft downy hair (lanugo) which covers its body falls off, and the baby learns to suck. At thirty-eight weeks the baby is considered to be full term, although the normal gestation is forty weeks.

CHAPTER TWENTY-SIX

I feel absolutely huge. Everyone tells me I am not, but I have never been pregnant before — never had to share my body with anyone else in this extraordinary way — and as I cart my little passenger around, in and out of cars and through the small openings of sheds and outhouses; as I lever myself out of the depths of my uncles' saggy sofa and have to abandon yet another favourite garment that refuses to do up, I feel cumbersome and clumsy and also deeply unattractive.

I recall with puzzlement the comments of pregnant friends, who "couldn't wait for the baby to *show*" and can no longer remember a time when mine didn't. What was it like to do up belts, wear a bikini, have a waist? I have bought several smock-like garments at the market, and have let out my jeans on a piece of elastic, and wonder at the proudly pregnant bellies of girls who seem happy to walk around with their bumps completely naked and their belly buttons turned inside out (at least mine hasn't done that yet).

My father has been with us for a week now, and despite this overwhelming evidence, is still obviously in a state of denial where my pregnancy is concerned. Since he never refers to it, it's become the elephant in the room (or perhaps I have become the elephant in the room; I certainly feel like one). Occasionally he will refer to a time 'when you're better, Ruth', as though having a baby were some kind of illness, but otherwise he manages to pretend it's not happening. Dad has always had this knack of ignoring the embarrassing or the distasteful, and at the moment he's surpassing himself.

'What does he say to you, Mum?' I ask my mother, but she just shakes her head.

'He doesn't talk about it.'

'What, not at all?'

'Not at all.'

'And what happens if you mention it?'

She gives a helpless little shrug.

'You mean, you don't mention it?' I'm not surprised, but I do feel a bit hurt.

'Well, no. I can't, Ruth. He's so worked up about the insurance people and the fact that he can't get hold of anyone when he wants to. There's no point in worrying him further.'

And I suppose this is true enough. Dad spends long hours on the phone, keeping a meticulous note of every minute he spends, and leaving money in a little pot on the window sill, getting increasingly impatient with whoever he's talking to, and giving a running commentary to anyone who'll listen.

'They're playing that tune again. Greensleeves, isn't it? You'd know it, Ruth ... oh, here we go. "This call may be recorded for training purposes". Whatever for? They presumably know what *they're* saying, and *I* haven't said anything yet. My call is very important to them. Well, I should hope so. "If you know the extension, then dial the number now". Well, I don't know the extension; why should I? Are these people stupid? Now I've forgotten what I'm supposed to press next. I'll have to go back to the beginning.' And more change rattles into the pot.

My parents seem to have slipped back into their marriage as though it had never been disrupted, but maybe this can be explained by the fact that neither of them has had to step down or lose face in any way. My father had to have somewhere to live, and this was the obvious place, and Mum hasn't moved at all. She is still here with me and Eric and Silas.

So perhaps this has satisfied both parties. They are kept busy, travelling back and forth between Applegarth and home in an attempt to rescue such belongings as they can from the ruins of the house. I accompany them on one of these forays, but my room is so badly damaged that all I can find among the still-smoking rubble are the remains of a very singed teddy bear, half a dolls' house and a rusty horse shoe. They are not much to remember my childhood home by but better than nothing, and I put them tenderly in a cardboard box to take back with me. I have no idea what I'm going to do with them, and for once, my parents don't ask. Perhaps the three of us, briefly united in our loss, are prepared to make allowances for such small shows of sentiment.

Otherwise, Mum keeps busy with her domestic chores and Dad with his negotiations over matters of insurance and house repairs. They attend Mum's new church together, and seem surprisingly comfortable with one another. I know that Dad is uneasy about Silas's taxidermy activities, and thinks that it's all 'most unhygienic', but since this isn't his house, he can't really say much. As for Eric and his Ark, Dad avoids this entirely, although I can see that Eric is longing to update him with his progress. There is more than an element of mischief in this, because Eric, armed with his dossiers of what he considers to be irrefutable facts, senses victory (he has a lot to learn about my father) and hankers after a little taste of it now. But Dad isn't going to fall into that trap, so the Ark has joined the baby and become another no-go area. As for the Virgin of the hen house, no-one mentions that. No doubt Dad will find out about it, but I think we all hope it will be later rather than sooner.

Meanwhile, Mikey calls in with news of Amos. I am enormously excited.

'Tell me! Tell me, Mikey! Where is he? What's he doing?'

'Hold on. Not so fast. The news isn't all good,' Mikey warns me.

'Why? What's happened? He's not had an accident, has he?'

'No. As far as I know, he's fine. I tracked him down to a cruise in the Caribbean, but apparently he's had a row with the conductor and disembarked on Barbados. No-one's heard from him since.'

'A row? What sort of row?'

'I've no idea. They're pretty pissed off with him, though, so I didn't like to ask too many questions.'

'Oh, Amos! How *could* he!' I'm very close to tears.

'Well, he didn't know did he? About the baby, I mean. As far as he's concerned, he's his own man. He can do what he likes.'

'But I need him. I need him *now*. Not in six months or a year or whenever it is he's planning on coming home.'

'Of course you do,' Mikey soothes.

'And now it could be ages before he appears again.'

'That's possible,' Mikey agrees. 'But he's bound to come back to England pretty soon, isn't he? There can't be that many jobs on Barbados for itinerant trombone players, and presumably he has a living to make.'

'I suppose so.'

'You've decided that you do love him, then?' he asks me, after a moment.

'I don't know. I can't really know until I see him, and even then, *he* mightn't love *me*.'

'Of course he'll love you,' Mikey says. 'If I were straight, I'd certainly love you.'

'Oh, Mikey. What am I going to do?' I wail.

'You'll just have to be patient. You've still got — how many months?'

'About three.'

'Three more months to find him. A lot can happen in three months. And I'll carry on looking. I've got a friend who's got a brother in Barbados.'

'How big is Barbados?' I ask him.

'I've no idea. It doesn't sound big, does it?'

I agree that Barbados doesn't sound that big. Quite small, really. And Amos is very hard to miss.

'What a nice young man,' my father remarks, when Mikey has gone (they met for just three minutes). 'Now, that's the kind of young man you want, Ruth. Steady and sensible. Yes. Just what you need. Better than that bearded fellow.'

Oh, Dad. If only you knew. But I decide not to tell him about Mikey's sexual preferences as I think he's had enough shocks for the time being. And it's no good reminding him that Amos is the father of my child. Dad remembers what he wants to remember, and he certainly doesn't want to remember that. Mikey apparently has assets which Amos doesn't have, and my father has never trusted beards.

The house, which was so tranquil when I arrived, is beginning to feel rather full. It's not that my parents take up much room; it's more that everyone is suddenly having to be awfully careful how they behave. It wasn't so bad when it was just Mum; she was becoming relatively relaxed and was even learning to fit in. But with the advent of my father, things are more difficult. My uncles have the patience of saints. They put up with Grace before meals, temper their language, and try to conceal the more earthy aspects of life at Applegarth. But I feel the strain on their behalf, and I also feel responsible. Had I not been here in the first place, my parents would no doubt have found somewhere else to stay — after all, don't insurance companies pay for hotel accommodation in circumstances such as this? — and Eric and Silas would have been able to carry on their untroubled existence without interference.

But if the house feels full, it is about to become more so.

Exactly ten days after my father's arrival, Kaz falls out with Blossom. No-one manages to get to the bottom of what exactly happened (although a man called Angus and a fifty-pound note come into it somewhere), but there it is. Another crisis, and yet another homeless person.

You would think it was impossible to fall out with Blossom, since no-one is ever, as it were, *in* with her. But apparently the fragile relationship between mother and daughter, having reached breaking point, has finally snapped, and Blossom has turned Kaz out of the house.

'It won't be for long.' Kaz stands on the front doorstep at midnight in the pouring rain, her car parked in the mud behind her. 'But at this time of night ... I couldn't think of anywhere else to go.'

'Have you no friends who could put you up?' I ask her (being the only one still up, I answer the door).

'Not really.' Kaz heaves a rather large suitcase into the hallway. 'Most of my friends are dancers like me, living in digs or with their parents. They haven't got room.' She grins at me from under her dripping fringe through eyes sooty with rain and mascara, and I wonder yet again how, whatever the circumstance, Kaz always manages to look ravishing. 'Any chance of a drink?'

'Whatever have you got in that case?' I ask her some minutes later, as we sit in the kitchen drinking (sloe gin for Kaz. Tea for me).

'Oh, you know. Clothes, make-up. Stuff for work. Don't worry, Ruth.' She pours herself another drink. 'I'll make it okay with the boys —' this is Kaz's preferred name for Eric and

Silas — 'and I'll even do extra hen house duty. In this weather you should be glad of me.'

'My father's here, too,' I remind her.

'You leave him to me,' Kaz says. 'Trust me. He'll be a pushover.'

Sure enough, when Dad meets Kaz at the breakfast table the next morning, after the initial surprise, he appears completely won over. She does what I think of as her class act; not exactly flirting, but demure and deferential, with just a little touch of the Princess Diana thing she does with her eyelashes. She listens with rapt attention to everything he has to say, and is most sympathetic about the insurance people.

'You're so right,' I hear her say. 'These people have got you just where they want you, haven't they? I've no time for them at all.' (I am pretty sure that Kaz knows nothing at all about house insurance, and cares even less).

'What an — interesting girl,' says Dad, when Kaz goes out to help with the animals. 'In spite of all those rings and things; a most interesting girl. And so sympathetic, too. I have to hand it to you, Ruth. You've made some very nice friends since you've been here.'

Eric and Silas don't appear quite so pleased at the sudden appearance of their new guest, but they take the news stoically.

'Oh well. She can always sleep in the attic,' says Eric. 'So long as she doesn't intend to entertain any gentleman friends.'

When I relay this information to Kaz, she laughs.

'He needn't worry. My boyfriends wouldn't touch this place with a bargepole,' she tells me. I've met one or two of them, and they tend to be of the posh, moneyed variety; wealthy young men who spice up their dull lives by paying to watch girls like Kaz.

'You don't sound very grateful.'

'Of course I'm grateful. I've a lot of time for the boys, bless them. But would you want a romantic liaison in this tip of a place? I think not.'

I can imagine nothing I'd like better, but Kaz wouldn't understand.

CHAPTER TWENTY-SEVEN

With the onset of winter, interest in the Virgin of the hen house begins to ease off a little, and I think we are all relieved. For while she has been less trouble than we anticipated, hen house duty on dark wet afternoons is something we can all do without, and while we have restricted the number of afternoons to two, it is still a commitment.

'Couldn't we pack the whole thing in for the winter?' I suggest to Blossom. 'After all, there aren't that many visitors now, and the weather's awful.'

'Nope.' Blossom gives me one of her looks.

'Just for a couple of months?' I can't believe I'm begging favours from someone who, when it comes down to it, is just a hired hand. But this hired hand is in a very powerful position, and she knows it, for without her, Eric and Silas would find it almost impossible to cope.

'Nope.' The look becomes dangerous. Blossom is preparing to make trouble.

'Blossom, we've got a lot on. Whoever's looking after things, it's always a disruption. Silas still isn't a hundred percent. He needs a bit of peace and quiet. And Mum and Dad don't approve —'

'Not my problem.'

'No. Maybe not. But *you* don't have to live here.'

'Wouldn't if you paid me.'

The idea of paying Blossom to live with us is laughable, but I'm in no mood for humour. I decide to try another tack.

'Well, just until the new year, then. How would that be?'

Blossom pauses, as though to consider.

'Think about it,' she concedes.

'That would be great.'

'Let you know Thursday.'

I'm too relieved to enquire as to the significance of Thursday. The prospect of even a few weeks without the tramping of strangers past the garden is too good for me to wish to endanger it by pushing my luck any further.

But I shall never know whether Thursday would have brought the anticipated reprieve, for I am not the only one who has been making plans.

The very next day we receive an unexpected visit from Mikey and Gavin. This is not unusual, as Mikey frequently calls in on his travels, and I'm always pleased to see him. But he doesn't often bring Gavin with him, and has never before brought Gavin in a wheelchair.

'Oh, dear. What's happened? Have you broken something, Gavin?' I ask, when Gavin and his wheelchair have been unloaded from the back of Mikey's car.

'We've come to visit your Virgin,' Mikey tells me.

'What are you two up to?'

'We're not up to anything. It's just that Gavin's decided to return to the Catholic Church and he wants to see it again.'

'But what's wrong with him? Is there something the matter with his legs?'

'You'll see.'

It's a relatively warm Saturday afternoon, the first sunshine we have seen for a couple of weeks, and there is a good gathering of pilgrims admiring the Virgin, praying and taking photographs. They draw back respectfully when they see the wheelchair, and Mikey parks his charge in front of the Virgin, where he and Gavin bow their heads apparently in prayer.

I am puzzled. Hitherto, Mikey has shown little interest in our Virgin, but perhaps Gavin, in returning to his faith, has managed to take Mikey with him. After all, it's quite possible. I'm sure that Mikey would dance barefoot on hot coals if Gavin asked him to, he is so besotted. On the other hand, why haven't they explained the wheelchair? Surely Gavin hasn't suddenly been struck down by some grave and unmentionable disease? Mikey and I have never had any secrets from each other. I would hate to think that he didn't feel he could trust me after all these years.

Meanwhile, people gather round the wheelchair, asking questions. What's wrong with Gavin? Has he always been unable to walk? If he's looking for a miracle, maybe he should try Lourdes. Someone's aunt came back from Lourdes cured of a tumour. People exchange views and experiences of Lourdes, and the gathering becomes something of a party.

Then quite suddenly, Gavin leaps from his wheelchair, flinging out his arms as though about to embrace some invisible giant.

'A miracle! It's a miracle! I can walk!' he cries, hugging Mikey and turning to the other visitors. 'Look, everyone! Oh, praise the Lord! I can *walk*!'

'Crippled from birth —' it is now Mikey's turn — 'and will you look at him now? Just look at him! He's walking with the best of us. We came looking for a miracle, and here it is. A miracle! Much better than Lourdes,' he adds tactlessly (I'm pretty sure that Mikey knows nothing at all about Lourdes).

Together, they pirouette round the wheelchair, while their fellow-pilgrims give little cries of astonishment and joy. A couple fall to their knees in thanksgiving, someone murmurs Hail Marys, while the rest gather round and ply Gavin with questions. What does it feel like? Has he really lived his life in a wheelchair? Did he have any kind of vision? Did the Virgin move? *Did she speak to him?*

But the performance is over. Gavin and Mikey reward their audience with radiant smiles and handshakes all round, before running off toward the house murmuring about having to make phone calls and letting Gavin's dear mother know the good news (Gavin's dear mother, I know for a fact, died when he was eleven).

'How could you, Mikey? *How could you*?' I demand, when we get back to the house. 'That was in the most appallingly bad taste.'

'It was fun, though, wasn't it? You have to admit, Ruth, it was a laugh.' Mikey tries to put his arm round me.

'It was not a laugh.' I push him away. 'It wasn't fun, either. Not for anybody else. What about all those poor people? They think they've just seen a miracle, and it was just you two making fools of yourselves. And of them. It was an unforgivable thing to do.'

'Oh, get a life, Ruth. Whatever's happened to your sense of humour?'

'My sense of humour is perfectly intact, thank you. I just don't happen to think it's amusing to play tricks on vulnerable people.'

'We're sorry,' says the newly-healed and now subdued Gavin. 'We really didn't mean any harm.'

'Oh, don't apologise to her, Gav. We haven't done anything wrong.' Mikey is unrepentant. 'Ruth's just in a bad mood.'

There are few things more infuriating than being told you're in a bad mood when, basically, you are not. It comes second only to being told that 'it must be the wrong time of the month' (at least he can't say that to me at the moment).

'Right. That's it. Go.' I point to the door. 'Just go.'

'What? No cup of tea?' Mikey looks astonished.

'No cup of tea. No cup of anything. Remember, I'm in a bad mood. You said so yourself.'

'But I didn't mean —'

'*Just go*, Mikey, would you? And take that bloody wheelchair with you.'

After they have gone, I find that I am shaking; shaking with anger, but also with disappointment and hurt. I thought I knew Mikey better. It's true that he has always enjoyed the odd practical joke, but he has never to my knowledge done anything so lacking in consideration for other people's feelings. But apparently I have misjudged him. It's tempting to blame the Gavin effect, but at least Gavin had the grace to apologise. I have to conclude that the whole thing was Mikey's idea.

My parents have been out for the afternoon with Eric and Silas, bonding over an ancient stone circle (this has been a pleasing development, as hitherto there has been little socialising between them), and they return just as Mikey and Gavin leave.

'Couldn't they stay?' Eric asks (Eric is fond of Mikey, who is always interested in Ark-related developments).

'No. They had to go.'

'Oh, what a shame.'

'I'll tell you about it later.'

When I finally get Eric and Silas on their own, I tell them about the "miracle", but they are disappointingly unperturbed.

'Oh well. No harm done,' says Silas, examining a dead frog (frogs are a new departure; advanced stuff, so I'm told, and in short supply in the winter, so Silas is pleased).

'You think so?' I ask him.

How little my uncles know about the power of miracles! For word spreads rapidly, and before we know it, we are inundated with visitors, with and without tickets. They come at all times of the day, and occasionally even at night, carrying torches. Thursday, the day of Blossom's decision, comes and goes unnoticed, for there is now no question of closing the hen house; more, the problem of how to manage what is rapidly becoming a crisis.

'Of course, it's trespass,' I say. 'It's your land. Surely there's some law to protect you.'

'Nowadays, the law seems to be more on the side of the person breaking it,' says Silas, who knows a man who was prosecuted for chasing a burglar with a sawn-off shot gun. 'We'll ask Blossom. She may have an idea.'

Blossom is typically unhelpful, but does refer the problem to Father Vincent, who pays us another visit accompanied by his new curate, with Blossom in the unlikely role of mediator.

'Oh, I say! That really is amazing.' The curate, who appears a great deal more impressed by the Virgin than Father Vincent, crosses himself. 'She looks so — *real.* And they say there's been a healing as well?'

'No. No healing. Just a practical joke,' I tell him.

'But I've spoken to witnesses. People who were there at the time. They said there was this man in a wheelchair —'

'The man in the wheelchair was perfectly able-bodied. He was an accomplice in a particularly cruel trick.'

'Ah.' The curate looks disappointed. He is young and fresh-faced and eager, and I feel sorry to have to disappoint him. 'But if it helps more people with their faith, surely that can't be bad.' He turns to Father Vincent for assurance.

'Faith built on deception isn't faith,' says Father Vincent firmly. 'Let's go back to the house and talk about it.'

I know from my brief acquaintance with Father Vincent that he is hoping to be offered a drink, and he's not disappointed.

Over mulberry wine (just a cup of tea for the curate, who's driving) we discuss the problem.

'You could donate the hen house to the church,' the curate suggests (we have been invited to call him Father Ambrose, which seems a terribly portentous name for someone so young).

'No room,' says Father Vincent, pouring himself more wine.

'And what about the hens? It's their home,' says Silas.

'Don't they mind all these visitors?' Father Ambrose asks.

'Strangely enough, they don't. I think they're getting used to it,' I tell him. 'In any case, they run around all over the place during the day time, so they only use it at night and for laying.'

'Electric fence?' says Father Vincent. 'For the visitors, not the hens, of course.' This is not a very Christian suggestion, but I think the wine is beginning to take effect.

'Someone would sue,' says Eric gloomily.

'We could try to get more volunteers from the church to supervise, and maybe collect money for some kind of cause,' I suggest. 'At least that would do some good.'

'What cause?' Eric asks.

'Chickens.' Blossom who has been silent for some time, speaks up.

'What do you mean, chickens?'

'Rescue chickens.'

'Rescue what chickens?' Eric is becoming irritated.

'Battery.'

'I don't think a chicken charity would be appropriate for Our Lady,' says Father Vincent. He has difficulty with the words 'chicken charity', and I'm relieved that Father Ambrose is doing the driving.

'God's creatures,' says Blossom piously.

'No doubt. But a human charity might be more — appropriate,' says Father Ambrose.

'Both, then.'

'It's certainly a thought,' says Silas. 'If we can — police things properly, and Eric and I don't have to do too much. It might be managed.'

'Leave it to me,' says Father Ambrose, who is obviously much taken with the whole Virgin project. 'Would you let me — organise it?'

'We'd be absolutely delighted, 'Silas assures him. 'If you're sure you've got the time.'

'There are some things one has to make time for,' Father Ambrose assures him earnestly. 'It will be a privilege.'

'The path's in a terrible state,' says Eric, after we have all had time to digest Father Ambrose's proposal. 'All those people tramping about have churned it up badly.'

'Gravel,' says Blossom.

'Expensive,' counters Eric.

'Lazzo knows someone.'

'Does he, indeed?'

Eric's suspicion may be well-founded.

'Legit,' Blossom pre-empts him.

'Not free, though,' says Silas.

'Good as.'

So after a lot of discussion and almost two bottles of mulberry wine, the decision is made. Lazzo will get a load of good-as-free gravel from his contact and reinforce the path with it. Father Ambrose will recruit more volunteers from the church to take over hen house duty and try to control the numbers by means of strict notices and more official-looking tickets, and we'll give it a try.

'Just a month's trial, mind,' says Eric, and Silas nods agreement. 'If that doesn't work we'll have to resort to something drastic.'

'What's drastic?' Kaz blows into the kitchen and helps herself to a glass of wine.

'It's a long story,' I tell her.

Kaz eyes Blossom suspiciously. 'If it's anything to do with Mum, I'd say no if I were you.'

'Too late,' says Blossom triumphantly.

And I'm afraid she's right.

CHAPTER TWENTY-EIGHT

Within a week, Father Ambrose has taken over responsibility for the Virgin of the hen house, and things have improved enormously. Lazzo has laid down his gravel, collecting boxes have been put in place (Battery Rescue, the chicken charity, to appease Blossom, and Oxfam for those pilgrims who prefer human beings to chickens), and some very official-looking reusable tickets have been produced. Pairs of volunteers, complete with shiny badges, supervise the hen house during agreed opening hours, and on the whole, the punters are co-operative.

December is if anything worse than November. There is no Christmas-card frost twinkling in the trees; no bright sharp wintry mornings; and not a trace of snow. There is just more rain and more mud, dark afternoons followed by nights of penetrating cold. The house is not what you'd call cosy, since the heating system is erratic and the rooms are large with high ceilings. I have always wondered about high ceilings. Why is it that big houses built before the luxury of central heating invariably have these lofty rooms, where (presumably) what little heat there is rises ceiling-wards to hover unhelpfully above the heads of those it is intended to keep warm, while the draughts sweep unchallenged under the ill-fitting doors?

And then there is the prospect of Christmas.

Out of a sense of duty, I have always tried to spend Christmas at home with my parents. This is another of the many downsides of being an only child: without me, my parents will not have a family Christmas, since (apart from Eric and Silas) they have no other family to have it with. Our

Christmases are never the jolly occasions enjoyed by other families. There are no crackers and paper hats; none of the drinking and merrymaking enjoyed by so many of my friends. We all go to church, after which my mother cooks a capon since, as she points out every year, there's no point in roasting a whole turkey for just the three of us. (For my own part, I have never been entirely sure what a capon is, except that it is a sort of inferior turkey substitute which only appears at Christmas, having undergone some kind of intimate operation). After lunch, we gather by the startling bright green plastic Christmas tree (Woolworths, circa 1980) to listen to the Queen and exchange presents.

When I was small, I always had a Christmas stocking, although there was never any pretence as to the existence of Father Christmas, since my father considered it 'wrong to tell lies to a child'. Nor for me the visit to Santa's grotto in the local department store, the excitement of waiting for a festive old man to clamber down the chimney, or the carefully prepared sherry and mince pies set out on the hearth. It was made absolutely clear to me from the start that Father Christmas was a myth, together with the munificent tooth fairy who frequented the homes of my more fortunate friends. If I have anything to do with it, the baby is going to believe in Father Christmas until it's at least eighteen, and will make a small fortune from the teeth placed under its pillow.

As I trudge back and forth with buckets of animal feed, I wonder what Christmas will be like here at Applegarth. My parents are still staying despite knowing full well that the insurance people are willing to pay for accommodation (I suspect that removal to an hotel would be seen to constitute some kind of climb down on the part of one or other of them); the rift between Blossom and Kaz has, if anything deepened, so Kaz is still living here; and Lazzo, who apparently misses his sister, is spending increasing amount of time with us, although he still goes home to sleep. If things carry on like this, I foresee a very full house at Christmas, not to mention a disconcerting clash of customs and beliefs.

But two weeks before Christmas, we receive a visitor.

It seems to be my lot to find unexpected visitors on the doorstep, but this is probably because I am nearly always in. My parents are increasingly out, seeing people about repairs to their house or attending prayer meetings with their new church friends, and Eric and Silas never answer the door if they think someone else is around to do it. As for Blossom she rarely answers doors at all, as she says it is not in her job description.

The man on the doorstep is middle-aged, lean and rather good-looking, with nice eyes and an anxious smile.

'My name is Kent Riley. I'm looking for my father,' he tells me, fending off the advances of Mr. Darcy.

'Your father?'

'Yes. Ridiculous, isn't it? At my age, I mean. It's taken me ages,' he adds, and I notice that he looks frozen.

'You'd better come in.' I hold the door open for him, 'although I'm not sure you'll find your father here.'

'Well, it's worth a try.' Mr. Riley takes off his muddy shoes and looks round the hallway with interest, as though expecting to be presented with an identity parade of missing fathers. 'I never met him, you know.'

'Oh, didn't you?'

'My mother wouldn't even tell me who he was.'

'Your mother?'

'She died six months ago.'

'Oh. I'm sorry.'

'That's all right.'

'Who is — your father?'

'I'm not sure. But I think his name was Purves, and I know he lived here.'

'Ah.' Purves is the surname of Eric and Silas, and they have lived here all their lives. I take a couple of deep breaths. Eric? Silas? Eric or Silas a *father*? Surely not.

'You don't have another name for — your father?' I say, leading the way to the kitchen. Silas's frog is spread-eagled on the kitchen table. I quickly cover it with a tea towel.

'No. My mother used to get so upset at the thought of my getting in touch with him, that I gave up asking her about him. After all, I've done okay without a father so far. But she left me a letter at the solicitor's saying that I might find my father at this address. So I thought I'd come and see if — well, if he's still alive.'

While we are having this conversation, my thoughts are spinning. What do I do? Silas mustn't be upset at the moment, as it's bad for his heart. My parents certainly shouldn't be involved due to the private nature of the business in hand. Kaz would certainly say something tactless. This leaves Eric.

'I'll just fetch my uncle,' I say. 'He might be able to help.'

Eric is very preoccupied with the problem of bamboo shoots and pandas, and is reluctant to leave his investigations.

'Can't you see to this man, Ruth?' he asks me, looking longingly at his charts and notes.

'No, I'm afraid I can't. This is a personal matter, and nothing to do with me. I probably shouldn't even know about it,' I tell him.

'Oh, well. If you're sure.'

'I'm sure.'

Eric greets our visitor, and offers him a drink.

'I think perhaps I ought to be going.' I edge towards the door.

'No, no, Ruth. Do stay.' Eric pours a cloudy liquid into glasses (the label has come off the bottle. I hope it's not weed killer).

'But this may be private,' I tell him.

'Nonsense,' says Eric. 'Now.' He turns to Mr. Riley. 'What can I do for you?'

'It's complicated.' The man looks desperately round him, as though searching for some kind of assistance. 'Is your name — Purves?'

'Yes. Eric Purves.' Eric tastes his drink and then holds his glass up to the light. 'Parsnip, I think. Yes, I'm sure this is the parsnip. Not at all bad, as I recall.'

'Well, I think you might be my father.'

'Ah.' Eric puts down his glass. He appears amazingly calm. 'What makes you think that?'

Mr. Riley explains about his mother, the mystery of his paternity, and the letter.

'I'm so sorry to bother you with all this, particularly after all this time. It must come as quite a shock to you. But you see, I really need to know.'

'Of course you do.' Eric pauses. 'And who — who was your mother?'

'Mary Riley. She never married, so if you knew her, that would have been her name.'

'Mary Riley,' Eric muses, as though mentally going through a check-list of past lovers. 'Yes. You know, I think there was a Mary Riley. It was a long time ago, of course. A very long time ago.'

At this moment, Silas comes in. He greets Mr. Riley cheerfully, and then starts hunting for his frog.

'I'm sure I put it down here somewhere,' he says. 'Ruth, have you done something with my frog?'

'Silas, I think you'd better listen to Eric,' I tell him.

'Yes. Silas, Mr. Riley thinks I'm his father.'

Mr. Riley is still apparently reeling from the identical twin effect, and I can't help feeling sorry for him. After all, there are just so many shocks someone can be expected to cope with in one afternoon. I refill his glass, hoping this might help.

'And are you?' Silas asks. 'Oh, here it is!' He recovers his frog from under the tea towel and places it on the draining board.

'I suppose I could be,' Eric says. 'He's Mary Riley's son.'

'Mary Riley, Mary Riley.' Silas says thoughtfully, 'Oh, *that* Mary Riley! I remember. She was a lovely girl. Nice sense of humour.'

I hope her son has inherited the sense of humour, for I have a feeling he's going to need it.

'So, what do you think?' Mr. Riley looks pathetically from one to the other.

'Well, we both *knew* Mary Riley,' says Silas carefully.

'Oh yes. We both knew her,' Eric says. 'Quite well, actually.'

'How well?' Mr. Riley has decided to be blunt.

'Very well.' Silas and Eric exchange glances.

'What, both of you?'

'Both of us.'

'You mean you shared — relationships?'

'Oh, not always,' Eric tells him, 'By no means always. But sometimes, when one thing ended, another would begin. You know how it is.'

'Are you saying — are you saying that either of you could be my father?'

'I think we're saying it's possible.' Eric refills everyone's glasses. 'What did you say your name was?'

'Kent. Kent Riley.'

'Why Kent?'

'My mother said I was conceived in Kent.'

'Surrey.' My uncles speak in unison.

'I beg your pardon?'

'Not Kent. Surrey. If it — you — were anything to do with us, it was definitely Surrey,' says Silas.

'Perhaps she thought that Kent Riley sounded better than Surrey Riley,' says Eric.

There follows a discussion about Kent and Surrey, and what Mary Riley might or might not have been up to in either county.

'You don't sound very surprised by all this,' Mr. Riley says, after everyone has decided that Kent is on the whole prettier than Surrey.

'Oh, I think we're surprised all right,' Silas says, 'but nothing's been proved yet, has it?'

'No. We need proof,' says Eric.

'Well, I've no problem with that,' says Mr. Riley (Kent, I suppose we should call him, especially as it looks as though he may be family).

'Of course, if you can prove that one of us is your father we'll have to share you,' says Silas.

'Why's that?'

'Shared DNA. Our DNA is identical, so while we might find out that either of us could be your father, we wouldn't know which one.'

'Oh. Oh dear.'

'Why? Does it matter?'

'I don't know. I hadn't really thought about it. I'd resigned myself to having no father at all, and now it looks as though I may have two. It takes a bit of getting used to.'

'And we had resigned ourselves to having no sons at all, and now we'll have to make do with half each,' says Eric, who has overdone the parsnip wine and is becoming pink-faced and merry. 'Have you any children?' I think this is greedy of Eric. Isn't a son enough, without expecting grandchildren as well?

'No. I never married.' No-one points out that it is just been shown only too clearly that marriage is no prerequisite for the fathering of children.

'Oh well. Never mind.'

'I don't, most of the time,' Kent says, 'but I think I'd like to have been a father.'

'It's not too late.' Eric laughs. 'Look at us! We never expected children, and now it looks as though we might have one after all!'

While this discussion is going on, it occurs to me that Eric and Silas may not be the only ones to have discovered a new relation, for I may be about to acquire a cousin. Never having had a cousin before — never really having had much in the way of family at all — I am very pleased with this idea.

'Mr. Riley — Kent — what do you do?' I ask him. 'For a living, I mean.'

'I'm a piano tuner.'

There follows a long, interested silence.

'Not — not a blind piano tuner?' asks Silas.

'Certainly not a blind piano tuner. Many of us can see perfectly well.'

Eric and Silas are clearly disappointed, and I feel enormously sorry for Kent. He has more than likely just found two possible fathers, and already he has proved to be a disappointment.

'Well, I think it's wonderful,' I tell him. 'We can play duets.'

I think of the poor neglected piano in the room next door. Our new-found relation may be just the person to bring it back to life.

CHAPTER TWENTY-NINE

It is decided that what with the approach of Christmas and the amount of work generated by the extra care needed by the animals in this most unforgiving of seasons, any DNA investigations can wait until the new year. But our new relation seems here to stay, at least for the time being.

Meanwhile, it transpires that whatever Mary Riley may have been up to in her lifetime, she contrived to save quite a lot of money, all of which she left to her only son. Kent is now what he himself calls 'a free man'. His piano tuning days are over. He has let his mother's house, and bought himself a nice little caravan, which he has fitted up with all mod cons. With this in tow, he intends to tour the country, looking up friends (and putative fathers) and visiting those towns and cities he has never managed to see before. Kent says that he has 'done' abroad, and that it is wildly overrated. It's time to reacquaint himself with the country of his birth. He admits that he was sad to leave his piano behind, but his inheritance wouldn't stretch to a caravan large enough to accommodate it.

Needless to say, Eric and Silas have invited him to stay on 'so that we can all get to know each other', so the caravan is now parked behind the outhouses, and Kent is rapidly becoming one of the household. I'm delighted, my parents are slightly puzzled and Blossom is indignant ('too many people,' she complains, although Kent keeps well out of her way). Kaz is another story.

When she first meets him, she's polite enough, but after a day or two, she begins to show a suspicious amount of interest in him.

'This Kent person,' she says casually, while we are seeing to the pigs. 'He's rather nice.'

'How, *rather nice*?' I ask her.

'Quite sexy, actually.' Kaz bends over the bucket of swill she's mixing.

'Oh Kaz, you can't!'

'Can't what?'

'You know perfectly well what I mean. For a start, he's too old for you. And anyway, aren't you seeing someone else at the moment?' For these days, it's hard to keep up with Kaz's love life.

'Oh, him. He's boring. I was giving him up anyway. No. I think it's time for someone more mature.' She winks at me.

'Kaz, you can't just *use* Kent because you want someone more mature. Hasn't the poor guy had enough shocks for the time being?'

'What's got into you, Ruth? I'm not using anyone, and Kent is a grown man and can make his own decisions.' She looks at me thoughtfully. 'You know, I think you're jealous!'

'Don't be ridiculous!'

But in a way, she's right. Having found this new almost-relation, I'm oddly reluctant to share him. Silas and Eric, as putative fathers, are different. But Kaz has no claim on Kent, and I want to keep it that way.

'Well, nothing's happened yet,' says Kaz peaceably, as we return to the house. 'We'll just have to see, won't we?'

My parents have been given just as much information about Kent as Eric and Silas consider they need; they have been told that he is the son of an old friend ('true, in a way') and that he has come to visit. Further information will be forthcoming if the DNA results prove to be positive. As Silas points out, there is no point in shocking them unnecessarily. Both my uncles agree that my mother might well be pleased to have a nephew, but the circumstances (not to mention the confusion) surrounding his provenance might prove more difficult to explain, never mind accept.

I am in a seventh heaven, for at last I have someone to make music with. While I clean up the piano, digging out everything from spiders' webs to old socks and even a dead mouse from its dusty innards, Kent does his best to tune it.

'I don't think I can bring it up to concert pitch without breaking strings,' he tells me. Fortunately, I am not blessed with perfect pitch, so I can just tune my violin down a fraction and we are ready to go. The piano is more honky-tonk than Steinway, but any piano is better than no piano, and I for one am not complaining.

Kent proves to be an excellent pianist. I am unsurprised — I have come across many piano-tuners who are similarly gifted — but my uncles are amazed. Like many people, they have hitherto regarded piano tuners as second-rate musicians (if they can be counted as musicians at all), but Kent rapidly wins them over, and he and I entertain everyone with an evening of Mozart and Beethoven.

Even my parents are impressed.

'He plays very well. For a piano tuner,' I hear Mum say to Dad.

In addition to his music, Kent adds a great deal to the running of the household. He's an excellent cook, bachelor-tidy in his habits, and good with the animals. He takes an interest in Silas's taxidermy, and even assists Eric with his researches (although I suspect that he considers them to be a waste of time).

As I watch him stooped over some task, or see his long fingers moving over the piano keys, I become increasingly convinced that he is indeed the son of Eric or Silas. In addition to the physical resemblance, he even shares some of their mannerisms. The way he shakes his head when he's puzzled; the occasional amused lift of an eyebrow; the sound of his laugh. All these remind me of Eric and Silas. And while I was initially unsure as to whether having a son would be a good thing for my uncles, I've now been completely won round. I think that Eric and Silas are beginning to feel the same, for while they accepted Kent's arrival with equanimity, I know they must have been disturbed by it. Now, it is as though they have always known him. He is, quite simply, part of the family.

I am not the only one to have noticed a resemblance.

'Family, is he?' Blossom asks me, after Kent has been with us a week. It's a question which she's obviously been longing to ask, and the waiting's finally got too much for her.

'He's the son of an old friend,' I tell her. 'She died recently.'

'Hmm.'

'What do you mean, hmm?'

'You know what I mean,' says Blossom. '*You know.*'

But now something happens to take my mind off life at Applegarth, for I have news of Amos. I've alerted everyone I can think of (friends, friends of friends, colleagues from the orchestra, even a dentist we once shared in London) and finally someone from the orchestra has received a postcard from Barbados, and has thoughtfully forwarded it to me. Palm trees and blue skies adorn the front, but on the back, the news isn't good.

Having a wonderful time in this amazing place. The people are so friendly that I feel as though I've come home. Even found a band to play in. May stay here for ever! December in England seems a very long way away. What's there to come home to?

ME! I want to tell him. There's me to come home to, and our baby! Oh Amos! Please come home!

But my tears fall uselessly onto the postcard, trickling across the sandy beach and the palm trees and smudging the ink of Amos's handwriting. He has nice handwriting, and it occurs to me that I have never seen it before. There has never been any reason for us to correspond. And now, when there is every reason, I have no address to write to. Supposing Amos really does decide to stay on? Supposing he never comes back? He has always had a penchant for dark-skinned women. He could well settle down with a Caribbean wife and a brood of tawny children, with never a thought for (or come to that, any knowledge of) the child he's left behind. Perhaps, in years to come, my son and I will voyage across the sea and try to find him. But of course by then it will be too late. We shall merely be an embarrassment; a cruel reminder of the life he's tried to leave behind.

I suppose I could try writing to the British embassy in Barbados. Do embassies concern themselves with such domestic matters? Almost certainly not. Perhaps I should go to Barbados now to search for him? But I haven't enough money, and I wouldn't know where to start. Also, the idea of travelling, once so attractive, has become daunting to me in my pregnant and vulnerable state, and the prospect of running the gauntlet of airports and queues and the complications of foreign officialdom on my own is not one I relish. I need my family and friends; I need continuity; I need to feel *safe*. Spinning across the world in search of Amos doesn't sound at all safe, especially as it is more than likely that I wouldn't find him. Briefly, I wonder whether Mikey would come with me. But Mikey is still sulking in the aftermath of the wheelchair episode, and in any case, it wouldn't be fair to take him away from Gavin at this early stage of their relationship. I shall just have to continue waiting, and see what happens. I wish most fervently that I had never seen that postcard. My friend meant kindly in sending it to me, but it has done nothing to raise my spirits.

'What's up, Ruth?' Kaz has come into the kitchen to make herself some coffee.

I tell her about the postcard. Kaz already knows about Amos, and has been on the whole sympathetic.

'Mm.' Kaz pours hot water into a mug. 'Are you sure you really want this guy?'

'No. Not absolutely sure. But I think I do.'

'Better to have no man than the wrong man,' Kaz tells me.

'Do you think you'll get married one day?' I ask her.

'I might, if I could find someone like Kent,' she teases. I decide to ignore her. 'But probably not. The only married couple I've ever had anything to do with were my parents. They were a nightmare together.'

'What was your dad like?'

'Oh, mousy, hen-pecked. A miserable little man, he was. Though I blame my mum.'

'Did she make him very unhappy?' I have often wondered about Blossom's marriage.

'She certainly did. But then, he asked for it. He was such a wimp. And he wouldn't fight back.'

'Why didn't he leave her?'

'Search me. She told him to often enough.'

'Wasn't she at all upset when he died?'

Kaz laughs.

'Not at all. At least no-one can call Mum a hypocrite.'

'And Lazzo? Was he — close to your father?'

'No. In any case, Lazzo wasn't Dad's.'

'Ah.' I was wondering how it was that the combination of a mousy little man and Blossom had managed to produce anything as large as Lazzo. 'How does she reconcile that with her faith?'

'I told you before. Mum's selective when it comes to her faith. She takes the bits she wants, and discards the rest.'

'How handy.' I pause for a moment, envying Kaz's ability to look ravishing whatever she happens to .be wearing (today, dirty dungarees, an old flat cap belonging to my uncles and a torn trench coat). 'Who was Lazzo's father?'

'No idea.' Kaz spoons sugar into her coffee, and props herself against the sink.

'Does no-one know?'

'Mum probably does, but she's not telling, and Lazzo doesn't seem to care. I'm glad she had him, though. He's a good lad, is our Lazzo.'

'Yes. He's wonderfully straightforward, isn't he.'

'Heart of gold,' Kaz agrees.

'And is Lazzo a Catholic?'

Kaz laughs. 'Well, he was an altar boy when he was little, but he ate all the communion wafers and was dismissed. Sacrilege, they called it, and Mum was furious. But I think he was just hungry, poor kid. Our Laz was always hungry. But no. He's not really a Catholic any more, though Mum does sometimes try to drag him to Mass.'

After Kaz has left the room, I ponder on the subject of God. Do I believe in Him? I was force fed with so much religion as a child, that I used to think that I had been put off for life, but of course God and religion are not necessarily the same thing. Thinking about it now, I decide that I probably do believe in something like God. Wide night skies, an expanse of sea, the music of Bach, the poetry of Shakespeare — they all seem to come from something beyond a mere coincidence of genes or particles. But they also seem to me to have little connection with the petty rules and regulations and the repetitive hymns, often sung to the accompaniment of a guitar, which are the life blood of the church attended by my parents. These prettify and reduce God, like the paintings of Holman Hunt, making Him small and ever so slightly sickly. My God, if I have one, is huge and powerful and mysterious.

But then, what right have I to belittle a faith which gives so much comfort, and in which my parents have invested so much of their lives? Isn't it possible that we are all right, in our different ways?

I wander outdoors and make my way up to the hen house. A weak winter sun is shining on the Virgin, making her appear even more lifelike than usual, and someone has placed a bunch of Christmas roses on the ground beneath her. I envy the pilgrims their faith. It would be wonderful to believe that our Virgin really is a divine sign, and that the real Virgin Mary is still alive and well and doing good in the world.

You know what it's like, I tell her. You didn't exactly plan your pregnancy, either, did you? You must have had a pretty difficult time. Please help me to cope.

And please, if you have any influence at all, help me to find Amos.

CHAPTER THIRTY

Christmas at Applegarth is very different from any Christmas I've experienced before. The house is as full as ever, and Lazzo joins us for the day (Kaz tells us that Blossom doesn't do Christmas, and probably won't even notice her family's absence). The turkey — an ill-tempered bird of enormous proportions who has spent the last few months chasing us round the garden and biting our legs — has been despatched and prepared, Mum has made a Christmas cake, and a real Christmas tree stands in the hallway, decked out with decorations which go back to my uncles' and Mum's childhood. Numerous dusty bottles of wine are brought up from the cellar, their labels washed off for identification purposes, and everyone has Christmas stockings.

'What, all of us?' Mum asked, when she was told what was to happen.

'All of us,' Silas told her. 'Eric and I always give each other a stocking, but as there are so many of us, we thought we'd all draw lots and do each other's.'

I draw Kaz, and wonder what on earth I can put in it, for Kaz has a mind of her own when it comes to matters of taste. But in the event, she is thrilled.

'I've never had a stocking before,' she tells me, as she unwraps little parcels of chocolate and bath essence and some rather naughty knickers from the market. 'I always wanted one as a kid, but Mum said no.'

'Didn't you get presents?' I ask her. 'You must have had something?'

'Money usually. And maybe some sweets. Nothing much else, though. If I have kids, they're going to have stockings just like this one.' She pops a Malteser in her mouth. 'What about you, Ruth? Will you give your child a Christmas stocking?'

'Oh, yes. I should think so.' It occurs to me that the baby should probably have one next year, but what does one put in the stocking of anyone so small? I know nothing at all about babies. Do they eat sweets? Play with toys? *Do* anything? No doubt I shall find out.

My parents pay lip service to the stocking ritual (Mum has drawn Lazzo, and Dad, Silas), but I can see their hearts aren't in it, and they hanker after the kind of Christmas they are used to. After a meal which is more mediaeval banquet than traditional Christmas lunch, they make their excuses, and drive off to spend the rest of the day with some of Mum's new friends from church. In a way I'm pleased, for at least they are united in their discomfort at the goings-on at Applegarth. I feel for my mother's situation, but I would hate my parents' split to be permanent. Maybe it's something to do with the perversity of my generation, for while we aren't necessarily too bothered about marriage for ourselves, we nonetheless expect out parents to stay securely within its boundaries.

After they have left, everyone else continues to make inroads into the home-made wine, until Eric and Silas fall asleep in their chairs. Kaz, who is by now very drunk indeed, is draped across the table singing Jingle Bells, one pert little breast attempting to escape from the confines of her strappy little top. Kent, who says he needs some fresh air, is feeding the chickens. As for Lazzo, he is still admiring the contents of his stocking. Mum's efforts have been unimaginative — among other things, sweets, socks, and a keyring — but she couldn't have had a more appreciative recipient. Lazzo has unwrapped all the little parcels, and arranged his gifts in a neat row. I can see he's longing to open some of the sweets, but doesn't like to spoil the appearance of his arrangement.

'Go on, Lazzo. Have one. That's what they're for,' I urge him (although after the excesses of lunch time, I personally can't imagine ever wanting to eat again).

Lazzo picks up his packet of sweets and turns it over in his hands. Then he puts it back in its place.

'Have one of mine.' I take pity on him.

'Ta.' Absently, Lazzo takes a handful of toffees, which vanish without apparently any need for chewing on Lazzo's part. 'Never had presents like this,' he tells me, picking up his keyring and stroking it.

'Have you got some keys you can put on it?' I ask him.

'Nope.'

'What, none at all?'

'Nope.'

'How do you get into the house when you go home?'

'Key's under a stone.'

'Oh. Would you like a key?'

Lazzo's face brightens, and I forage in my bag and find an old front door key from a long-ago flat, wondering why it is that people never get around to throwing away old keys. Carefully, Lazzo attaches the key to his keyring, then holds it up for me to admire.

'Perfect,' I tell him.

Lazzo nods happily. His capacity for finding pleasure in small things never fails to amaze me, and I feel oddly humbled. Here is someone who has never (as far as I know) experienced much in the way of parental love and appears to have very few possessions, and yet he appears perfectly content with his lot. I have heard Lazzo swear, certainly, and he has a very colourful vocabulary in that department, but I have never heard him complain. Whatever he is doing, he gives the impression that that is the thing he wants to be doing above all else. He may not be particularly clean (I notice that among Mum's gifts there is a large can of cheap deodorant) and his table manners are appalling, but he is gentle and courteous and, in his own way, chivalrous. I don't think it would be an exaggeration to say that I have grown to love Lazzo.

'What's your mum doing today?' I ask him.

'Bed,' Lazzo tells me.

'What, all day?'

'Yeah. Always does.'

'What about church?'

'Midnight.'

Of course. I'd forgotten that that was what Catholics do at Christmas. It always seems to me to be a very sensible arrangement; get the formalities out of the way as early as possible, and then get down to the serious business of celebrating.

'So she's all by herself?'

'Doesn't mind.' Lazzo helps himself to another half dozen toffees.

'Did she — give you anything? A present?'

Lazzo laughs.

'Nope. Says I get board and lodging. Shouldn't expect anything else.'

'Do you mind?'

'Nope.' Lazzo finishes up the toffees.

'Did you give her anything?'

'No money.'

This is true enough, for Lazzo never appears to have any money. Although Blossom has cautioned against it, my uncles insist on paying him something for the work he does for them, but I know for a fact that he hands it all over to his mother. She feeds him and buys his few clothes, and if he did have money of his own, he'd probably spend it unwisely.

'Got fags off our Kaz,' he offers.

'That's nice.'

'Yeah. Five hundred. Keep me going.'

'They certainly should.'

By now, Kaz appears to have passed out. Lazzo carries her into the sitting room and deposits her on the sofa, where she lies snoring gently. One of her arms dangles over the edge like that of Chatterton in his famous portrait, and her right breast has finally broken free of its moorings, its rosy nipple pointing triumphantly towards the ceiling. Most people in this situation would look dishevelled and decadent. Kaz simply looks beautiful. Nonetheless, I cover up the rogue breast with a coat, for while Lazzo doesn't appear to have noticed, I would hate to embarrass Kent on his return.

By seven o'clock, everyone is beginning to recover, and we receive a Christmas visit from Mikey and Gavin, who come bearing gifts and forgiveness.

'I think I've sulked for long enough to make my point,' says Mikey, giving me a hug.

'I think you have.' I return his embrace. 'But I'm afraid I haven't bought you a present. I didn't know you were coming.'

'Neither did we. It was a spur of the moment thing. We were going to have our first Christmas on our own, but we got bored and decided we needed a party, so we've come to see you.'

'But we're not having a party.'

'You are now.' Mikey fetches bags from the car, and unpacks pork pies and crisps and nuts and Christmas crackers, and yet more drink. 'There! A party! Now, where's the corkscrew?'

When my parents return at eleven, they find Mikey's party in full swing, with a drunken game of charades in progress. Kaz and Kent, together with several cushions, are under an old raincoat pretending to be a camel, with Gavin, his head covered with a tea towel, as its Arab owner and Lazzo some kind of tree. Mikey and I are doing the guessing, but Silas, who is supposed to be on our team, is asleep, and Eric is fretting because he's realised that he hasn't accounted for camels on his Ark, and is wondering whether he needs to have dromedaries as well, or will the camels do for both?

'You don't hear much about dromedaries, do you?' he says. 'Camels, yes, but not dromedaries. What do people do with dromedaries?'

'I've no idea,' I tell him.

'Camels drink a lot,' he murmurs. 'Oh dear.'

'It would seem,' says my father, taking off his coat, 'that everyone has been drinking a lot.'

This strikes Mikey and me as terribly funny, and we roll on the sofa, crying with laughter. Eric merely looks hurt. Both halves of the camel collapse on the floor, Silas wakes up with a start, and the tree wanders off into the kitchen to look for more beer.

All in all, I think you could say that it's been a very merry Christmas indeed.

CHAPTER THIRTY-ONE

It is now January (if anything, even worse than November, with its grey twilight days and penetrating cold), and everyone is tired and grumpy. Meanwhile, I have commenced ante-natal classes.

After two sessions, I've decided that nothing can be quite so smug as a room full of cosily pregnant women lying on cushions on the floor doing their breathing exercises, each cocooned in a warm blanket of reproductive self-satisfaction. While I thought I would welcome the opportunity to talk to women of my own age and in the same condition, I had no idea of the self-centredness of pregnancy, and after two coffee breaks' worth of conversation about backache and breastfeeding and Braxton-Hicks contractions, I long for talk of anything but babies. What do these women actually *do*, apart from being pregnant? Have they lives, jobs, interests? It would appear not, or at least not at the moment. Right now, their lives centre round their bumps, the wonder of what's inside those bumps, and most importantly of all, how it's going to get out (we are all first-timers. Presumably second-time-round mothers are too busy to bother with all this, or maybe they feel they already know enough. I envy them).

Of course, Silas wanted to come with me, but fathers' evening (the only time when men are invited) doesn't happen until later, and in any case, I don't think it would be appropriate. In the absence of a genuine father, I have been invited to call on the services of a "birthing partner", but so far, I've decided against it, since there doesn't seem to be a suitable candidate. Silas, who is dying to be chosen, is out of the question, my mother (the obvious choice) seems unsure, and Kaz, who has volunteered for the part, is not in my good books.

For Kaz is beginning to make headway with Kent.

She hasn't told me so. In fact, she hasn't told me anything at all, but I can tell from her demeanour that something has happened. She sings as she goes about her work, volunteers to do the most unpleasant of jobs and has even made her peace with Blossom, although she continues to live with us. I know for a fact that she has dumped the "boring" boyfriend, and since the latest club didn't work out after all, she's short of work, and living here she has little opportunity to meet anyone else.

Kent, too, has changed. Always a cheerful person, he now literally glows with happiness, and nothing is too much trouble. On several occasions I have intercepted covert glances and smiles between the two of them — the kinds of secret smiles particular to lovers — and wherever possible he and Kaz contrive to work together. Kaz has been teaching Kent to milk the goats, and I've even caught her giving him what appeared to be a pole dancing demonstration in the garden, using a long-abandoned telegraph pole by the hedge.

'What on earth is Kaz doing?' Eric asks, as we watch from the kitchen window. 'She's going to hurt herself if she tries to climb that thing. It's probably rotten by now.'

'She's not trying to climb it. She's — dancing with it.' I know my voice is tight with hostility, but just at the moment, I can't help it.

'Now I've heard everything!' Eric has never understood the pole dancing thing. 'Don't you go trying anything like that, Ruth. You could do yourself serious damage.'

'I wouldn't dream of it.'

At this moment, Kaz begins to swing effortlessly by one arm, her head thrown back, legs stretched out at an impossible angle, looking as ravishing as ever despite her torn shirt and filthy jeans while Kent watches, apparently mesmerised. Suddenly, I'm overwhelmed with jealousy. I know this is nasty of me; they are both free and single, and they are both people I'm fond of. I should be pleased for them. But up until now — notwithstanding a possible relationship with Eric and Silas — Kent has been *my* friend; my almost-relation. He's been the person I play music with; the one who really understands and shares my passion. And now it seems as though he's found an altogether different, more exciting kind of passion; something I can't share in at all. And I don't like it. Besides, I'm the one who needs a partner, not Kaz. Until recently, Kaz has had putative lovers beating a path to her door, while I, with my impending motherhood, have no-one at all.

After two weeks of this, I can't stand it any longer.

'Kaz, how *could* you?' I ask her, as we muck out the pigs together. Kaz is doing most of the work since my size (which to me appears colossal but which I'm told is quite normal) prevents me from doing much in the way of bending.

'How could I what?' Kaz pushes Sarah out of the way with the handle of her shovel (Sarah hates her home being disarranged, and always makes herself as unpleasant as possible).

'Kent.'

'Ah.'

'Yes. Ah.'

'Well, what's it to you?' She stands back and wipes her hands on her jeans.

'I — I'm —'

'Jealous?'

'Of course not!'

'I wouldn't blame you,' Kaz says. 'He is rather gorgeous, isn't he?'

'Not particularly.' I'm in no mood to collude in this kind of conversation. 'Anyway, when did it all start?'

'I suppose — inside the camel.'

'*What*?'

'You know. At Christmas, when we were playing charades, and Kent and I were a camel. Under a rug. We — kissed.'

'How romantic.' If I wasn't so cross, I'd laugh.

'Yes. It was rather. I was going to tell you, but I knew you'd be like this.'

'I'm not being like anything. It's just — I don't like seeing him being taken advantage of.'

'Ruth, no-one's taking advantage of anyone. We just — like each other. We get on.'

'But you've got nothing in common!'

'Oh yes we have.' Kaz winks. 'More than you think.'

'Have you — well, have you —?'

'Not yet. No. But we probably shall.'

'And you've got a cosy little love nest waiting for you in the caravan, haven't you?'

Kaz closes the door of the sty and leans against it. 'Ruth, do you have to be like this? I thought we were friends.'

'Yes. No. I don't know.' And to my horror, I burst into tears. 'I'm sorry. I really am. It's just that I'm fat and tired and unlovely, and you're young and beautiful, and — and I feel so alone!'

Kaz puts her arms round me and pulls me into a hug, and for a few minutes we stand there in the drizzle as I sob into her shoulder and she pats my back and makes the kinds of soothing noises that Lazzo makes for the animals.

'Come on,' she says, pushing me gently away. 'It's freezing out here. Let's go back into the house and I'll make us some tea. And Ruth?'

'Yes?'

'Don't tell the boys about — about me and Kent yet, will you? It may come to nothing, and it's early days.'

I promise that I won't.

Later on in bed, I am awakened by the activities of the baby, who seems to be playing football with my liver, and my thoughts turn again to Kaz and Kent. Maybe it's not so bad after all. Neither of them seems to have had it easy so far, and don't they both deserve a little happiness? If Kent turns out to be my cousin, and he and Kaz stay together, then Kaz will be a kind of cousin, too, and I've always wanted more relatives. Kaz would make a good relative; maybe even the next best thing to a sister. She's kind and funny and loyal. I reflect that I could do a lot worse.

As I rearrange my pillows and turn onto my back, I conclude that my problem is that I'm now surrounded by couples. Eric and Silas have each other, as do Mum and Dad. Even Sarah has what might be called a gentleman visitor, who is delivered from time to time from the back of a very dirty truck and stays just long enough to guarantee another litter of piglets. I have only met him once, and he is if possible even more ill-tempered than she is, but none the less, he is her mate (although no doubt the mate of many others, besides), and he seems to do the business to the satisfaction of both parties. I'm the only one who's alone.

Mikey has heard from his contact in Barbados, who has made a few enquiries but come up with nothing in the way of news of bearded trombone players, or indeed any trombone players at all. It seems that Barbados is bigger than I had imagined, and any search for Amos would be of the needle and haystack variety. Amos may even have already tired of it and left. As I drift off to sleep, I dream of Amos and me running towards each other across a palm-fringed beach, like a Caribbean Cathy and Heathcliffe.

'Ruth! Ruth!' Amos calls, but his voice and image become fainter and fainter until I find myself alone, and when I awake again, my pillow is damp with my tears.

CHAPTER THIRTY-TWO

It's becoming increasingly apparent that Silas is unwell again. He is breathless and pale, tires easily and complains of swollen ankles and palpitations.

'I think it's come back,' he tells us, leafing through his health bible. It is a new one, which Eric gave him for Christmas since the old one was falling to pieces. It was not something Eric wanted to buy, since he had had more than enough of the last one, but he had to agree that Silas would only fret without what he sees as an essential aid to living. The new book is big and shiny and up-to-date, illustrated with the kinds of photographs that most people would do a great deal to avoid, and Silas loves it.

'Look.' Silas jabs a finger at a diagram of a heart valve. 'That's what it's supposed to look like. I think mine must be shot to pieces.'

'But you don't know what your heart looks like,' I object. 'How can you possibly tell?'

'I can feel it.' Silas places a hand on his chest. 'It's fibrillating again. The valve just isn't working properly. Look, Ruth.' He shows me a picture of a non-functioning valve. 'That's what's happened to it. I think I'm in mild heart failure.'

He goes on the explain about "mitral regurgitation" and "oedema" and says that this almost certainly means he should have an operation.

'Anyone would think you wanted an operation,' I object. 'No-one *wants* operations.'

'Well, of course I don't actually *want* one,' Silas says, just a little too cheerfully. 'But if I have to have one, then so be it.'

'You should see the doctor anyway,' Eric says. 'You need a thorough check-up.'

'All in good time, all in good time,' Silas says, opening his book again. 'I want to make quite sure I know all the facts before I start seeing doctors again.'

'But the doctor will know all the facts. *You* don't have to,' I object.

Silas regards me gravely over the top of his spectacles.

'You can't be too sure,' he says. 'And it's my body. I think I should be the one to decide what to do with it.'

Since none of us can argue with that, we have to leave Silas to get on with it, but I know that poor Eric is terribly worried, and I feel for him. In matters of his own health, Silas, usually the most thoughtful of men, can be very inconsiderate, for surely he, more than any of us, should understand how Eric is feeling.

'You must be awfully worried,' I say to Eric, when we are alone together.

'Of course I am. But what can I do?' He is currently preoccupied with the subject of koala bears and eucalyptus, and for once I'm grateful for Eric's Ark, because at least it's something to help keep his mind off his brother. 'He's so stubborn. It would be easier if he didn't enjoy all this so much. He's having a wonderful time with that bloody book of his. I wish I'd never given it to him. It only encourages him.'

'He would have bought it for himself anyway,' I remind him. 'You know what Silas is like.'

'True.' Eric puts down his pen. 'Did you know that the koala bear is a marsupial? Isn't that interesting?'

The following day, Silas collapses at the lunch table. As we once again await the arrival of the ambulance, Eric curses himself for not doing something sooner. It should never have come to this, he says wretchedly. We should have bundled him into the car and shipped him off to the doctor with or without his permission. If anything happens to Silas, he tells us, he will never forgive himself. Mum, too, feels responsible; even I feel responsible. In fact, it seems to me that everyone feels responsible except the patient, who is lying serenely on the kitchen floor issuing instructions through lips the colour of damsons.

'Don't talk, Silas,' Eric tells him, 'You're just tiring yourself out.'

'Take — my — pulse,' whispers Silas.

I take his pulse. I can barely feel anything, and what I can feel is thin and thready and very irregular.

'What — is — it?'

'Difficult to tell. A bit irregular.'

Silas nods. 'As — I — thought.' He smiles, and I find myself actually feeling angry with him. How could he? How could he be so cheerful when everyone else is so worried? Doesn't he spare a thought for Eric? For Mum? Apparently not. Silas is doing what he does best; he is Being Ill. And don't we all enjoy doing what we do best?

In hospital, Silas has all the tests he had last time, and is fully vindicated. His mitral valve has become virtually useless, and he needs a new one.

'There,' he says, sitting up in bed and talking through a plastic oxygen mask. 'I was right all along.'

'So you were,' says Eric, who is by now paler than Silas.

'They say they're going to operate as soon as possible,' Silas tells us. 'I'm not sure what kind of valve they're giving me. Apparently the organic ones are very good, but the metal ones last longer.' I notice that his bible has managed to get into the hospital with him, and sits proudly on his bedside locker beside a bowl of fruit and the stuffed frog, which Silas considers to be his finest work. The nurses do not like the frog, and the words "bacteria" and "cross-infection" have been mentioned, but no-one has had the heart to remove it. 'They can sometimes repair valves, but mine has gone too far.' He pauses for breath. 'I — told — you — so,' he adds, 'only the other day. Didn't I tell you,' he pauses again, panting through the steady hiss of oxygen, 'it was shot to pieces?'

Silas's operation is scheduled for the following week. We are told that if it is left any longer, there is a risk of his condition deteriorating so much that he will be unfit to undergo surgery at all. In the meantime, he has further tests, and is given drugs to "stabilise his condition". He looks terribly ill, but remains in good spirits, enjoying all the attention and making notes on everything pertaining to his illness and its treatment. As for the rest of us, we have been warned that Silas is a very sick man, and that while his chances are good, we must take into consideration that he is no longer young. While I think we have all managed to work this out for ourselves, it is not comforting to have it spelt out by someone in the know. Sometimes I wish that the medical profession would keep their more disappointing thoughts to themselves.

Poor Eric is beside himself with worry, and is unable to concentrate on anything, and Mum isn't much better. I also feel very sorry for Kent, who having only recently discovered that he has two fathers, is now having to come to terms with the fact that he may end up with just one (and a broken one at that, for who can imagine Eric without Silas?). Dad, on the other hand, is coming into his own, and while his offers of leading us all in prayer are politely declined, his support is very welcome. He makes telephone calls, does shopping, and drives people to the hospital to visit Silas. He even feeds the chickens.

While I'm sure he does all this with the best of intentions, I also feel it must help to take his mind off recalcitrant insurers and unreliable plumbers, for work on the house is only just getting started, and my father is not a patient man.

The day of Silas's operation is one of those extraordinary January days when spring decides to put in a fleeting, tantalising appearance; a brief reminder that winter isn't here to stay, and that whatever else is happening, there's light at the end of the seasonal tunnel. There are snowdrops in the garden, and the first hints of birdsong, the sky is a pale, washed blue, and the air is fresh and fragrant. As we drive to the hospital for our vigil (for it's unthinkable that we should not be in the building while Silas has his operation), I think we're probably all feeling the poignancy of the contrast between our own emotions and the beauty of the world outside.

I have always thought that waiting is one of the hardest things we have to do in life. Whether it's waiting for exam results, or for the longed-for phone call from a lover, or even for something relatively unimportant like the arrival of a visitor, it seems to have a paralysing effect. I can never get down to anything when I'm waiting. It's as though life is put on hold, and nothing can move forward until the thing which is awaited has happened and I am released once more into activity, whatever form that may take.

It's like this today. Eric requested that Mum, Kent and I should accompany him to the hospital, and here we all are in the Relatives' Room, which is bland and perhaps purposely characterless, with its pale walls and its fawn-upholstered chairs and its jug of plastic roses. Waiting. I can almost hear the time ticking by, although the clock on the wall makes no sound, and while there is plenty we could be saying, we all seem lost for words. There are magazines on the table, but none of us has touched them, and I have brought a book, but couldn't think of reading it. I am praying to the God I don't really believe in, Mum is almost certainly doing the same, Kent is standing by the window studying the distant view of the car park, and Eric is sitting on the edge of a chair, as though at any moment he may be required to leap up and do something. I have paid two visits to the coffee machine outside to purchase plastic cups of something warm and murky, and a nurse has popped in a couple of times to see if we're okay. Otherwise, the silence ticks by virtually uninterrupted. I don't think I have ever known time pass so slowly.

After two hours and fifty-five minutes (yes, I've been counting. I'm sure everyone's been counting), a doctor arrives in blue theatre scrubs. I think we all immediately know that something is wrong.

'Yes?' Eric jumps to his feet. 'How is he? What's happened?'

Very carefully, the doctor closes the door behind him and turns to face us.

'I'm afraid there's been — a complication,' he tells us.

'A complication? What complication? How is he? What's happened?' Eric lets rip with a barrage of questions.

'I'm afraid —'

'Yes? Yes? Come on! Out with it! *What has happened to Silas?*' Eric grabs hold of his sleeve. 'Tell us. You have to tell us!'

'I'm trying to tell you.' Gently, the doctor disengages himself from Eric's grip. 'The operation itself went well, and the new valve is functioning nicely. But unfortunately your brother — he is your brother isn't he? — suffered a haemorrhage during surgery. He lost a lot of blood very quickly, and while we replaced it as fast as we could, his blood pressure fell dangerously low. There is the possibility of —'

'What? The possibility of what? What's going to happen to him?'

'The possibility — just the possibility — of brain damage.'

Time stops ticking. For a few moments, life itself seems to stand still. In these few moments I know that whatever happens, I shall never forget this day, this moment, this horrid little room, which seems suddenly redolent of all the grief, all the tragedies, all the bad news which has been released within its walls. I shall remember Eric's mismatched socks, just visible beneath his trousers; the stain — coffee? — on the carpet, shaped rather like a map of Italy; the hideous roses, with their faded plastic petals; the single leafless sapling outside the window; the tiny vapour trail of a distant aeroplane across the ice-blue sky.

And the sound. The first sound which breaks the silence. The soft, heartbreaking sound of Eric weeping.

CHAPTER THIRTY-THREE

The next few days are an agony of waiting, punctuated by the mundane tasks needed to keep ourselves (not to mention the animals) alive and give some semblance of normality. Ordinary everyday jobs like cleaning my teeth or washing up the dishes take on a strange irrelevance; I keep stopping to ask myself what I'm doing them *for.* What does it matter if dirty plates stack up on the draining board, or my toothbrush goes unused for a couple of days? Who *cares*? I suppose I have been fortunate. Up until now, I have never had any kind of brush with tragedy. I recall with equanimity the long-ago death of my grandfather; he was old, and I scarcely knew him. When I was about twelve, the family cat was run over, and I did shed tears over him. But this is so much bigger, its potential for grief so much greater. I have grown to love my uncles dearly, and my sadness is compounded many times over by that of Eric, who is quite distraught. Silas is being kept sedated to "give his body a rest", and the extent of any damage won't be known until they withdraw the drugs and let him wake up. Eric spends his days sitting by Silas's bed in the Intensive Care Unit, among the forest of tubes and drips and the beeps and sighs of the machinery upon which Silas now depends, and his nights pacing up and down in his room, which is next to mine, sometimes weeping, sometimes listening to the BBC world service on the radio. I hear him going downstairs at two and three in the morning to make cups of tea, his footsteps slow and apologetic and infinitely weary.

'Are you all right, Eric?' I join him in the kitchen, unable to bear the idea that he is down here suffering on his own while everyone else is asleep.

Eric looks up. He seems mildly surprised.

'Oh, Ruth. What are you doing down here?'

'I came to see you.'

'Ah.' He pauses, kettle in hand. 'Cup of tea?'

'Please.' I sit down at the table. 'Eric what can I do to help?'

He sits beside me, nursing his mug between his hands. 'Nothing. There's nothing anyone can do. That's the trouble.' He manages a pale smile. 'You see, we've never been apart before.'

'What, not ever?'

'Not ever. Well, maybe a night or two here and there, but never longer than that. As children we did everything together, and we've lived together ever since. There's been no need to be apart.'

'Oh, Eric. I'm so, so sorry.' I'm unable to think of anything else to say, because of course there's nothing anyone can say. All I know is that Eric's heart is breaking, and however much we may want to help him, he is beyond our reach, in a world of his own.

'I can't think of anything else, do anything else. I can't even be anything else. All I am is Silas's brother. Waiting.'

Waiting. That word again. Eric is suspended between the chance of hope and the expectation of grief, and for the time being at least, has come down on the side of grief, and in his state of suspense (which when I think about it now, takes on a whole extra meaning) is totally disabled.

I take his hand and rub it gently between my own. It feels terribly cold, but I doubt whether Eric is aware of it. He's probably been pacing about for ages in his unheated bedroom.

He hasn't even bothered to put on a dressing gown. I get up to fetch a coat from the hall, and put it round his shoulders.

'You'll catch your death,' I tell him, 'And then what use will you be to Silas if — when he needs you?'

'I suppose we always assumed we'd die together,' he says, and I know that he hasn't heard a word I've been saying. 'Silly, isn't it? But we were conceived together, born together, went to school together. We even started shaving on the same day. There wasn't much to shave, but we shaved it off anyway with our dad's old razor. And we felt so proud. Real men, we told each other. Not boys any more. *Men.*'

'I've often wondered what it must be like to be a twin.' I stir sugar into my tea, which is much too strong.

'And I've often wondered what it must be like not to be one. To be an individual, unique, entirely different from everyone else. As children, we were always being compared with each other. Our school reports, exams, team games.' He sighs. 'We both hated games. We were the ones to be picked last for team games, but it was still a competition to see which of us would be picked the very last. Usually no-one knew which of us they were picking anyway, as they could never tell us apart.'

I know that not all twins — even identical ones — are as similar as this; some in fact contrive to be quite different. There were identical twins in my class at school who went to considerable lengths to make themselves as individual as possible, even to the extent of wearing their school uniforms in different ways. Few needed (or indeed, dared) to confuse them. But it seems that Eric and Silas have always delighted in their similarity and the confusion it causes, and don't appear to need to establish their individuality, although it's certainly there for anyone who takes the trouble to get to know them.

'He's still alive, you know,' I say, after a moment. 'They say there's a chance he'll make a full recovery. You told me so yourself.'

'Yes. But when I see him lying there, he looks so — so *not Silas*, somehow. Almost as though he's already gone.'

'I don't think anyone looks their best when they're unconscious,' I tell him gently.

'No. You're right.' He pulls the jacket more closely around him. 'I suppose I was always the pessimist. I left the optimism to Silas. I mean, look at the way he approached this operation. Anyone would think he was going on holiday.'

'Yes. He'd have been so interested in all this, wouldn't he? It seems such a waste that he's not awake to — I don't know — to *enjoy* it.'

'Yes. He would have loved it, wouldn't he? All the attention; all those drugs and machines and things. I've been keeping notes, you know.'

'What notes?'

'A kind of diary. What happened when; which doctors came to see him and what they did and said. That kind of thing. In case … well, for when he gets better.'

'That's such a nice idea, Eric. He'll love it.'

Eric smiles, as though for a brief moment he's actually forgotten the seriousness of Silas's condition, then I watch his expression change as reality kicks in again.

'Oh Ruth. What would I do without him? Or if he's damaged; if he's unable to speak or understand. How will I bear it?'

I give Eric a hug. 'I think you have to do the "one day at a time" thing,' I say. 'I've always hated that expression, but there's no other choice, is there? We have to — oh, I don't know — keep the home fires burning for Silas. For when he comes home. Whatever condition he's in. There's not a lot we can do for him at the moment, but we can do that.'

'You're right, Ruth. Of course you are. And I found this amazing hare on my way back from the hospital this afternoon. He's never done a hare before. You don't often see them near the road, do you? But this one's enormous, and absolutely perfect, although it must have been knocked down.'

'It sounds wonderful. What — what have you done with it?'

'I put it in the freezer. Double wrapped. Right at the bottom. Underneath Dorothy.' (Dorothy was a daughter of Sarah's, who having proved to be barren has recently been despatched and butchered into neat little packages). 'She'll never find it there.'

We exchange complicit smiles. Mum accepts most of the things which go on at Applegarth, but draws a line at Silas putting his specimens in the freezer where we keep the food. I don't suppose even she would object under the present circumstances, but Eric's right. It's better that she shouldn't find out.

There is the sound of footsteps coming down the stairs, and Mum joins us in the kitchen. I notice for the first time that she seems to have aged since Silas's illness.

'What are you two doing?' she asks, surprised.

'Tea and sympathy,' Eric tells her. 'Like some?'

'What, tea or sympathy?'

'Either.'

'A bit of both, I think.' Mum puts her arms around Eric and for the first time I notice how alike they are. I suppose that because of the twin thing, I've never considered that my mother might resemble her brothers, but now I see that she shares their eye colour, and her expression — one of sadness and concern — is very like Eric's.

We sit round the table together talking softly, trying to reassure each other that "everything will be all right". While I join in, I still wonder why it is that people always say this to each other in times of crisis, as though defying fate to deal the blow they fear, while as often as not it's perfectly obvious that things are very far from all right, and moreover, are unlikely to become so.

There's a knock at the back door, and I unlock it to find Kent, wearing a coat over his pyjamas.

'I saw the kitchen light on. Is everything okay?'

'Well, nothing's new, if that's what you mean.' I fetch another mug from the cupboard.

'I'm not — intruding?' He takes off his boots and places them side by side on the doormat.

'Of course you're not. Come and join the party.'

Poor Kent. One of the family, and yet not one of the family, this must be so hard for him. Mum still doesn't know his full story, although I think she may have her suspicions, and Dad certainly knows nothing. And while I'm sure he must have told Kaz about it, his real position, whatever that might be, is as yet unknown and unacknowledged. He must be in an emotional no man's land at the moment, but is too sensitive and thoughtful a person to draw any kind of attention to himself.

'Can I do anything?' he asks now.

'No. No-one can do anything. That's the trouble,' Eric says. 'The not doing anything.'

'Who's not doing anything?' Kaz wanders into the kitchen, ruffled and bleary-eyed, her skimpy nightie ill-concealed beneath a kind of giant cardigan. She and Kent exchange one of their glances, but I no longer mind. Now is not the time for petty jealousy.

'All of us,' I tell her. 'For Silas.'

'Well, we can cheer up for a start. Silas would hate all this.' She stifles a yawn, and treats us to one of her infectious smiles. 'While there's life, and all that. What you all need is a drop of this in your tea.' She fetches a bottle of brandy left over from Christmas, and pours a generous measure into everyone's mug (except mine). 'Warm you up,' she explains. 'It's freezing in here.'

Only Kaz could get away with such inappropriate jollity, and I could hug her for it. Her good humour (fuelled, I suspect, by the effects of love) infects us all, and soon everyone's mood improves. Eric even manages a laugh, and Mr. Darcy, who has been sleeping by the Aga, wakes up and thumps his tail on the stone floor.

'That's better,' says Kaz with satisfaction. 'Tomorrow's another day.'

'Tomorrow's already here,' I tell her. 'You ought to get back to bed, Eric. You need to get some sleep, or you'll be in no fit state to go and see Silas.'

But as the clock in the hall strikes the hour, the telephone rings. For a few seconds we sit staring at one another, frozen into immobility. Time seems to stand still. I hear my heart thumping in my ears, and am aware of everyone holding their breath, as though waiting for something to happen.

Then Eric clears his throat.

'Answer that, could you, Ruth?' he says, and I notice that his hands are shaking. 'I don't think — I don't think I can bear to.'

CHAPTER THIRTY-FOUR

Pneumonia. Such a pretty word, I've always thought; a girl's name, perhaps, or some kind of flowering shrub.

But of course, in reality, not pretty at all. Potentially deadly. I believe they used to call it "the old man's friend" because it often provided merciful release from some lingering painful illness, or perhaps from a life which had outlived both comfort and purpose. *But not Silas!* Not Silas's life. Not after all he's already been through.

'How?' Eric asks. 'How did he get pneumonia in here? He should have been safe. *We thought he'd be safe!*'

'He's a very sick man. You have to understand that.' The doctor looks very young, exhausted, ruffled from sleep.

'We know he's a sick man. But we didn't expect him to get even sicker.' Eric is beside himself. '*How — did — this — happen?*'

'Please sit down. The nurse will make you some tea.'

'*I don't want tea.* I've done nothing but drink tea for days now. Tea isn't the answer!'

'Sit down, Eric.' Mum pulls gently at his sleeve. 'Sit down and listen to what the doctor has to say.'

Eric crumples into a chair, and the doctor explains. The pneumonia has developed suddenly and rapidly; Silas's resistance is lowered due to his illness; they are doing all they can. He talks of x-rays and antibiotics, of more drips and further tests. Silas's chances are not good, but he is "holding his own". The next couple of days will be crucial.

Afterwards, when the doctor has gone, Eric sits with his head in his hands.

'I don't know how much more of this I can take,' he says to no-one in particular.

'You have to, Eric. You just have to,' Mum tells him. 'For Silas. We'll go and see him, shall we? I'll come with you. You stay here, Ruth, and phone home. Everyone will be wondering what's happening. It's not fair to keep them waiting.'

I go outside to use my mobile, and phone Applegarth, where Kaz, Kent and Dad are waiting for news, then I fetch myself coffee from a machine. I feel exhausted beyond any tiredness I have ever felt before. The baby has reduced (hardly the right word, but I can't think of another) me to a lumbering elephant of a woman, and as I cart my exhausted body and its small passenger back to the relatives' room and find myself a chair, I wonder how it is that many women go back and do the whole pregnancy thing over and over again, ending up sometimes with three, four or even more children. For whatever I may feel about my own child, now or when I get to meet it, I know for a fact that I shall never want another. I'll have done my bit; I shall have replaced myself on the planet, and formed the next link in the family chain. I certainly don't need to do it again.

It's funny how thoughts of my imminent motherhood, occasional at the best of times, have gone out of the window since Silas's illness. The baby is there, and presumably it will eventually emerge (apparently in about five weeks' time), but I have put it to the back of my mind. I have received a reproachful phone call from the midwife enquiring as to why I'm no longer attending her classes, but it seems self-indulgent to spend time huffing and puffing on a cosy nest of cushions while the rest of my family are going through all this. No doubt when the time comes, I'll push the baby out. People do it all the time. Apparently, it's impossible *not* to push babies out when the time comes. So why all the fuss?

For the moment, all that matters is that Silas should get better. It may be that a part of me is only too willing to be relieved, if only temporarily, of thoughts of the future, or simply that I am still maintaining a degree of denial. I shall never know. What I do know is that if Silas recovers, I shall be willing to cope with anything. I will go to ante-natal classes every day if required to do so; I'll be a model mother and even a model daughter; I'll even sacrifice any hopes of seeing Amos again, if only Silas will get better. Please, Silas. Please, please, *please* get better.

'Are you okay?' A nurse comes into the room, and I realise that I've been crying.

'Yes. Yes, I'm all right.'

'Well, you don't look it.' She closes the door behind her. 'Are you his daughter?'

'No. He's my uncle.'

'You're close, are you?'

'Yes. I suppose we are.' I'd never thought about it before. 'I live with him — them.'

'That must be hard. Especially with a baby on the way.' She touches my hand. 'When's it due?'

'Due?'

'The baby.'

'Of course. The baby.' I push my hair out of my eyes and blow my nose. 'About a month, I think.'

'Not long to go, then.'

'No.'

'Can I get you a cup of tea?'

'Please.'

Tea again. Where on earth would we be without tea? I suppose the French and the Italians have coffee on these occasions, but what about, say, the Americans? What do they drink in times of crisis? Iced tea, perhaps, at least in the summer. I've read about iced tea, but never actually tried any. Iced tea, lemon tea, herbal tea... My thoughts drift and swirl, and I see people — lots of people — drinking tea; Japanese women cross-legged on the floor, sobbing as they pass round tiny decorated cups; people queueing by the huge shiny urn used by one of Mum's women's groups; I see teapots, kettles, tea bags, tea leaves. The seahorse/rabbit appears and tells me it hates tea, and why can't I give it milk like a normal mother? *Normal mothers* don't give tea to babies, it tells me. Why can't I behave like a normal mother? It fades away, weeping, and now I am in a boat going to look for Amos. The boat is operated by pedals, but my feet won't reach them and there's no-one around to help. I panic as the boat begins to quiver and tremble, as though tossed by a succession of tiny waves.

I wake up whimpering to find Mum gently shaking my shoulder.

'Ruth? It's all right, dear. Don't cry.' She touches my cheek. 'Come on. It's time to go home.'

'Why? What's happened? How's Silas?' The anxiety of my dream is still with me. 'He hasn't died, has he?'

'No. He hasn't died. He's — stable.'

'Hospital-speak,' I tell her, now fully awake, and I think of all those other hospital clichés: "as well as can be expected," "fighting for his life" (how can anyone who is seriously ill *fight*?), "comfortable". It's almost as though hospital staff are issued with a list of words and phrases which are supposed to give comfort but which fool nobody. 'How is he really?'

'Unconscious, of course, but they say his chest is a bit clearer. Eric's staying on. I'm going home to have a bath and a nap. I'll come back later.'

'What about me? When can I see him?'

'Well, I suppose you could pop in quickly now. Just for a couple of minutes. We'll ask.'

I've hardly been inside the Intensive Care Unit up until now, leaving the visiting to Mum and Eric. It's a strange place, with an atmosphere and rhythm of its own, isolated and apart like a womb; a world within a world. Staff move around in theatre scrubs, speaking softly, attending to the recumbent forms around them. They look smoothly efficient, more like technicians than nurses, but then I suppose in these circumstances efficiency is more important than the touchy-feely nurses of my imagination.

I remember Eric describing his brother as looking '*so not Silas*', and he's right. It's hard to connect the still figure beneath the clinical white sheet with the Silas I know. This figure breathes — in-out, in-out — fluids are dripped in and others drain away, but everything is mechanical; everything is *not Silas*. Eric is sitting beside him holding his hand, but his eyes are closed, and we don't disturb him.

'Let's go.' Mum whispers, as though we are in church.

I nod, too choked to speak, and together we tiptoe from the room. As we leave the building and make our way to the car park, the grey wintry sky threatens rain, bleak skeletons of trees reaching out towards it as though in supplication. Like those other memories of the day of Silas's operation, I know that whatever happens, I'll always remember these things; this sky, these trees, the echoing of our footsteps along the deserted walkway; even the car park, which is half empty. Only the workers and the wounded and the families of the seriously ill visit hospitals at night.

We drive home together in silence. Dad and Kent have gone back to bed, but Kaz has stayed up to wait for us, and is dozing in a chair. Wordlessly, she gets up and holds out her arms to me, and I stumble into them.

'Oh, Kaz,' I sob. 'He looks so *awful.*' Kaz's arms scarcely reach around me now, but the closeness of her and the familiar smell of her perfume (something expensive; a gift from a boyfriend?) is infinitely comforting.

'I've made porridge,' she tells us.

'*Porridge*?' Mum looks puzzled.

'Porridge,' says Kaz, 'is what you need. With brown sugar and lots of cream.'

'Porridge? At a time like this?'

'Especially at a time like this.' Kaz fetches bowls and spoons, and a big jug of cream from the fridge. 'Comfort food,' she explains. 'Plus, you need something to soak up all that tea.'

'How did you know about the tea?' I ask her.

Kaz laughs. 'I'm right, aren't I?'

'Spot on.'

'Well, then. Be good girls and eat up your porridge. It'll do you good.'

CHAPTER THIRTY-FIVE

To add to our troubles, we have a chicken crisis.

Somewhere, somehow, news of our chicken charity collecting box has been translated into an appeal for actual chickens. It is probably a simple case of Chinese whispers; after all, the leap from chicken charity to chicken sanctuary is a relatively small one. But whatever its provenance, in the course of the past couple of weeks, we have found ourselves suddenly inundated with unwanted chickens. There are rescued chickens, hen-pecked chickens, neglected chickens and even a few happy healthy chickens. There are also two vicious cockerels, and, oddly, a small white duck.

'Chickens are us,' remarks Eric, in a rare moment of humour. 'And they aren't even laying. What on earth are we going to do with them all? And those half-naked ones — they must be freezing.'

'We could knit them little jackets,' says Kaz.

'Not funny, Kaz,' I tell her.

'No. Sorry.'

'But at least we can eat one of those cockerels before they eat each other.'

The bird in question is duly despatched and casseroled, leaving his fellow to take out his fury on Mr. Darcy and any human being who comes his way. Meanwhile, the cockerel in residence — an unassuming, harmless little bird called Henry, who has been in sole charge at Applegarth for years and has successfully fathered generations of fluffy yellow offspring — becomes withdrawn and depressed, and the resident chickens, who all know each other and have their place in the pecking order (what else?) are confused and disrupted by so many uninvited guests. There isn't room for them all in the hen house, so at night such newcomers as we can find are rounded up and herded into a small leaky shed. The rest have to fend for themselves and run the gauntlet of the neighbouring foxes. It is not a happy situation.

Fortunately, food isn't a problem, for pilgrims come bearing offerings of corn and scraps (perhaps since the Virgin herself is not in a position to accept gifts, it's felt that the chickens might like to do so on her behalf), but the sheer numbers of chickens are becoming a considerable problem. Chickens escape into the road and are run over; chickens leak out into the fields and outbuildings and even into the house; chickens roost in the greenhouse. There seem to be chickens everywhere.

'How about a sort of chicken exchange?' suggests Kaz, having discovered another feathery corpse in the driveway. 'Like a bring and buy, only chickens rather than white elephants.'

'So long as the buy outnumbers the bring,' says Eric. 'We certainly don't want any more chickens.'

'I'll organise it,' Mum says suddenly. 'Why don't you leave it to me?'

We all look at her in surprise. Mum has never shown much interest in the livestock, and has tended to avoid the chickens because of her feelings about the Virgin (Mum still has problems with the Virgin, and Dad won't discuss the matter at all).

'Well, if you're sure,' says Eric.

'I'm sure. I need a project. Something to keep my mind off, well, you know.'

We know. And Eric gratefully accepts Mum's offer. She spends an afternoon making a large sign to the effect that chickens may be collected and taken away, provided the prospective owners check with her first and guarantee a good home.

'What's a good home?' I ask her.

'Oh, you know. A decent run, food and water. That kind of thing.'

'How do you know people won't just take them home and eat them?'

'That's a risk we'll have to take.'

'Pick your own chicken,' Kaz muses. 'Well, it's certainly a novel idea. What are people going to take the chickens home in?'

'That's up to them,' Mum says. 'They'll have to bring a cage or something.'

'How are they going to catch them?' I ask her. 'It's not like picking strawberries. Strawberries keep still. Chickens don't.'

'That's up to them, too. But I suppose we could make a sort of net. Perhaps Lazzo would make one. He's good at that sort of thing.'

'How are we going to stop people taking *our* chickens?'

'They'll have to be shut in the run for the time being.'

'They won't like that.'

'I'm afraid that's tough,' says Mum. 'They've had it too good for too long. It's time they were — contained.'

So our chickens are padlocked into their run, which has sole access to the entrance to the hen house, while their new friends are left the freedom of the garden. It doesn't seem a very fair arrangement, but as Mum says, for the time being, there's nothing else for it. And when all's said and done, they are only chickens.

But the chickens are not used to being restrained in this way, and, encouraged by Henry, set up a considerable racket in their attempts to escape from their prison, while the new, free-range chickens tease and provoke them from the other side of the wire mesh.

'Told you,' says Blossom, who didn't actually tell us anything but hates anyone other than herself having ideas where the animals are concerned.

'Well, what would you do?' I ask her. 'Have you a better idea?'

'Nope.' Blossom chases an invading chicken out of the back door. 'Not my business.'

'Well, if it's not your business, then perhaps you'd best keep your ideas to yourself.'

This is not like me, for as a rule I go to great lengths to be polite to Blossom, but since Silas's illness she has been quite impossible. Eric, ever charitable, says it's probably because she misses him, and I suppose he could be right, but a bit of support wouldn't come amiss. Blossom knows the score; she must see how we're all struggling to keep going; and yet she continues to be if anything even more ill-tempered than usual.

'What is the *matter* with your mother?' I ask Kaz, having tripped over the flex of the vacuum clear which has been left out in the middle of the kitchen.

'Search me.' Kaz is doing her make-up, peering into a tiny mirror propped on the window sill (she's filling in for another dancer tonight, although she's "scaling down" her professional activities as Kent apparently isn't happy about them).

'She's being so *nasty*.'

'That's Mum,' Kaz agrees, applying plum-coloured eye shadow with a tiny brush.

'But why? Why is she so thoroughly unpleasant all the time? What's her problem?'

'You know —' Kaz applies the finishing touches to her eyelashes and puts away her mirror — 'I've been asking myself that ever since I could think, and I've never come up with an answer.'

'How on earth did you survive? As a kid, I mean.'

'Dunno.' Kaz shrugs. 'Just got on with it, I suppose. And I had Lazzo. I'd never have survived without our Laz. And Dad. Dad wasn't much use, but at least I could talk to him. And he was in the same boat as Lazzo and me.'

'Three against one?'

'Yep. Although the one always came out on top.'

'I'll bet.'

'There. How do I look?' Kaz stands up and runs her fingers through her hair (which she's recently dyed pink).

'Fabulous. As usual.'

'Ta.' Kaz grins. 'Hope the punters feel the same way.'

'Oh, they will. If they've got any sense.' I hesitate. 'How's — how's it going with Kent?'

'I thought you didn't approve.'

'I don't — didn't. But then I realised I was being selfish, and you were right. I was a bit — well, jealous.'

'I told you.'

'Okay, no need to gloat.'

'Sorry. That wasn't very nice of me, was it? Poor Ruth. You need to find your Amos, don't you?'

'Yes. Oh, yes!' I feel again the familiar ache of loneliness, which sees to increase with my size. 'But you still haven't answered my question. How's it going?'

'Great. It's going really great. He's so kind. You know, I don't think I've come across many really kind people. Plus, he's good looking, and sexy —'

'Too much information, Kaz. I get the picture.' I hesitate. 'Kaz, would you — would you marry him?'

'It's a bit early for that! But d'you know, I think I might. And then, just think — I'd be family, wouldn't I? I'd love to be part of this family.'

'So he's told you about — about Eric and Silas.'

'Yep. I think it's really cool to have two dads, and I think he's coming round to the idea, too. And I'd have two fathers-in-law!'

'I never had you down as the marrying kind.'

'Me neither.'

'And your mother would have to wear a hat!'

We both laugh. 'She wouldn't come,' Kaz tells me. 'Whatever the circumstances, she'd find a reason not to come. Mum hates weddings.'

'But surely, *your* wedding —'

'Especially my wedding. Trust me.'

'Well, you'd have all of us. Lazzo could give you away. Oh — and I'll help you choose the dress!'

For what could be more fun than dressing Kaz up as a bride? She could get married from Applegarth, and we might even have a marquee (provided enough uncluttered space could be found). Despite my initial reservations, I find myself feeling quite excited at the idea.

'Hold on a minute, Ruth. We're not quite there yet! But thanks for being — nice about it.' Kaz picks up her bag. 'Gotta go. See you later.'

As Kaz's car rattles off down the driveway, scattering chickens in its wake, I realise that for a whole five minutes or so I have managed not to think about Silas. But now reality kicks in with a thud, and I feel my spirits sink. Weddings —

celebrations of any kind, come to that — are off-limits at the moment, and may be so for some time to come.

I fetch a bucket and start mixing pig feed.

CHAPTER THIRTY-SIX

Despite the gloomy prognostications of the doctors, Silas continues to hold his own. He isn't exactly better, but he's no worse, and a note of optimism creeps into the household.

Poor Eric is worn out with his vigils, refusing to take a day off, and must have lost nearly a stone. He looks almost as ill as his brother; more so in a way, because there is an artificial glow to Silas's skin which has nothing to do with his condition but which gives an appearance of health. No-one would confuse the two of them now; they don't even look like brothers, never mind twins. The GP has given Eric pills to help him sleep, but I don't believe he takes them, preferring to remain on permanent alert in case he's needed at the hospital. His Ark plans remain rolled up in a drawer; he hasn't touched them since Silas's operation. And while I'm still pursuing a bit of research for him on the subject of birds (and believe me, if the mammals are complicated, the birds are many times more so), I haven't liked to update him on my progress. The Ark, like so much else at Applegarth, is going to have to wait.

Meanwhile, I have had some news. A postcard has arrived for me at my parents' address from Amos, and while there's not a lot on it, it's still news. Amos is apparently on a ship on his way home, together with a small Caribbean band he founded while in Barbados. He has had a "great time" and tells me that the trombone goes "amazingly well" with steel drums (I can't imagine it, but where music's concerned, Amos is usually right). He will be arriving back in England "soon", and hopes "to meet up some time".

The casual note of the postcard is not cheering. "Soon" isn't nearly specific enough for me, and no-one wants to "meet up some time" with the man they love (or even the man they think they might love), but never mind. Amos is alive, and is not staying in Barbados for ever, and this has to be good news for me. Of course there is no return address, and since he hasn't given me the ship's name or company, I can't contact him that way. But it would seem that some time in the not too distant future, I may be seeing Amos. I only hope it's sooner rather than later, for whatever I may feel, the baby won't delay its arrival just to accommodate its parents.

'Is that the chap with the beard?' asks my father, who has obviously read the postcard.

'That's the one,' I tell him.

'Hmm.'

'What do you mean, hmm?'

'Looked untrustworthy.'

'Dad, just because he has a beard —'

'Not just the beard.'

'What, then?'

'He had shifty eyes.'

I think of Amos's lovely brown eyes (more lovely and more brown with absence, of course) and despair. It could just be that no-one's good enough for his little girl, but I immediately dismiss the thought. It would be lovely if this were the case, but simply not Dad. He's not the *my little girl* type. No. Beards and shifty eyes notwithstanding, he doesn't approve of my condition, and therefore by association the person who put me in it. I just hope that Amos doesn't rock up at my parents' house only to find signs of the recent conflagration and no-one to enlighten him as to my whereabouts, for the reconstruction works are not going well, and the house is still in a pretty sorry state, although piles of bricks, some scaffolding and a cement mixer are all signs of hope for the future.

But of course, if Amos should experience a momentary fear that my parents and I have all perished in the blaze, he can always ask the neighbours. Now there's an idea! I shall get my mother to leave a note with the people next door to the effect that if anyone comes looking for me, they should contact me at Applegarth. I am delighted with this idea, and plan to put it in motion forthwith.

Lazzo comes into the kitchen.

'Nice postcard,' he remarks.

'Yes, isn't it.'

'Lots of sea.'

'Yes. There is quite a bit.' The postcard is in fact almost entirely sea, with one tiny island in the distance and what might be a palm tree.

'Made the net,' he continues, pulling a packet of cigarettes from his pocket and looking at them longingly (he's not allowed to smoke in the house).

'Net?'

'For the chickens.'

'For the — oh yes. Well done.'

'See it?'

'Yes please.'

Lazzo brings in a complicated construction consisting of a long wooden pole with what looks like a wire tent on the end.

'There.' He puts it down on the floor.

'Goodness!'

Lazzo grins at me. 'See it work?'

'Oh — right. Yes of course.'

We go out into the garden, Lazzo wielding his net, and search for chickens. Typically, they all seem to be hiding, but at last he spies one behind the greenhouse, and sets off in surprisingly rapid pursuit. There is a lot of squawking and flapping, plus one or two choice expletives from Lazzo, and the chicken is brought back for my inspection. It looks ruffled and very cross, but otherwise in good shape.

'Why, that's great, Lazzo. Really ingenious. I just hope the pilgrims can run, because the chickens certainly can.'

'Do it for them,' says Lazzo, beaming (he loves praise, I suspect because it's in pretty short supply at home).

'You aren't always here,' I remind him.

'Mobile.'

'Oh, yes.

Lazzo has recently acquired a mobile, and is completely wedded to it. I've no idea whom he phones, and why, especially since he is a man of such very few words, but he spends a lot of time labouring over misspelt text messages, experimenting with ring tones and playing its various electronic games. The fact that there's no reception here causes him much frustration. When I have had occasion to phone him on it from the landline, he seems unsure how to reply, and there's usually a lot of huffing and puffing, peppered with little clicking noises, before I actually get him to hear what I have to say.

'You mean you don't mind us phoning you to come and catch chickens?' I ask him.

'S'right.'

'Ok then, that's what we'll do. You can be chief chicken-catcher.'

Lazzo beams again, and while it occurs to me that perhaps I should have asked Mum first, since this is now her project, I'm sure she won't mind. Running fast after chickens is not what my mother does best, and I think she'll probably be delighted to have someone else do it for her.

Eric returns from the hospital earlier than usual to tell us that the doctors are planning to start reducing the dosage of some of Silas's drugs and try taking him off the ventilator.

'I'm not sure I want them to,' he says. 'In a way, I prefer not to know. As things are, there's still hope. But if they take him off the drugs and he doesn't regain consciousness, well, that's it then, isn't it?'

'Not necessarily,' says Mum. 'It could take time, couldn't it?'

'I think if he's going to get better, it'll happen quite quickly.'

'Is that what they said?'

'More or less.'

'When are they starting?' I ask him.

'Tonight, after his consultant's been round. I'll go in first thing tomorrow, of course.'

'Do you want anyone with you?' Mum asks him.

'Would you come, Rosie?'

'Of course.'

'D'you mind keeping an eye on things here, Ruth? We'll — we'll keep in close touch.'

'Of course I don't mind. I'd be happy to.'

Following Eric's news, the waiting seems to intensify for all of us, and once the routine evening jobs are done, none of us are unable to settle to anything. Mum tries to make a cake, but omits some vital ingredient and has to throw the whole thing away. Eric paces to and fro like a lost soul. Poor Kent, still on the periphery of the family, retires to his caravan "to give us space". And I try to practise the violin, an activity which has become increasingly difficult of late because of the tiredness induced by my pregnancy. Only Dad is gainfully employed, bullying the builders who are trying to rebuild the house. Of course, I don't know this for sure, but from the conversations he relays back to us, it sounds to me very much like bullying. The builders are either the laziest men on the face of the earth (Dad's perception) or have the patience of saints (mine).

The following morning, Mum and Eric leave early for the hospital. I busy myself around the house, hindered by Mr. Darcy, who senses trouble and follows me round like a shadow, and by Blossom and her vacuum cleaner. After I've tripped over the flex for the third time, I finally lose patience.

'Blossom, please, please would you look where you're going with that thing? Someone's going to do themselves an injury.'

'Their look-out,' Blossom says. She looks a bit pale even for Blossom, and I noticed that she didn't have a biscuit with her coffee earlier on (always a bad sign).

'Are you — are you all right, Blossom?'

'Course.' Blossom turns away, but not before I detect what look very like tears in her eyes.

'Are you — worried about Silas?'

'Might be.' She sniffs and blows her nose on a tattered Kleenex.

'He'll be all right, you know, Blossom. I'm sure he will.' I put a hand on her arm, realising that it's the first time she and I have ever had any kind of physical contact.

'Better be. The old bugger.' There's the ghost of a smile. 'Taken flowers up to the Virgin,' she confides. 'Some nice early daffs. Said a prayer for him, too.'

'Well, that was kind.' I feel quite exultant, having finally found the soft side of Blossom, but realise it would be dangerous to push my luck any further. 'Would you like another cup of coffee?'

'Wouldn't mind,' says Blossom graciously. 'Any biscuits?'

The morning drags. Every time the phone rings, I jump, but so far it's been a man about a blocked drain, a wrong number, and Dad fretting about the right sort of bathroom tiles. Did Mum say blue patterned, or plain? He can't remember. At the moment I can think of few things I care about less than bathroom tiles, so he gets pretty short shrift. I reflect that my father has ill-timing down to a fine art. At midday, we receive a brief bulletin with the news that Silas has been taken off the respirator and is breathing on his own, but is still unconscious. Is that good news or bad? No-one seems to know.

Kent and Kaz join me for lunch, but none of us is very hungry, and my half-hearted attempt at artichoke soup goes virtually untouched. A couple of pilgrims/chicken-lovers turn up asking for chickens, and after an unseemly scuffle involving half a dozen people and a great many chickens (Lazzo isn't answering his mobile) we manage to capture five, plus, incidentally, the white duck. The duck is given a reprieve and the chickens set off in the back of a very posh Volvo, where they can be seen hurling themselves against the rear window in a flurry of feathers as they depart down the drive (the putative owners having forgotten to bring a receptacle). The minutes and the hours tick by.

At five thirty-four, the phone rings again. I leap to answer it, treading on Mr. Darcy's tail and knocking over a lamp.

'Oh, Ruth!' Mum sounds beside herself.

'Yes? What? What is it Mum? Is Silas all right?'

'Oh Ruth.' Mum is sobbing now.

'Please, Mum! *What's happened?*'

'Silas. It's Silas.'

'Yes?' Of course it's Silas! Does anything or anybody else in the world matter at the moment?

'He's — Oh, Ruth! — he's asking for his frog!'

'His frog? What frog?' For a moment, the significance of Mum's news escapes me.

'*His* frog. You know. The stuffed one. Oh, Ruth, isn't it wonderful? *Silas is asking for his frog!*'

'Yes. Yes of course.' My fuddled brain struggles with images of Silas and frogs, and a myriad other questions. Then the significance of what she's saying finally hits home. 'You mean he's conscious? He's talking? He's *okay*?'

'Yes! That's exactly what I mean. You can't imagine what a relief it is —' do you want to bet? — 'and Eric is, well, Eric's —'

'Pleased?'

'Not just pleased. He's *so* relieved. I don't think I realised how desperate he's been until Silas spoke to him.'

'Oh, Mum! That's fantastic!'

'Isn't it? Of course, he's got a long way to go still, but it really looks as though he's on the mend at last.'

'What are you doing now?'

'I think we'll stay just a bit longer, then we'll come home. I believe Eric might actually sleep tonight.' She pauses. 'Ruth?'

'Yes?'

'What *did* we do with that frog?'

CHAPTER THIRTY-SEVEN

Silas is being a terrible patient. He has been home just five days, and is driving us all up the wall.

'It says in my book...' are the words we are learning to dread, for Silas's bible has something to say on every tiny symptom, and Silas would have us know everything it has to say.

I have to admit, I'm disappointed. I was looking forward to looking after Silas; a Silas who would depend on us for his care, a Silas who would be sweetly undemanding, a Silas who would — dare I say it — be *grateful.* I imagined him lying on the sofa in the sitting-room swathed in blankets, sipping sweet tea or delicious home-made soups, taking little walks at times convenient to the rest of us, getting better every day (of course) but doing it without causing any trouble.

Not so. Silas is very far from grateful. He is restless and bored, tapping his way round the house (he's been persuaded to use a walking stick until he's a bit steadier on his feet) interfering and generally making his presence felt. I know I'm not the only one to dread that tap-tapping, and the demands which accompany it, for the rest of the household too are becoming irritable and fractious.

'What does he want *now*?' Eric sounds exasperated at the imperious tinkle of the little bell Silas keeps by his bed. 'I've only just been up to him. He's had his breakfast, he's got the newspaper and the telephone. I've re-filled his hot water bottle. What else can he possibly want?'

'I'll go,' I tell him. 'You stay here and finish your coffee.'

When I enter his room, Silas is sitting up in bed with his reading glasses perched on the end of his nose, consulting his book.

'I think I'm getting a rash,' he tells me. 'It says here —'

'Oh, Silas! Not that book again! Why don't you put it aside for a bit and read something else? How about a nice cheery thriller?'

'It says here,' Silas continues as though I haven't spoken, 'that a penicillin allergy usually begins with a rash. I think I must be allergic to penicillin.'

'You've been on penicillin for ages. Surely it would have shown up before now?'

'Not necessarily. It says here —'

'Let me have a look at you.'

Silas pulls up his pyjama top to reveal a pink, healthy chest (healthy, that is, if you ignore the large scar running across it).

'It looks fine,' I tell him.

'It itches.'

'You're probably too hot. It's awfully stuffy in here. Shall I open a window and let some fresh air in?'

'Gracious, no!' Silas looks shocked. 'I might catch a chill.'

Even I know that catching chills from open windows is more old wives' tale than fact, and I suggest to Silas that he looks up "chill" in his bible.

'You're not taking this seriously,' Silas tells me.

'Silas, we've done nothing but take you seriously recently. We've worried ourselves sick, we've thought of little else, but —'

'Really? Have you really?' Silas looks pleased.

'Yes. Really. But now you're on the mend, and of course we're all delighted, and we'll do anything for you within reason. But we've got other things to think of as well.'

'Yes. I see what you mean.' Silas looks chastened, and I fear I may have overdone it.

'But we don't mind. Of course we don't. We all love you, and we still worry about you,' I assure him, anxious not to give the wrong impression. 'You're our priority at the moment —'

'Oh good. Well then, about this rash —'

'Silas, that's not a rash! Trust me. I know about rashes. I used to be allergic to all sorts of things as a child. You could say I'm something of an expert on rashes. And you *haven't got a rash.*'

'It's still very itchy.'

'It's probably dry. All that time in hospital with that central heating. It's probably dried your skin out. And no —' as Silas reaches for his book again — 'you don't need to look up dry skin. I'll give you some baby lotion. I use it myself. It's quite harmless, and very soothing.'

'Then could you —'

'Yes. I'll put it on for you.'

Half-an-hour later, Silas has been anointed and reassured, and is mercifully asleep. I know he should be up and about — we've been told he needs to keep moving, and much of the time he's only too happy to oblige — but it's such a relief to have him out of the way, that I leave him. He's got the rest of the day to potter round the house, and for the time being, we can get on with our chores.

'Now you've got an idea what it will be like when you've had the baby,' Mum says, only half-teasing. 'You have to get on with things while they're asleep, otherwise nothing gets done.'

Ah. The baby. There's apparently only about three weeks to go before it's due to make its entrance (or rather, its exit), and I've still hardly done anything about it. I've bought the basic necessities with help from Mum and generous contributions from Eric and Silas, but I haven't made any plans. I'm booked into the local hospital for the actual birth, and my uncles have said I can come back here afterwards, but that's about the sum of it. Mum keeps trying to encourage me to think about the future, and even Dad has enquired as to "what I intend to do" after the baby's arrival, but I simply don't know. Like a rabbit caught in headlights, I can't see beyond the moment. I still can't imagine a baby, or myself as a mother. Friends phone to ask how I am, Mikey is beside himself with excitement, Mum is knitting mountains of fluffy little garments, even Kent is excited; but for me, despite indigestion, backache, exhaustion and all the bounding activity that goes on inside my bloated body, the baby still has no reality.

I humour Mum by returning to my ante-natal classes, but I appear to have missed quite a lot, and I still find the sessions boring. Mum, who has put her squeamishness to one side and agreed to be with me for the birth, has started accompanying me, and learns how to rub my back, operate the gas and air and encourage my deep breathing. I find all this bewildering, but Mum is fascinated, and so I let her take over, reasoning that so long as one of us knows what to do, things should be okay.

'What are you going to call your baby, Ruth?' she asks me. 'Have you thought of any names?'

And of course, I haven't.

'How about Lucy for a girl? After Grandma?'

'But it's a boy. Blossom said so, and they told me at the hospital.' Is Mum too in denial? I know she would like a granddaughter, but she can't change the baby's sex just by calling it Lucy. If only life were that simple!

'A boy, then. What about a boy's name?'

'Malachi.' The name comes to me suddenly. 'I shall call it — him — Malachi.'

'Oh.' Mum looks both surprised and disappointed. 'Why? I mean, why Malachi?'

'He was a prophet.'

'I know he was a prophet, but you don't have to name your child after a prophet. There are lots of other good biblical names. John, Matthew — that's nice — Joseph, Peter —'

'No. Malachi.' Malachi, son of Amos, although I don't say this to Mum. The name pleases me. It's unusual, and has a nice ring to it.

'What would people shorten it to?' Mum asks.

'I've no idea. Does it have to be shortened?'

'People always shorten names.'

'They lengthen mine.' This is true enough, although my parents rarely call me Ruthie.

'He mightn't like it.'

'He mightn't like any name I choose. The whole thing's a bit of a gamble, isn't it?' It occurs to me what a huge responsibility it is naming a baby; giving it a label which it has to carry for the rest of its life, and which might not suit it when it grows up. I recall a schoolfriend — large and plain and lumpen — who had been given the name of Grace. Her parents couldn't have known how unsuitable the name would turn out to be, but in the end, they weren't the ones who had to live with it. At least Malachi doesn't give rise to any particular expectations (except perhaps a beard, and a penchant for seeing into the future). And it is undeniably dignified.

But Mum has gone on to speculate about second names (presumably in case the first one is rejected), and I let her get on with it. Four weeks still seem a long way away. Anything can happen in four weeks.

In the event, several things happen.

The first is a devastating raid by a fox, in which a great many of the immigrant chickens perish, together with the white duck.

'Bloody, bloody thing,' rages Eric, gathering up the tattered corpses. 'I can understand it taking just one. One is reasonable. Even a fox has to eat. But all these! All this waste. It's just been killing for the fun of it.'

'Isn't that what foxes do?' I ask him.

'Yes, but that doesn't make it any less infuriating.'

'They weren't really our chickens, were they?'

'That's not the point. And your poor Mum's terribly upset.'

This is true, for Mum has been taking her duties as chicken custodian very seriously, and now she blames herself.

'I should have locked them all up,' she mourns. 'I had a go, but some of them refused to be caught, and it was so cold last night that in the end I gave up. But it was wrong of me. I was being lazy. I could have caught them if I'd tried harder.'

'Mum, chickens are stupid things. It's not your fault if they decide to stay out all night. They know the score. There's a cosy shed there for them if they want it. You did your best.'

'And we can't even eat them.' Eric says. 'That blasted fox has mangled them to bits. I've a good mind to go out with my gun and see if I can catch him. He's bound to come back for more.'

'And if you shoot him carefully, I could stuff him.' Silas has joined us in the kitchen. 'See if you can get him through the ear. Yes. That would be a good place. The ear. You're a good shot, Eric. I'm sure you could do it. That'd preserve the pelt, and would be a nice clean kill.'

'That's thoughtful of you, Silas.' There's an edge to Eric's voice. 'Anything else I can shoot for you while I'm out there? An owl perhaps? A bat?'

'No. Just the fox.' Silas seems impervious to Eric's tone. 'Though a bat would be wonderful,' he adds wistfully. 'I wonder whether anyone has ever stuffed a bat?'

The next thing to happen is the disappearance of Mr. Darcy. One minute he is happily rolling in chicken manure (which of course we have in abundance, and which is his preferred emollient), and the next, he has completely vanished.

'It's so unlike him,' Eric keeps saying, as we hunt through sheds and outbuildings, whistling and calling. 'He's never done anything like this before. He's such a *home* dog.'

'And lazy,' suggests Kaz.

'That too.' But I can tell from Eric's tone that we shouldn't speak ill of the disappeared.

Mr. Darcy isn't a hunter, nor does he go out in search of the opposite sex. He's never been known to fight, and he doesn't go near the main road. He's a stay-at-home dog, occasionally a guard dog, if he can be bothered, but not a wanderer. The whole thing is a mystery.

Hitherto, I have taken Mr. Darcy for granted. He and I get on well enough, he's been a great asset for my busking, and has given me welcome companionship on windy days outside the pound shop, not to mention a talking point for the punters. He is not a creature of beauty, being a strange mixture of collie, terrier and several other rare and not-so-rare breeds, but he is unique. If he resembles anything at all, it is the result of one of those children's games where you add little bits of different animals to make an entirely new species. I would be happy to bet that there is no other dog on the face of this planet who looks like Mr. Darcy.

'Do you have a photo?' I ask Eric.

'There might be one somewhere.'

'We could make a poster.'

'But where would we put it? We're miles from the town. He can't have made his way there on his own.'

'Unless he's been stolen.'

Eric gives me a pitying look. 'Much as I love our dog, I think it very unlikely that anyone would want to steal him.'

'He could be shut in somewhere.'

'That's what I'm afraid of.'

Lazzo, who can eat up the miles like a giant in a fairy story, goes off on foot to search farther afield, and Silas, who needs to be kept occupied, is given the task of phoning such neighbours as there are to make enquiries and to ask them to look in their sheds and garages. Blossom crashes around with her vacuum cleaner, berating us all for our inattention (were we supposed to mount a round-the-clock guard against the possibility of anything happening to Mr. Darcy?), and the rest of us try to get on with our lives. But the ancient chipped dog bowl, the smelly blanket by the Aga, the dog hairs all over the furniture, the half-toothbrush — these are poignant reminders, and we all find it difficult to settle to anything.

A day later, we receive a further blow when Dad, attempting yet again to supervise jobs about which he knows nothing, falls off the roof of his house.

'Everyone keeps telling me how lucky I am,' he says, as he lies in hospital with concussion and three cracked ribs. 'Falling off a roof is not lucky.'

I know what he means. If you don't fall off a roof, no-one tells you how lucky you are, but if you do, then you are apparently lucky not to have killed yourself or at the very least, sustained life-threatening injuries, and people don't hesitate to remind you constantly of your good fortune.

'I'd like to know how they'd feel,' Dad grumbles. 'It's not funny. Falling off a roof.'

The faith and the optimism which carried him through the fire seem to have deserted him, but I suppose even Dad has his limits. It's been a horrible six months for him by any standards; he has a disgraced daughter, he's lost his home, nearly lost his wife, and now this. I think he's entitled to be fed up. Mum stays with friends so that she can visit him, and after two days' observation he's allowed out.

Of course, he comes back to Applegarth — where else can he go? — where he and Silas bond over their medical problems and get on remarkably well. Dad is introduced to Silas's book, and together they pore over it, looking for *complications*. Dad thinks the book is wonderful. He would like a copy for his birthday, he tells us, but Mum is not amused, and says that one hypochondriac in the family is quite enough.

Meanwhile, the weather is appalling — cold and sleety, with an icy north wind — and the heating breaks down. As I lumber up the garden carrying buckets of pig feed, with motherhood just a fortnight away, I wonder what else can go wrong. I also wonder — selfishly, no doubt, but perhaps with just a little justification — when it will be my turn to have some attention, because at the moment, I'm a bit short on it. As I lean over Sarah's door to fill her trough, I shed tears of exhaustion and self-pity, getting nothing for my troubles but a surly grunt and an evil look from one piggy eye.

'Sarah,' I tell her, 'you should count your blessings. You have no idea what a lucky woman you are.'

CHAPTER THIRTY-EIGHT

Eric has shot the fox. He had to get up long before dawn, but he finally got it, and has returned in triumph.

'But you shot it through the head,' Silas protests. 'Look what a mess you've made of it! I said aim for the ear. The ear would have been perfect.'

'It may surprise you to know,' says Eric, who is cold and hungry and very tired, 'that my priority wasn't to provide you with a specimen. My priority was to kill the fox in order to protect the chickens. And that's what I've done.'

'Well, I think it's an awful shame,' says Silas sulkily. Silas has had a good night's sleep, breakfasted on hot porridge with brown sugar and cream, and is cosily wrapped up in the new dressing gown Mum gave him for Christmas. I sense trouble.

'If you think that I'm going to sit around on a freezing night trying to get in exactly the right position to shoot a fox through the ear — the *ear*, for goodness' sake! — then you're very much mistaken. Besides. You've already done a fox. Why do you need another one?'

'I wanted a pair. I thought we could have one on either side of the fireplace.'

'Over my dead body!'

'Over *your* dead body? *I'm* the one who's nearly died!'

'And don't we all know it!'

'What's that supposed to mean?'

'It means,' says Eric, peeling his gloves off hands which are blue with cold, 'that I've had enough of your illness. It means that there are other people in this house besides you. Ruth, for instance —' oh, please don't bring me into it! — 'who's exhausted; Rosie, who's been working her socks off; Lazzo and Kaz. Blossom, too. Brian, who's had a nasty accident. And Kent. You are not the only person who needs looking after.'

'I never asked to be looked after! I'm up and about, doing my bit ' —

'You're up and about interfering, and quoting that bloody book at everyone —'

'You gave me *that bloody book*, as you call it.'

'And you asked for it!'

Mum, Kent and I listen in astonishment. I have never heard my uncles exchange so much as a cross word, but it would seem that when they get going, they can argue with the best of us.

'I think I'll be going.' Kent edges towards the door.

'Me too. I've got the chickens to feed.' Mum joins him.

'That's right! Abandon us, why don't you?' shouts Silas.

'Well, I don't think you need us at the moment,' Mum tells him. 'You seem quite capable of fighting without any help from anyone else.'

'WE ARE NOT FIGHTING!'

We leave them to it. There is no point in trying to intervene, and although it can't be good for either of them, we should have seen something like this coming. Eric and Silas have been under considerable strain, not helped by a houseful of people. Accustomed to a peaceful life on their own, the past few months must have taken their toll, and I can't help feeling partly responsible.

'Still arguing, are they?' Blossom who has been hovering outside the kitchen door, looks pleased.

'I've no idea.'

'Sounds like it.'

'Well, if it bothers you, you can always do a spot of vacuuming. That should drown them out.'

'Telling me my job, are you?' Blossom bridles.

'I wouldn't dare,' I assure her.

The argument rages for some time, and is followed by a sulk. I thought I knew a bit about sulking, having been something of an expert when I was in my teens, but my sulks were nothing compared to that of Eric and Silas. The sulk hangs over all of us like a malevolent grey blanket, rendering the atmosphere indoors even more depressing than the cold and the mud outside.

'They used to do this as children,' Mum tells me. 'They could keep it up for days.'

'But they're usually so close.' I find their behaviour puzzling.

'It's because they're so close. They know exactly how to annoy each other.'

'But how can they annoy each other if they're not saying anything?'

'I've no idea. But it seems to work.'

'How did — does it end?'

'One of them apologises.'

'That doesn't look very likely at the moment.'

'You'll see.'

Eric is researching water buffaloes, and Silas is looking something up in his bible. They are both pretending to be happily occupied, but even I can see that they're miserable.

But in the event, the row between Eric and Silas is overtaken by a bigger and more serious altercation when two days later, Dad and Eric fall out over Eric's Ark.

To be fair, Dad has done his best to avoid the issue, aware, presumably, that it would be bad manners to pick a quarrel with someone who has been such a generous host. But Eric, still sore from his argument with Silas, finally gives in to the temptation to taunt Dad with his findings, and Dad, who is having serious problems with a recalcitrant electrician, falls into the trap.

'For a start, there's the weight of water,' I hear Eric saying, as I come into the sitting room.

'What do you mean, the weight of water? What's the weight of water got to do with it?' Dad asks.

'The weight of the rainwater; enough water, remember, to reach the top of Everest. It would sink the Ark before it had even started.'

'But it says in the Bible —'

'Never mind what it says in the Bible. The Bible story is a myth.'

'It most certainly is not!'

'It has to be. Because the whole story is nonsense.'

'How dare you —'

'Quite easily, actually.'

'If the whole story is nonsense, how come you're spending so much time going into it all? You tell me that!'

'I'm doing it to prove *how much* nonsense it is. I've given it the best possible chance; I've spent hours doing research. You ask Ruth. She's been helping me —' thank you, Eric — 'and I can tell you, there never was an Ark. There couldn't have been. Some kind of boat, perhaps, with some chickens, a goat, a few bits and bobs. Enough to keep a family going for a while. But not a whopping great Ark full of animals. It's a preposterous idea.'

'They found the remains on Mount Ararat. How do you explain that?'

'They found the remains of something, but it's by no means clear it was an Ark.'

'Of course it was the Ark! The Bible says —'

'No, no, *no*!' Eric is almost hopping with frustration. 'You can't keep saying that. It's a cop out! Think, man. *Think*. Question it, think round it, use your common sense!'

'Well, really. I didn't come here to be insulted!'

'No. You came here because you burnt your house down.' Oh dear. 'And when I try to explain to you the extensive research I've been doing, you completely dismiss it.'

'Well you're dismissing the Bible. The word of God.'

'The *story* of God, more like. Take the water buffalo.' Eric ploughs on, regardless of my father's indignation.

'Take *what*?'

'The water buffalo. It's just one example. How do you expect that to survive on the Ark? You tell me that.'

'I don't know anything about water buffaloes.'

'Exactly! And I don't suppose you know anything about lemurs, or wildebeest, or humming birds or spiders —'

'I don't have to know all about these things to believe what the Bible says.'

'So if the Bible says black is white, you'd believe that?'

'Now you're being ridiculous.'

'No. *You're* being ridiculous. You can't just abandon your common sense and your reasoning because of what the Bible says. Work it out. Think about it. Like I have.'

'Well, I think all this — *work* you've been doing is simply destructive. You're trampling all over beliefs people have held dear for generations. You have no right —'

'I have every right. I'm a scientist —' steady on, Eric — 'and I look at things logically.'

'Well you seem to have spent an awful lot of time trying to prove what you think you already know.' Dad indicates Eric's charts and notes. 'I'm surprised you haven't got more important things to do.'

'I'm doing it because I want to show not just that the whole thing is ridiculous but just *how* ridiculous it is. I'm not just telling you you're wrong; I'm *proving* it.'

'Well you haven't proved anything to me.'

'That's because you're not listening. You've decided what you want to believe, and you refuse to look at what's staring you in the face. It's rubbish. All of it. Rubbish. The Ark, the animals, the Noah family — just eight people, remember, to look after all those hundreds of creatures. That in itself is a bit far-fetched, *and* they had to catch them all in the first place — whichever way you look at it, it's a logistical impossibility.'

'You're enjoying, this, aren't you?' says Dad, after a moment.

'Of course I am. It's fascinating. I shall be quite sorry when I've finished.'

'I mean the argument. You're enjoying arguing with me, questioning my beliefs.'

'Well —'

'There! I told you! You're just doing this to annoy me. Admit it.'

'Of course I'm not. Do you really think I would spend months on a project just in order to annoy you? But to prove you wrong — now that's a different matter. I would certainly do it to prove you wrong. You and anyone else who takes the Bible literally. When we had that — discussion last year, I decided that I'd go into the whole Ark business, and I'm grateful to you, I really am. It's been fascinating.'

'Don't you patronise me,' says Dad, clambering back onto the high horse from which Eric has just about managed to dislodge him.

'Oh, don't be so pompous, Brian. It doesn't suit you.' It does, but I've got enough sense not to intervene. 'Come and have a drink. We've just opened some rather nice turnip wine. You must try it.'

'You know I don't drink.'

'Silly me,' mutters Eric.

'You said it,' counters Dad, and drawing himself up to his full but not very substantial height, he takes himself off to bed.

'Wasn't that a bit naughty, Eric?' I ask him, when Dad has left the room.

'Probably.' Eric grins. 'But he's so easy to wind up. And we were going to have this discussion sooner or later, weren't we?'

'You call that a discussion?'

'Oh, come on, Ruth. Don't you go all disapproving on me. Come and have a little taste of the turnip wine. I'm sure just a little taste won't hurt the baby, and I hate drinking alone.'

CHAPTER THIRTY-NINE

The following morning, all rows and sulks are forgotten, for Kent has received the result of his DNA test.

'Well, that's it,' he says, looking rather stunned.

'Yes? What did they say? What's the result?' Silas asks him. 'Come on. Don't keep us in suspense.'

Kent folds his letter and replaces it carefully in its envelope. 'It's — positive.'

'Wonderful! That's wonderful isn't it, Eric?'

'Wonderful.'

'Wonderful,' echoes Kent, studying his letter.

'Well, aren't you pleased?' Eric asks him.

'Yes, of course. Of course I'm pleased. It's just that it's a bit of a shock. I knew it was possible, otherwise I wouldn't have come here in the first place, but after all this time it seemed such a long shot, and I'd prepared myself for disappointment.'

I think I understand what Kent must feel. I too always expect the worst, and try to prepare myself for it. The down side of that is that I'm not ready for the good news when it comes. Kent apparently feels the same.

'I'd already been wondering what to do if the answer was no,' he continues. 'After all, you wouldn't have wanted me hanging around here if I wasn't your — if I wasn't related, would you?'

'Yes we would!' my uncles speak together.

'A "no" result wouldn't have made you a different person, and we've loved having you around,' Silas adds. 'In a way, this doesn't change anything, does it?'

'It does for me,' Kent says. 'It gives me a whole new view of who I am. It takes a bit of getting used to.'

'Come and feed the pigs with me,' I suggest, sensing Kent's mixture of feelings. 'A breath of fresh air is what you need.'

'That is one seriously nasty animal,' Kent says, five minutes later, as we lean over the door of Sarah's shed.

'Isn't she? But I'm fond of her in a funny way. She's certainly a character.'

The character looks up at us, her jaws slobbering swill, giving us the evil eye as only Sarah can.

'What's to be fond of?' Kent asks. 'I don't get it.'

'Not a lot.' I laugh. 'I suppose it's because she's part of Applegarth, and believe it or not, she's a wonderful mother.'

'I can think of mothers I'd rather have.'

'Speaking of mothers...'

'Yes.' Kent sighs. 'Well, mine was a character, too. She was a pretty good mother on the whole, but she put herself about a bit, too.'

'Just as well for you that she did,' I remind him.

'True. I suppose in a way she couldn't help herself. She was so pretty. Even in old age, she had these amazing blue eyes, and a nice pair of legs, and a kind of twinkle. She was giving the milkman the glad eye right up until the day she died. Everyone loved her.'

'Do you miss her?' I ask, after a moment.

'Oh, yes. Of course I do. For years, there were just the two of us. She never had a live-in lover. She said it was because of me, but I think she wanted to keep her options open.'

'Or maybe she just didn't find the right man to live in with.'

'That's possible, too.'

'And now, this.' I bring the conversation back to the matter in hand.

'And now this,' Kent agrees. 'I know I must seem ungracious. Ungrateful even. It's just that I really had prepared myself not to be their son — doesn't that sound odd? *Their* son? — and was already making plans. And now — well, I've got a lot of catching up to do. There's so much I want to ask them. Family things, personal things. Things I haven't dared to ask before. Up until now, I've tried to keep a bit of a distance. I didn't want to get too attached to them and — all this. Now, they're family, and everything's different.'

'And you've got a cousin.'

Kent squeezes my shoulder and smiles; Eric's (or is it Silas's?) smile.

'I've got a cousin,' he agrees. 'And a rather lovely one at that.'

'Thank you, kind sir.' With my enormous bulk it's a very long time since I felt lovely, and although I'm sure Kent's just being kind, I can't help feeling pleased.

'Not at all. I've always wanted a cousin. Mum was an only child, so I was a bit short on family.'

'Me too.' I hesitate. 'Kent — I'm really pleased about, well, about you and Kaz.'

'She's told you, has she? I didn't think anyone knew.'

'I'm a woman, Kent. Women notice these things.'

'And — the others?'

'No-one's said anything, so I don't think so. But you both look so happy it's a bit hard to miss!'

'I've never felt like this about anyone before,' Kent confides. 'But — and you mustn't tell Kaz I said this — I've thought long and hard, and I've decided there can't be a future for us.'

'What? Why ever not? You're not already married, are you?' Because if Kent has a secret wife hidden away somewhere, I'm going to be seriously angry with him.

'No. Nothing like that. It's — our ages. I'm too old for her, Ruth. I'm nearly twice her age. It wouldn't be fair.'

'Isn't that for her to decide?'

'She says it's not a problem, but while it's fine now, what about the future?'

'In my experience, the future rarely turns out the way you expect it to. Just look at me! Besides, Kaz is a big girl. She knows what she's doing.'

'And I know what I'm doing,' Kent says sadly. 'And it's not right, Ruth. It's not fair. But please don't say anything to her. It's up to me to break it off. And I will, when the time's right.'

'Then is it fair to — to keep on with the relationship at all if you're going to end it?'

'Probably not. I suppose at first I thought it would run its course, and things would sort themselves out. But now it's getting serious, and I don't know how to stop it.' He sighs. 'I'll have to tell her soon, but, well…'

'Not yet?'

'Not quite yet.'

'Well, it's up to you of course, but it'll break her heart.'

'I know. Oh Ruth, what have I got myself into?' He leans his elbows on the door of the sty and rubs his face in a way that is so reminiscent of Silas that I wonder that we ever needed that DNA test at all.

We stand for a few minutes watching Sarah wolf down the last of her breakfast and snuffle round her trough for the remaining fragments.

'She goes free range when the weather's okay,' I tell him, thinking it's time we changed the subject.

'What a terrifying thought!'

'No, actually she's all right when she's out. She just hates being cooped up.'

'I can imagine.'

We turn back towards the house.

'May I ask you something?' I have a burning question, but am not sure whether or not it's the right moment.'

'Ask away.'

'Do you mind — I mean, does it matter to you which one is your father?'

'Funnily enough, no it doesn't. They are so much two of a kind, even if I knew, I think I'd see them both in the same light. It might be a little awkward when it comes to my introducing them to people — and I'm longing for them to meet some of my friends — but no. I honestly don't mind not knowing. In a way, it makes it all more interesting.'

'What's going to be really interesting is telling Mum,' I tell him.

'She must suspect something like this.'

'Oh, yes. But Mum is a great one for burying her head in the sand. If something is hurtful or distasteful, or if it doesn't come up to her exacting standards, she tries to ignore it. Mum doesn't do confrontation. Dad, on the other hand, weighs right in and tells everyone what he thinks. There's nothing reticent about my father.'

'I've noticed.'

'And I don't think he suspects anything because, apart from anything else, he's terribly unobservant. He won't have noticed how like Eric and Silas you are.'

'Am I really?'

'Oh yes! Can't you see it?'

'I think I've been trying not to. But yes. A bit. I can see I'm a bit like them, but probably more like Mum.'

We have just reached the house when a very smart car creeps cautiously up the drive, and a very familiar dog jumps out. He is wearing a new posh collar, and there is a well-dressed woman following him and carrying a matching lead.

'*Mr. Darcy!*' I hold out my arms, and Mr. Darcy leaps into them, licking my face and covering me with mud. His feet may be muddy but his fur is clean and fluffy, and he smells sweetly of lemons. Someone has given Mr. Darcy a bath. 'Where have you been, you bad dog? We've been so worried!'

'Oh dear.' The woman totters through the puddles in her unsuitable shoes, looking embarrassed. 'I did hope he wasn't yours as we've rather fallen for him.'

'But where did you find him?' I push Mr. Darcy down, and he turns his attentions to Kent.

'I think he must have come back with us in the car when we collected those chickens.'

'But he's been gone nearly a week!'

'Yes. Well, we've only just realised what must have happened. We never saw him get into the car or get out of it. As far as we were concerned, he just turned up. We phoned the police —'

'So did we!'

'Well, they weren't much help. Anyway, we thought he must be a stray. He was awfully hungry.'

'Mr. Darcy is always hungry,' I tell her. 'But he definitely belongs here.'

'Yes. I can see that. Oh dear. What shall I tell the children?'

'You could buy them a puppy?'

'That wouldn't be the same at all. Tiger — we called him Tiger. Don't you think it suits him? — is house-trained, you see, and has such lovely manners.' Tiger? *Lovely manners*? Perhaps this is the wrong dog after all. But the little tear in his left ear, the lop-sided wag of the tail, the beetling eyebrows —

these are all Mr. Darcy. He looks a little sheepish, as well he might, but there is no mistaking his identity.

I briefly consider inviting our visitor in, but this is Kent's day, and besides, at the moment I don't think I can face another lot of explanations, plus the identical twin effect (this woman looks the susceptible type), so I wave her politely on her way.

'Does he often go off with people like that?' Kent asks.

'He loves riding in cars, but he doesn't usually hijack other people's.'

'Oh well. No harm done, and he's home, which is the main thing.'

Back in the kitchen, Mr. Darcy receives a rapturous welcome from my uncles. Even Blossom can't hide her relief.

'Decided to come back then, did you?' she asks him, wiping mud off his paws with an old towel. 'Dratted animal. Don't know when you're well off.'

'We can have a double celebration!' says Silas.

'What double celebration?' Blossom demands.

'Oh dear.' Silas turns to Eric.

'She'll have to know sooner or later.'

'Yes. But know what, exactly?'

'We've just discovered I'm a relation,' Kent says. 'Isn't that good news?'

'Son, more like,' says Blossom.

'Well, yes. Possibly.'

'Whose?'

'I'm afraid that's personal,' says Eric quickly.

'Yes. Personal,' echoes Silas.

'Personal, my backside.' Blossom, sniffs. 'Got a right to know,' she adds.

'No, Blossom. You haven't. Not yet, anyway,' Eric says. 'This is a private family matter.'

'Ruth know, does she?'

'Yes.'

'Humph.'

'Ruth's *family*,' Silas tells her. 'It's only fair that she should be told.'

Blossom gives me an evil look. While she seems to have little use for her own family, she hates to be reminded that she's not a member of ours.

'Oh come on, Blossom. Surely you understand,' Eric says.

'Only been here five minutes,' Blossom says, presumably referring to me.

'She's still family,' Eric says.

'Been here years, I have,' Blossom retorts.

'That's true. And we're very grateful.'

'Grateful!' scoffs Blossom.

'And you get paid,' Silas reminds her.

'Paid! Paid, indeed!' Blossom slams out of the back door.

I've no idea what Blossom means by this, but she is clearly not pleased. I dread to think what she'll do next, for Blossom does an interesting line in revenge, and I don't fancy the idea of anything like that being directed at me.

'What will you tell Mum?' I ask, after she's gone.

'That's what we've been wondering,' Silas says. 'But we think it'll have to be the truth.'

'A version of the truth,' Eric adds.

'Yes. We've decided to tell her that Kent is Eric's. That'll be one shock less for her to cope with. I'll be his uncle,' he adds. 'I'm quite happy to settle for uncle. In public, anyway.'

'Good luck, then.'

'Yes. I think we're going to need it.'

In the event, Mum takes the news pretty well, although she's undoubtedly shocked. I think she has hitherto believed her brothers to be dedicated celibates, and to have incontrovertible evidence of a sexual liaison, however long ago that might have been, is going to take a bit of getting used to. But she does agree that Dad need not know, at least for the time being, and she seems quite pleased to have a nephew.

Two days later, I come across Blossom in the hallway. She has a knowing glint in her eye, and I sense trouble.

'Had a visitor,' she tells me, switching off the vacuum cleaner and folding her arms.

'Who, me?'

'S'right.'

'Well, who was it?' I take off my coat (I have just returned from the clinic).

'Big feller.' Blossom is watching my reaction, eking out her news and enjoying every minute of it.

'Yes?' I feel a frisson of fear. I suspect that Blossom's revenge has already taken place, and is going to be more wounding than even she could have anticipated.

'Beard,' says Blossom. 'Trumpet thingy.'

'Amos.' I can't believe it. I can't bear it. *Amos.* So close, and now gone. 'What did you tell him?' I try to keep my voice even. 'Where is he now?'

'Told him I'd never heard of you. Told him you don't live here.' Blossom is actually smiling. 'Went away.'

'*Blossom!* How could you? How dare you? *You had no right!*' I grab hold of the front of her pinafore and give her a little shake. 'It was a wicked, wicked thing to do!'

Blossom pulls herself free. 'Don't you touch me!'

'When was this? How long ago?'

'Two hours, about. Didn't notice.'

'Have you *any* idea what you've done?'

Blossom shrugs.

'You've turned away the father of my baby, that's what you've done. I've been trying to trace him for months and now I may never find him!'

'Not my problem.'

'But *why*? Why did you do this? What have I ever done to you?'

Blossom mutters something about my morals, and babies out of wedlock.

'And what about lying?' I counter. 'That's okay, is it? It's all right to tell lies to a total stranger? Lies about something which is none of your business?'

'Seems nothing's my business nowadays,' says Blossom mutinously.

'Just because Eric and Silas don't want you to know all about their private lives, you decide to take it out on me? That's not fair, Blossom, and you know it.'

'Done, now. Too late to do anything about it,' says Blossom.

'Did he leave a phone number? An address? Anything at all?'

'Nope.'

'And you didn't think to ask anyone else? Eric or Silas? My mother?'

'Out.'

'What, all of them?'

Blossom smirks, and I can see that she's lying, although I haven't any proof.

'Well, I think what you've done is unforgivable. I've tried to get on with you, Blossom. I've put up with your rudeness and your moods, and this is all the thanks I get.'

'Your problem.' Blossom switches on the vacuum cleaner again. 'Nothing to do with me,' she yells above the noise.

'Quite. It was *nothing to do with you.*' But of course, Blossom can no longer hear me.

It would seem that our little chat is now over.

CHAPTER FORTY

Kaz finds me weeping at the kitchen table.

'Hey! What's up? Bad news at the clinic?' Kaz sits down and puts her arm round my shoulders.

'No. Your bloody mother.'

'Oh dear.' Kaz hands me a roll of kitchen towel.

'Oh dear indeed.' I blow my nose. 'Sorry to talk about her to you like this, but she really is a cow of the first order.'

'Tell me about it.' Kaz sits down beside me. 'So what's she been up to this time?'

'She's been "up to" turning away Amos.'

'Your bloke?'

'Well, he never will be now, will he? Blossom told him no-one here had ever heard of me.'

'Oops.'

'He turned up — he actually came here looking for me. I left this address with my parents' neighbours so that if he ever came looking for me, he'd know where to find me. I was out, and it had to be your mother who answered the door. Blossom *never* answers the door. Talk about sod's law!'

'God, I'm sorry Ruth. Didn't he leave a message or anything?'

'No. Because as far as he's concerned, I don't live here, do I? I suppose I'm lucky she didn't tell him I was dead while she was about it.'

'I knew she was upset with you all, but not that upset. Oh dear. I'm so sorry, Ruth. I really am.'

'It's not your fault.' I tear off more kitchen roll and wipe my eyes. 'But oh, Kaz! What am I going to do? Amos finding me here was my last chance, and now it's gone. And so has he. He won't come back here again.'

'He mightn't have been the right one for you. You said so yourself.'

'Yes. But *I* wanted to decide. *My* decision. Not bloody *bloody* Blossom's!'

'I can see that.' Kaz strokes my hair. 'Is there anything I can do?'

'Not really. An itinerant trombone player ought to be easy to find, particularly that one, but apparently not. Amos seems to have this knack of disappearing.'

'How was the clinic?' Kaz changes the subject.

'Oh, fine. The midwife said about ten days to go.'

'That's good, isn't it?'

'You know, Kaz, I don't really care. I'm so tired, there's been so much going on, what with Silas's illness and everything. I've hardly had time to think about babies.'

'Ruth, you have to. It's ridiculous to say you haven't had time to think about the baby. The truth is that you don't want to think about it.'

'That's not fair!'

'Isn't it? You've had nine months to think about it, and you hardly ever mention it. It's almost as though there isn't a baby at all. You decided to keep it. You've had all your scans and things. Now you have to start planning for it. Looking forward to it, even.'

'You sound like my mother.'

'That's a good thing, isn't it? You need a bit of bossing about. You need someone to look after you.'

'I need Amos.' The tears start again. I imagine Amos's big arms around me, Amos telling me everything's going to be all right, Amos at my side while I give birth to our child, Amos bringing me flowers, and being proud. 'I need him so much, Kaz. You've no idea how much.'

'I can imagine.' Kaz pauses for a moment. 'Well, we'll just have to find him.'

'How? How are we going to find him?'

'Let's start with your friends. We'll phone them all up and see whether anyone has any idea of where he is.'

'But I did that ages ago.'

'Yes, but that was when he'd gone abroad. Now that he's back, you've got more chance of finding him. He must be somewhere, for goodness' sake! Someone must know where he is.'

I fetch my address book, and together Kaz and I go through it. Of course, many of my friends don't know Amos, but the musical world is a small one, and my friends from college and from the orchestra prove to be more help than I had anticipated. There have been several recent sightings of Amos, who has apparently been doing the rounds, looking up old friends. No-one seems to know where's he's living, or even to have his phone number, but Amos is apparently very much around, and looking for work in the London area.

'That's a start,' says Kaz, when we call a halt for a cup of coffee.

'London's a big place,' I remind her.

'Yes. But it's a lot nearer than Barbados, and you've left plenty of messages. I bet he'll get in touch soon. Just you wait.'

I am not good at waiting, although given the amount of practice I've had recently I certainly ought to be. But I have no choice. If Amos gets any of my messages, I'm pretty sure he'll be in touch, but there's no guarantee that it'll be soon. As for the baby, Kaz and I discuss this at length and we both decide that it would be best that he shouldn't know about it at this stage. As Kaz says, it might scare him off, and that's the last thing I want to do.

'Though I don't think Amos is the kind of person to be scared off by a baby,' I tell her. 'Or anything else, come to that.'

'Why take the risk?' Kaz asks me.

'Good point. He'll have to know some time, but perhaps not yet.'

Fortunately, at this point we are interrupted by several pilgrims who wish to adopt chickens, and since Lazzo is currently suffering from flu and Mum is out helping Dad choose kitchen units, the job falls to Kaz and me. Neither of us is good with Lazzo's chicken-catching device, so it takes us an inordinate amount of time to trap three particularly scruffy specimens (it seems the fox chose all the better-looking ones).

'But I wanted the ones with the little furry trousers,' their putative owner objects. 'These aren't nearly so pretty.'

'Little furry trousers are all very well,' says Kaz, nursing some nasty scratches, 'but they don't lay well.'

'Are you sure?' The pilgrim/chicken-lover looks dubious.

'Quite sure. Trust me. And these have all been blessed. By a bishop.'

'Have they really?' The woman looks impressed. I notice that she is carrying a rosary. Kaz says the religious ones are always the most gullible.

'Of course. You've no idea what a difference it makes. Now, take them home and enjoy them.'

'Kaz, really! You're almost as bad as your mother,' I tell her, as we return to the house. 'Blessed, indeed!'

'Well, I had to get rid of her somehow, and there's no way I'm chasing little furry trousers all over the garden. Little furry trousers run very fast indeed. Only Lazzo can catch them, and I'm not even going to try.'

'And is it true that they don't lay well?'

Kaz laughs. 'I've no idea.'

Today is not supposed to be a day for visits to the Virgin, but we receive three more lots of visitors before dark. Two are regulars, and know their own way around, and the third has brought a rather splendid pair of Rhode Island Reds.

'My son gave me these for Christmas,' he tells me. 'My wife died in the summer, and the children think I'm lonely. But I'm not sure chickens will help.'

I agree, wondering what kind of people could conceivably imagine that chickens would be an antidote to grief. A dog or cat might at least be company, but chickens?

'I'm sure we'll find them a good home,' I tell him, and then, because I feel sorry for him, I invite him in for a cup of tea. By the time I've heard his story of long years of caring for a wife gradually disabled by dementia ('the long good-bye, they call it,' he tells me) I feel ashamed for feeling so sorry for myself earlier on. After all, I'm still fairly young, I'm fit, and as Kaz points out, no-one has died. I resolve to pull myself together and start being responsible, beginning with an inventory of the pitifully small collection of equipment which awaits the advent of the baby.

'Two vests won't be enough,' says Kaz, watching me.

'Then I shall buy more.'

'And nappies. You've forgotten those.'

'Nappies, too.'

'You'd better hurry up. Time is not on your side.'

'Right. Tomorrow I shall go out and buy vests and nappies.'

'That's my girl,' says Kaz. 'I'll come with you. And we can go to that new little café that sells wonderful cream slices.'

'Aren't I big enough already?' I ask her.
'No-one,' says Kaz, 'is ever too big for a cream slice.'

CHAPTER FORTY-ONE

But during the vest/nappy-buying expedition, Kaz appears to have preoccupations of her own.

'Kaz? What's up?' I ask her, when we adjourn for coffee and cream slices. She looks pale, and she obviously hasn't slept, and I suspect that the news isn't good.

'I've slept with someone.'

'Kent. Yes. You said you were going to.' My heart sinks. For if they've slept together, breaking up will be so much harder.

'No. Someone else.'

'Goodness.' I put down my cup. 'But why, Kaz? And who?'

'An old friend.' Kaz fiddles with her teaspoon.

'Let me get this straight. You're supposed to be having a — thing with Kent, but you've gone and slept with an *old friend*! What on earth were you thinking of?'

'Long story.'

'Good thing we've got plenty of time, then.'

'You're not going to make this easy for me, are you?'

'Nope.' Though given Kent's feelings about the future, this may be one solution.

'I was — upset. Kent and I had this horrible row, and I needed cheering up.'

'I see. So the cure for a lovers' tiff is to dash out and find a replacement?'

'Oh Ruth, it wasn't like that at all.'

'Well, what was it like?'

'He's got this thing about his age, and I don't think it matters, and we had this argument, and it kind of — well, it got out of hand. I said some horrible things.'

'And he did, too?'

'No. Kent never does anything horrible. That's the trouble. He's so bloody *nice* all the time. He just goes all quiet and sad, and then I feel awful and make things even worse.'

'So let me get this straight. You were horrible to Kent, who didn't deserve it, and then you went off and slept with someone else. What a brilliant move!'

'Actually, he was the one who "went off". He said he needed to be alone, and he went back to his caravan, and I was upset, and I went to see Gary. Gary and I go back a long way. We just had a few drinks, but one thing lead to another. And Ruth, I'm so, so sorry. I feel terrible.'

'It's not me you should be apologising to.'

'I thought you'd — I thought you might understand. After all, isn't that what got you into your present mess in the first place?'

'Oh, no. *Oh* no. You're not comparing this — what you've done with my situation. I am not in a mess, as you so kindly put it. I may have made a mistake, but I didn't plan to get pregnant, and I did not let anyone down. Amos and I are — were — free agents. No-one else got hurt.'

We sit glaring at each other, while tears trickle down Kaz's cheeks and drip onto the checked tablecloth.

'Look, let's not fall out about this.' I decide that one of us had better rescue the situation before it escalates further. 'We need to decide what you're going to do.'

'I'll have to tell Kent, won't I?'

'Will you? Won't telling him make things worse?'

'I don't know,' Kaz says wretchedly. 'Oh, Ruth, what am I like?'

'Well, you're kind and funny, and — and bloody impossible!' I can't help smiling. 'But if you really love Kent, I'd leave this for the moment. It might make you feel better to tell him, but it certainly won't help the situation.'

'Mm.' Her hair is rumpled, and there are streaks of mascara down her cheeks, but she still manages to look as stunning as ever. 'Ruth, do you think — do you think twenty years older is too old?'

I've been thinking about this ever since my conversation with Kent, and I'm not sure. 'Yes and no. I think it's more a matter of you being mature enough to take on someone of his age. Running off and sleeping with someone else as soon as the going gets tough isn't a mature thing to do, is it?'

'I'll never do it again. If he stays with me, I swear I'll be faithful. I really will.'

'Well in that case, if I were you I'd go home and apologise nicely for the things you said, and try to discuss the situation as calmly as you can. I'm sure he'll listen if you can keep your cool. Then ask him to give you — you and him — a bit more time. After all, there's no hurry, is there? No-one's going anywhere.'

'Would you have a word with him?' Kaz pushes her plate towards me.

'If I get the chance, I will,' I promise, finishing off Kaz's cream slice and thinking that if I go on like this, I'm going to have one very fat baby.

The next day, I find myself alone with Kent in the orchard.

'About you and Kaz,' I begin.

'Has she been telling you about her — our row?'

'*Her* row, I think it was.' I laugh. 'Yes, she has. Kent, she really loves you. I know she's young, but could you give her a chance? I don't think Kaz has had much love in her life, and maybe someone like you is exactly what she needs.'

'I just feel that I'll be — taking advantage of her, I suppose.'

'Trust me. No-one takes advantage of Kaz,' I tell him. 'She's young, and she can be stupid, but she's also pretty canny, and I reckon she's been looking after herself most of her life. It's love that she needs.'

'Maybe. I'd love it to work out. She's a special girl, Ruth. Not just pretty. There are lots of pretty girls around. But few as — as special as Kaz. Perhaps you're right. Perhaps we should give it a bit more time.'

By now, the news of Kaz and Kent has got out, and everyone seems to know (everyone, that is, except my parents, who have a blind spot where such goings-on are concerned). Silas and Eric, those most accepting of men, seem quite happy about the situation, if a bit surprised. But Blossom is furious.

'Dratted girl!' she says, sending a tsunami of soapy water across the kitchen floor. 'Anything in trousers. Always been like that. Takes after her father.'

From what I've heard, nothing could be further from the truth, but there's no point in saying so.

'Don't you want her to be happy?' I venture.

'Happy? Humph.' Slosh, swipe. 'She wants to be *happy*, does she? I'll give her happy!'

She flings down her mop and slams out into the garden.

So it seems that yet again, the focus is on other people and their problems. Just as I have got Kaz on side and excited about the baby, her attention is lost to more pressing problems. And while I am still not as excited as I probably ought to be, I quite enjoy the excitement and the attention of others. For the first time since I came to Applegarth, I feel very much alone, and if I am honest, frightened. For whatever my feelings about it, the baby is going to come *out*, and it's going to hurt. That much I know. I've paid scant attention to the ante-natal classes, and I am ill-prepared for the rigours of childbirth. I have at least one friend who's sworn that she's "never going through that again", and has stuck to her word, enjoying her daughter but flatly refusing to have any more children. I have never been particularly good with pain, and Mum, while supportive, can be squeamish. Supposing she faints? Supposing we *both* faint? It won't be much of a welcome for a baby who didn't ask to be born and wasn't even wanted in the first place.

I wander into the sitting room and find Eric, who is preoccupied with the problem of humming birds. For it is not only bees and other insects that need flowers, he tells me. Humming birds do, too.

'But surely God wouldn't have expected Noah to have more than just two birds, and they could have been anything. Robins are nice and easy. How about robins?'

'No. The Bible says two of "every kind of bird, every kind of animal and every kind of reptile". So you can't get away with just robins. I've had to leave out a lot; it would take more than a lifetime to deal with every single species. But I've dealt with quite a few. Owls, eagles, ostriches — you've no idea, Ruth. It's incredibly complicated.'

I realise that the more complicated it becomes the more Eric enjoys it, but have enough sense not to say so.

'So you see, we'll have to have a garden, or even a small park, for all the creatures which can't do without living plants. At this rate, the Isle of Wight is definitely going to be too small. Perhaps something the size of Gibraltar.' He rubs his head. 'How big is Gibraltar?'

'I've no idea. Eric, you can't have a park on a boat. The soil would rot the boards and fall through.'

Eric sighs. 'Ruth, you're missing the point, like everyone else. I thought you at least understood. Of course it's not possible.

At least, not possible on an Ark. But on a structure the size of Gibraltar — whatever that is — and reinforced with concrete (I must ask someone about that) it might be possible. Or maybe I could line the foundations with plastic.'

'They wouldn't have had concrete in those days,' I remind him. 'Or plastic.'

'I know, I know. That's not the point, either.' He jots down a note to himself. 'Come to think of it, I believe there's a cruise ship with a small golf course,' he says thoughtfully.

'Is there really?'

'I believe so.' He folds up his charts. 'Ruth, are you all right?' He pats my bump. 'Not long to go now.'

'So everyone keeps telling me.'

'It won't be so bad, you know.'

'What? The baby? Childbirth? The — my — future?'

'All of them.' He holds out his hand, and draws me down beside him on the sofa. 'You'll be all right, you know. And we'll do anything we can for you. You'll always have a home here, if you need one.'

'I know.' I squeeze his hand, and my eyes fill with tears. 'Kent's so lucky.'

'Why? Why is he lucky?'

'To have you — you and Silas — as his father. Fathers, I mean.'

'You have a good father, Ruth. And he does care, you know.'

'Perhaps he does, but at the moment I want to *feel* that he cares.' I look down at our linked hands. 'I don't think my father has so much as touched me since I was a small child.'

'People have different ways of showing affection. Some just aren't the hugging kind.'

'I suppose you're right.' I lift Eric's hand and hold it against my cheek. It is rough and chapped from working outside in all weathers, but the feel of it is infinitely comforting, and I realise that what I miss more than anything else at the moment is physical contact with another human being.

'He's a fortunate man, your Amos,' Eric says, as though reading my thoughts. 'I hope he does come and find you soon, and discover that for himself.'

'Oh, so do I, Eric. So do I.'

I gaze out of the window, where a wintry dusk is already draining away what little daylight we've had. Somewhere out there, perhaps not very far away, is Amos. I wonder what he's doing at this moment; whether he's playing his trombone, perhaps having a pint in a pub with a friend, driving somewhere in his dreadful old car, making a curry (Amos makes good curries). If I believed in telepathy, I'd send him a message. As it is, I just have to hope that one of the smattering of messages I've left all over the country reaches him soon.

CHAPTER FORTY-TWO

March comes in like the proverbial lion. A biting east wind whisks the last few brittle autumn leaves round the frozen garden and penetrates under doors and the edges of ill-fitting windows. The animals huddle in their sheds, and we huddle indoors, wrapped in as many layers as we can lay hands on. I look like a Russian doll; as though within each layer of clothing there lies another, smaller woman, similarly clad. Mum, who has never been good with the cold, suffers terribly from chilblains, and Silas, who still hasn't regained all the weight he lost during his illness, feels the cold more than usual. He is banned from outdoor duties, although he protests that he is fine, and that the 'fresh air will do him good'. Eric points out that it's more likely to kill him, and fortunately the medical bible agrees, so Silas has to do as he's told. He takes comfort from the corpse of the hare, recovered from beneath the frozen remains of Dorothy. We all hope that the stuffing of this unfortunate animal will keep him amused until the warmer weather arrives. The only people unaffected by the cold are Lazzo, who strides back and forth, often in his shirtsleeves, seeing to the animals, and Kaz and Kent. Having for the time being at least resolved their differences, they appear to have recaptured their initial glow, and this seems to be enough to keep them happy, if not exactly warm.

The baby is late. I never expected it to arrive on time, considering that after so long in the womb, it should be allowed a little leeway. I have never understood how babies can be late. I can see that early could be a problem; even I know that premature babies are bound to be underdeveloped. But late? It seems to me more than likely that each baby comes in its own time, and that that time varies from baby to baby.

But the midwife disagrees, and mutters about weight loss and something called 'placental insufficiency'. I know that the reason I have lost weight is that indigestion prevents me from eating as much as I normally would, but the midwife, a busty bossy woman, doesn't listen. I tell her it's my body; she says what about the baby? I say it's my baby, too; she says I'm being selfish, and threatens to have it induced. I ask whether this can be done without my consent. She reluctantly admits that it can't. Well, then.

I sit around and wait. Because of my size and accompanying exhaustion, I was relegated some time ago to light duties — feeding the hens, helping Mum with meals, a spot of hen house duty — but now everyone insists on treating me like an invalid, and I'm hardly allowed to do anything at all. I read and try to play the violin, but my attention span is so limited that I can't concentrate on either. My sleep is disturbed by the activities of the baby, who appears to have no notion of day or night, and by bad dreams. I have a recurring nightmare in which the baby refuses to come out — in fact never comes out — and I get bigger and bigger as the years go by.

'He's a man now, you know,' says the midwife, who is still apparently in attendance. 'He's started shaving.'

The idea of a fully-grown man living inside me and actually *shaving* is so horrendous that it invariably wakes me up.

These days, I hardly recognise Kaz. Gone is most of the ironmongery which used to adorn her face, her hair is returning to its natural colour (a pleasant shade of honey) and she's trying to give up cigarettes (Kent hates them).

'Though it's bloody difficult,' she tells me, as we shiver together outside the back door while she has a smoke. She's down to seven a day, and rations them carefully so as to get the most out of them. 'If you've never smoked, you don't know how wonderful it is. That first long pull of smoke into your lungs — there's nothing like it.' She removes what is now a minuscule stub from between her lips, gazes at it wistfully for a moment, and then screws it carefully into the ground with her heel. 'Let's go in and get warm.'

We wake the next morning to snow. When I look out of the window, the garden and the fields beyond are carpeted in white. The roofs and corners of the outbuildings are rounded and softened by snow, making them resemble gingerbread houses, and the branches of the trees are bent low under its weight. There isn't a breath of wind.

Perhaps there's still something of the child in me, for I never fail to be excited by snow. The magic white light, which seems to glow on the walls even before you've opened the curtains; the softness of the silence; the treat of being the first to make footfalls in virgin snow. Of course, as a child, I had snowballs and snowmen to look forward to, and I think I can say I've grown out of those, but there is still something special about waking up to snow, especially when, as today, it is totally unexpected.

But it would appear that I'm the only one excited by the snow, for downstairs, everyone is grumbling. Snow means more work, of course. It needs to be negotiated or shovelled away; such animals as are still allowed out during the day will have to be kept in, which means more mucking out; everything takes twice the time when you have to tramp through snow.

'Blossom won't be in,' says Eric wearily.

'Why?'

'She never comes when it snows. Says the bike won't work.'

'Well, she may have a point.'

'She may. But I think the real point is that she doesn't like snow.'

But Lazzo turns up, full of good cheer, and between us all (for once, my offers of help are accepted) we get the jobs done. By lunch-time, the snow is pock-marked by trails of footsteps, crossing and re-crossing each other, and my excitement has evaporated as quickly as it arrived. My fingers are stiff with cold, my feet are numb inside my wellingtons, and I know without looking that my cheeks have turned an unattractive shade of purple. Maybe snow isn't so much fun after all.

But after lunch, Mikey and Gavin turn up.

'We've come to help you make a snowman!' Mikey says. 'To cheer you up.'

'What a ridiculous idea.' I'm no longer in the mood for snowmen. 'Haven't you got a job to go to?'

'It's Saturday.'

'Oh. I'd forgotten.'

'Come on, Ruth. It's your last chance to be a kid before you're a mother.'

'You think?'

'I know.'

So we make a snowman. Kaz and Kent join in, and when it's finished, I have to admit that it's the best snowman I've ever seen. It — he — is huge (Mikey made the finishing touches with the help of a stepladder), and sports a rather fetching trilby hat and a moth-eaten dinner jacket.

'There. Don't you feel better now?' Mikey brushes snow off his jacket and beams at me.

'You know, I think I do.'

'I said you would. It brings out the child in you.'

'That's actually what I'm waiting for.'

'So you are!'

We all howl with laughter, while my father, who doesn't do fun in any form, watches us pityingly from the sitting-room window and Mr. Darcy runs round and round in circles, dizzy with excitement. A lone pilgrim, waiting for someone to attend to her, watches in astonishment, and Eric and Silas applaud from the back doorway.

Today has turned out to be a good day after all.

CHAPTER FORTY-THREE

Late in the evening, the wind gets up again, and before long it's howling round the house and down the chimney.

'It's snowing again. Already drifting,' says Kaz, letting in a blast of ice-cold air as she comes in from checking on the animals. 'Bloody hell, it's cold. Put the kettle on, someone. I can't move my fingers.'

Kent obliges, and Kaz peels off several layers and then goes to warm herself by the Aga.

'I think they forecast a blizzard,' says Eric mildly.

'Now he tells us,' mutters Kaz.

'Well, what would you have done about it?' Eric is scribbling madly at the kitchen table, making notes from a textbook. 'D'you know what? I forgot all about the dodo!'

'What about the dodo?' Kent asks.

'It would have been on the Ark.'

'But it's extinct,' Kaz objects.

'It wasn't then, though, was it?' I can tell from Eric's tone that he was hoping someone would say this.

'Well, no. But do you have to have it?' I ask him. 'After all, you've left out other birds, haven't you? Why not leave out the dodo?' I have a ridiculous mental image of a pair of dodos waddling up the gangplank into the welcoming arms of the Noah family.

'Because it's important. The fact that it's extinct could mean it's quite old —'

'Or quite careless.'

'I wish you'd take this seriously, Ruth.'

'How can anyone take dodos seriously?'

'It nests on the ground, so it will have to be kept separate in case someone treads on its babies.' Eric makes another note. 'Apparently it wasn't very bright.'

'Now there's a surprise,' murmurs Silas.

'What did you say, Silas?'

'Nothing.' Silas has nearly finished his hare, and is enormously pleased with it, although apparently hares' eyes are hard to get hold of. 'Will rabbit's eyes do, do you suppose?'

It is at this stage, in the middle of the dodo/hares' eyes discussion, that two things happen at once. All the lights go out and my waters break.

'Bugger!' I stand shocked into inactivity, warm water trickling down my legs and seeping into my socks. What do I do next?

'It's only a power cut, Ruth. Not to worry,' says Eric, foraging in a drawer for candles and matches.

'No. It's the baby. I think it's started.'

There is a stunned silence (which, when I come to think about it, is odd, since it's what everyone seems to have been waiting for).

'Where's Rosie?' Silas asks, after a moment.

'She's gone up to bed. She was feeling a bit under the weather. Do you think you can hang on, Ruth?'

The idea of hanging on to a baby who has decided to be born is so ridiculous that I laugh.

'No,' I tell him, 'I don't think I can hang on. Or rather, I don't *know* whether I can hang on. I've never done this before. But don't disturb Mum yet. This will probably take ages.'

'Not a good night to have a baby,' Silas remarks, going over to the window and drawing back the curtain. Frenzied snowflakes are hurling themselves against the darkened window. They appear to be going up rather than down.

'Thank you, Silas.'

'Oh, I'm sorry, Ruth. But I'm sure you'll be ok. It says in my book —'

'Silas, this is not the time for your book. I need proper help. I think I should phone the hospital.'

'Yes. Yes, of course.' Silas sounds disappointed. 'Can I ring them for you?'

'I think I'd better speak to them myself.'

But it isn't only the power lines that have come down, and the phone is dead.

'Mobiles. Has someone got a mobile?' Kent asks. Kent himself doesn't use a mobile, and knows very little about them.

'No signal here,' Eric says. 'No-one can use a mobile from Applegarth.'

'We could try,' says Silas.

We try. Three mobiles attempt to phone the hospital, and fail.

The first pain rises like a wave in my stomach. It isn't too bad, but I think it means business. I look at the circle of helpless faces round the candlelit kitchen table, hoping someone will say something helpful.

'I'll drive her to the hospital. Get your things, Ruth,' says Kaz. 'And for God's sake, wrap up warm.'

'In that case we really do need to fetch Rosie. Brian, could you go and tell her? She'll need some warm clothing,' Eric says.

Dad, who has been standing helplessly in the background, seems only too pleased to have something to do, and hurries off upstairs, while I pack a small suitcase (this should have been ready weeks ago, but somehow denial got in the way, so I've probably left vital things out).

Ten minutes later, Kaz, Mum and I totter unsteadily out into the blizzard, together with Kent, who's coming as extra support. The snow is falling fast, blown in all directions by a wind which is threatening to become a hurricane, stinging our faces in icy gusts and forming steep drifts all over the garden. We scoop the snow off Kaz's car, our hands already numb with cold, and climb in. With four adults and a suitcase, the car seems very full, and fulfils my worst fears by refusing to start.

'We'll have to take the Land Rover,' Kaz says.

'Are you insured for it?' I ask.

'Ruth, this is an emergency. Insurance doesn't come into it.'

'I'll drive if you like,' Kent offers.

'Please.'

Kent fetches the keys, and we all pile in. By now, I'm so cold that it's somehow ceased to matter. I sit hunched in the front passenger seat, my arms wrapped around my stomach, waiting for the next pain. It comes in a gentle crescendo, but is still easily bearable. I'm beginning to wonder what all the fuss is about. So far (weather conditions notwithstanding) this is proving to be a doddle.

We make our way cautiously down the driveway, through drifts of snow, the windscreen practically obscured by a billion snowflakes which dance and dazzle in the headlights.

After about ten yards, the Land Rover comes to a gentle halt. Kent revs the engine, but nothing happens. He gets out to have a look.

'There's a huge drift,' he tells us, 'and a massive tree's come down. We won't be able to get out, even if we manage to clear the snow.'

His voice is practically drowned out by the wind, but his meaning is clear. We're stuck.

'Is there another way round?' he yells.

'No.' I know this for a fact. The track is the only route through the thickly wooded coppice which separates Applegarth from the road. Silas and Eric have discussed plans for a 'back way', but these have never come to fruition. To all intents and purposes, we're stranded.

'Oh dear, oh dear.' Mum's gloved hands make little flapping movements. 'What are we going to do?'

'First things first. We need to get Ruth back into the house,' Kaz says. 'She's frozen.'

'Can you walk?' Kent asks me. 'Because the car is well and truly stuck now.'

'I think so.'

'Come on, then.'

With Kaz and Kent on either side of me and Mum still fretting behind us, we begin to walk back to the house. We are facing into the wind, which is so strong we can almost lean on it without falling. It hurls the snowflakes into our frozen faces, snatching away our breath, as we stumble over the hidden ruts, pausing as I have another, stronger contraction. Although it's such a short distance, it takes us about fifteen minutes, and by the time we reach the house, we're all exhausted.

'Well, you said you loved snow. You've got snow,' remarks Kaz, as we stumble in through the back door, bringing with us a strong gust of wind and yet more snow.

Eric and Silas fuss over us, as they help us out of our wet coats and gloves. When we're more or less settled, Eric makes a big jug of cocoa (at least the Aga is still working). I am still shivering, despite the rug around my shoulder and the hot water bottle on what's left of my lap. Up until now, it's all been a bit of an adventure, but now reality has set in and I'm beginning to feel seriously frightened.

'It'll be all right,' Eric says. 'The baby probably won't be born for ages, and by then the phones will be back on.'

'You think?' I wish I shared his optimism.

'Well, I certainly hope so. And anyway, people give birth all the time, don't they? In many parts of the world, they just get on with it on their own.'

'At the edges of paddy fields,' I finish for him.

Another bigger contraction tightens my stomach and makes me gasp. I have a feeling this is not going to be such a doddle after all.

'Perhaps she should go to bed?' Kent suggests (it seems that already I'm becoming a third person; a helpless victim, incapable of being spoken to directly).

'No. She's better up and about, as long as she feels like it.' I can tell that Silas has his bible on his knees, and is referring to it surreptitiously under the table.

'Don't we need boiling water?' Eric says. 'I'm sure I've read somewhere that we need lots of boiling water.'

'I always wonder what they want all that hot water *for*,' Kent muses. 'They never seem to use it; they just get it ready.'

'The hot water's a myth,' says Silas. 'But we'll need sterile scissors — now, those *will* need to be boiled — and some kind of string or thread to tie the cord.' He brings his book out of hiding and lays it on the table. 'And of course a clean sheet or towel to wrap the baby in. But first we have to clear the baby's airway. Well, that makes sense, doesn't it?'

I give Kaz a despairing glance. I don't want my predicament medicalised by Silas and his book. I don't like his plans for what "we" are going to do. What I need is sympathy, and cosseting, and someone who knows what they're doing. I'm very much afraid that if someone doesn't do something soon, I'm going to cry.

'She will be all right, won't she?' Dad asks. He suddenly looks small and vulnerable, and even in my present parlous state, I feel oddly touched.

'Of course she is.' Kaz takes control. 'Ruth, how about a nice hot bath? It'll warm you up, and while you're having it, I'll put some clean sheets on your bed, and a fresh hot water bottle. It's going to be pretty cold up there without the central heating. And then I think you should try and get some rest.'

'I'll give you a hand.' Mum is obviously desperate to be of some help.

'Oof!' Another contraction. Everyone watches in awe, as I sit it out. I've forgotten my breathing exercises (puff? pant? a bit of both?) and for the first time, I wish I'd paid more attention.

'A bath would be lovely. Thank you, Kaz,' I say, when I can speak again.

'Was that painful?' Silas asks. 'It shouldn't hurt that much at the beginning. It should —'

'Silas, I think you should shut up. And please put that bloody book away!' Eric says.

'I'm only —'

'Trying to help? Well, you're not helping at all. You take Ruth upstairs, Kaz. Shout if you need anything.'

The bath is soothing — even the contractions are less painful in warm water — and it is with some reluctance that I get out.

'How often are you having the pains?' Kaz asks, bringing me clean pyjamas.

'You sound like Silas,' I tell her.

'No, I think it's important. If they're really frequent, it means the baby's well on the way.'

'And what would we do about it?' I ask her.

'Good point.'

'You arrived quite quickly,' Mum tells me. 'For a first baby.'

We look at each other in the flickering candlelight, and I think it's at this point that we all realise the awful truth. I am almost certainly going to give birth here, at Applegarth, with no medical help whatsoever.

'We'll manage,' says Kaz, after a moment.

'Course we will.'

'And we'll both stay with you.'

'Yes. Please do.' I hesitate. 'Kaz?'

'Mm?'

'You're not squeamish are you?'

'No.'

'Not ever?'

'Not ever.'

'Have you ever — fainted?'

'Certainly not.'

'And you, Mum? Will you be okay with all this?'

'Of course I will,' says Mum, smiling bravely.

'Good.'

'I'll move my mattress into your room and sleep here,' Kaz says. 'We'll leave the candle alight, just in case.'

'Shouldn't I be the one to stay with her?' Mum asks.

'You've not been feeling too good, have you, and we're going to need you later,' Kaz says. 'We'll call you if anything happens. And Ruth, you should get some sleep if you can. I think it's going to be a long night.'

Strangely, I do get some sleep. The contractions ease up a bit, and I'm able to doze in between. Towards dawn, the wind drops, to be replaced by an eerie stillness. In the white glow reflected from the snow outside, I can see the outlines of furniture, and Kaz curled neat as a kitten under her duvet on the floor beside my bed. I wonder whether it's worth going downstairs to see if the phones are working yet, but decide against it. Having got nicely warm, I'm reluctant to leave my bed. Besides, since no-one can get to us through the snow, there's not much point in making phone calls. It's not as though anyone can deliver my baby over the phone.

I feel another contraction, and manage to breathe my way through it quite satisfactorily. Kaz turns on her back and begins to snore gently. Once more, I drift off to sleep.

CHAPTER FORTY-FOUR

The baby means business.

I have been awake now for nearly an hour, and the contractions are getting stronger and a good deal more painful. There is none of the stop-start nonsense of last night. This is for real.

The news on my bedside radio (mercifully battery-operated) tells of storms and drifts all over the country. As usual, the British weather has been met with total astonishment by the British people, and everything has ground to a halt. There are people stranded in cars and trains, and sheep marooned in fields. All over the country, schools will be closed, and in Nottinghamshire, a woman has given birth in a village hall.

'At least this isn't a village hall,' says Kaz, returning from the kitchen with a tray of tea.

'There might be a doctor in a village hall.'

'And there might be an audience of several hundred. You wouldn't want that.'

'I suppose not.'

'How's it going?' Kaz wraps herself in her duvet, and sits on the edge of my bed.

'Painful.'

'How painful?'

'Pretty painful. Bearable, though.' I lever myself further up the bed.

'Should we fetch your mum?'

'No. Let her sleep for the moment, and I'll see how it goes.' I shiver. 'Gosh, it's perishing in here. The poor baby will freeze to death before it's even taken its first breath.'

'No it won't. Kent's lit a fire in the sitting-room, and you can lie on the sofa.'

'Where's Silas?'

'Doing the animals with Eric. But he's been looking things up in his book and he's dying to come and interfere.'

'Please don't let him!'

'What do you take me for?' Kaz grins. 'He wants to know how often your contractions are coming.'

'What did you tell him?'

'I said I'd no idea.'

'Good girl.' I wrap my hands round my mug of tea. 'And Dad? Is he okay?'

'I think he's praying. He said it was the only thing he could do. He's awfully worried, Ruth.'

'Poor Dad.' I could do with his prayers right now. 'I had this awful dream that the baby died and Silas insisted on stuffing it.'

'I wouldn't put it past him.'

'Neither would I. Are the phones back on?'

'No chance.'

'Bugger.'

'Bugger indeed.'

Another big contraction begins, and I almost spill my tea. I pant my way through it.

'Wow,' says Kaz, impressed. 'That was serious, wasn't it?'

'Just a bit.'

'You know, I thought I wanted children, but now I'm not so sure.'

'Thanks, Kaz.'

'You're welcome.' She puts down her mug. 'Let's get you downstairs before the next one.'

She helps me into my dressing gown, and down the creaking staircase. There seem to be a lot more stairs than there used to be, and I have to stop half-way for a breather.

In the sitting-room, a fire is blazing. Kent has pulled up the sofa and made it up with blankets and pillows. It looks quite cosy.

'Welcome to the delivery suite.' Kaz helps me on to the sofa and covers me with several blankets. 'I'll go and fetch some towels. We'll need towels. Breakfast?'

I shake my head as another wave begins. 'Please — keep — everyone — out. Ouf! And I think — it's time — to call Mum.'

Minutes later, Mum comes hurrying down, full of apologies. 'I was awake half the night, and then I must have dropped off. How's it going, love?'

'A bit — painful. But — I'm — managing.'

She sits down beside me. 'I won't talk. I'll just sit here quietly. But you tell me if I can do anything.'

The morning progresses slowly. Kent has set off on foot to see if he can tunnel his way out of Applegarth and find some kind of help, and Eric and Silas are busy seeing to the animals while Dad makes seemingly endless cups of tea for everybody. Meanwhile, Kaz, Mum and I are left to our own devices, with Mum rubbing my back and giving me sips of water, and Kaz timing my contractions.

'Every five minutes, regular as clockwork,' says Kaz, after what seems several days rather than a mere morning.

'What does that mean?'

'Didn't you listen to *anything* they told you?' Kaz says in exasperation. 'If I were having a baby, I'd want to find out everything I could.'

'Bully for you.'

'I don't understand you, Ruth.'

'I never asked you to.'

'Ruth dear — Kaz is only trying to be helpful,' Mum says.

'Well, it's not helping.'

Somewhere at the back of my mind there stirs a memory of being told about a stage in labour where women tend to lose their tempers and swear. Is this it?

Perhaps not.

'Sorry, Kaz,' I squeeze her hand.

'Me too.' She rearranges my pillows. 'This baby thing is exhausting isn't it, and I'm not even the one having the baby.'

Silas pops his head round the door, his face barely visible above a brightly-coloured muffler.

'Silas, you're supposed to knock,' says Kaz sternly.

'I'm so sorry, I just wanted to know —'

'Every five minutes,' Kaz tells him.

'Ah. That means —'

'Silas, we know what that means —' we don't — 'so please leave us to get on with it. Everything's fine.'

'Are you sure?'

'Quite sure.'

'Is Kent back?' Mum asks him.

'No. I think he'll be some time,' Silas says. 'The drifts are about eight feet deep in places.'

I spare a thought for Kent, who certainly isn't anything like eight feet deep, and hope he'll be all right. It would be awful if he were to give his life for me and my unborn child.

The time and the contractions tick by. The pain gets worse and more frequent, but I do my best not to make any noise, for I am uncomfortably aware that Silas is waiting somewhere nearby for an excuse to come and help.

'Mum, I need to push,' I gasp.

'Aren't you supposed to hang on a bit?'

'I — can't — hang — on!'

'Then perhaps you'd better go ahead, dear. I'm sure your body knows what it's doing.'

I push. It feels as though my whole body's trying to turn itself inside out, but nothing happens.

'Do you think I ought to — have a look?' Mum asks me, after several more fruitless and exhausting pushes.

'Please.'

Mum has a look.

'Oh, my goodness! I can see its head!'

'What, all of it?'

Kaz joins her, and they both peer under the blanket. 'Just the top,' she says.

'Hair?'

'Possibly. Gosh this is so exciting!'

'I'm — glad — you — think — so.' Another big push. I feel utterly drained. Whatever happens, this baby is going to be an only child.

'I think it helps if you put your chin on your chest,' Kaz says. 'And then push. I've seen it on the telly.'

'*Fuck off!*' The pain is overwhelming. All this pushing is going to kill me. 'Fucking, fucking baby!'

Mum makes a tutting noise, and despite the pain, I experience a wave of irritation, but Kaz wisely shuts up, and we all wait for the next contraction.

'Aaaaaaah!' This is a big one, accompanied by a searing pain.

'Oh, Ruth! Its head's out,' Mum tells me.

'Wow! This is amazing!' Kaz says.

'What — happens — now?' I lie back on my pillows, panting.

'Another push?'

'Here goes.'

The next push is a bit easier, and the one after that is accompanied by another sharp pain and a rather satisfying slither. There's a brief silence followed by a yell of protest.

The seahorse/rabbit has arrived.

'He's here. Your baby's here! Oh, Ruth! He's *beautiful*!' Tears are running down Mum's cheeks as she very carefully lifts up something slippery and howling, wraps it in a towel and hands it to me.

I look down into the face of my son. After a few moments, he stops crying, opening navy blue eyes beneath a slick of wet dark hair and gazes at me critically.

'Will I do?' I ask him softly.

'Oh, Ruth! Of course you'll do!' Kaz gives me a big hug. 'This is the most exciting day of my life. Congratulations!'

'Darling, you were amazing,' Mum says. 'Just amazing.'

I unwrap him and we all count his fingers and toes, wonder at his tiny fingernails, his neatly-drawn eyebrow and feathery lashes and his 'dear little knees' (Kaz's words). It is amazing that a year ago he didn't exist at all, and yet here he is, absolutely perfect in every way. A home-made human being.

'Could you — could you ask Dad to come in?' I ask Mum, after a few moments.

'Are you sure?'

'Yes. I'm sure.' Because now I want both my parents with me to share in this miracle.

Dad tiptoes into the room in his socks and approaches the sofa carefully ('like the shepherds in the stable,' as I afterwards say to Kaz).

'Oh, Ruth,' he says, very gently laying a finger on the baby's head. '*Ruth!*' And to my astonishment, I see that there are tears in his eyes.

An hour later, I am sitting up with my baby in my arms and we are drinking his health in elderflower champagne. The placenta (which had been completely forgotten in all the excitement) has been delivered, and in a moment of post-natal magnanimity, I even let Silas cut the cord with his newly-boiled scissors. Altogether, it's been something of a joint effort, and everyone seems inordinately proud, both of themselves and of me.

You read about childbirth (at least, most women do); you read about the different stages and what happens when and what you're supposed to do; you even read about the pain. Nobody, however, tells you about the afterglow.

I think now of all my favourite moments — performing a concerto with an orchestra; getting my diploma; the best possible sex; being in love (not necessarily the same thing) — but none can compare with this. At this moment, there is no-one and nothing in the world but me; me and this perfect little human being (how could I ever have thought of him as a seahorse/rabbit?). I never expected to feel like this; I didn't even know it was possible. But I believe that now — this moment — is the nearest I have ever been to perfect happiness.

'Hey!' I cry, to no-one in particular. 'I did it! *I did it!*'

As though in response, there are muffled footsteps outside and we hear the front door opening. There's the sound of raised voices, and a kind of scuffle, and a few moments later, Amos bursts into the room followed by Kent. They both look very cold and very wet, and Kent at least looks very cross.

'I'm so sorry, Ruth. I couldn't stop him. He wouldn't let me explain,' Kent says. 'I met him outside. He said he'd had an urgent message and needed to see you at once.'

'So you *do* live here!' Amos beams at me. 'When I came before, that weasily little woman said she'd never heard of you, and told me to go away. I only just got your message, and tried to phone, but I couldn't get through. What's the matter? Has something happened? Are you ill? It's taken me hours to get here. I had to abandon the car and —' he stops short. 'Whatever have you got there?'

'It's a baby.'

'*A baby?*'

'A baby.'

'Whose baby?'

'Your baby.'

'*My* baby?'

'Our baby.' I hold out our son to show him. 'Amos, meet Malachi.'

EPILOGUE

Six months later

I love September; still summer, but with a hint and promise of autumn, and (today at least) warm sunshine.

Malachi is sitting on a rug on the grass chewing at a biscuit with his one tooth. He catches my eye and smiles (Amos's smile), biscuity soup leaking down his front. Indoors, Amos is practising with all the windows closed (the neighbours are not fans of the trombone) and keeping an eye on his vat of home-brew (he has been picking up tips from Eric and Silas).

We've been living together in my flat ever since the Norwegians left, and things seem to be working out pretty well. We're neither of us in any hurry, but I think we are both hoping for a future together. Amos is a wonderful father, which considering he had no time at all to get used to the idea is pretty amazing. We argue frequently, laugh a lot, make love whenever the baby allows us to, and perhaps most importantly of all, are the best of friends. We both do a bit of teaching and Amos plays in a small jazz band. We get by.

My mother adores Malachi, and manages to ignore the fact that Amos and I aren't married, referring to Amos as her son-in-law. Since she and my father left Applegarth to move back into their renovated home, she has been much happier. I think this is in no small part due to her chickens.

While Mum was at Applegarth, she became very attached to her feathered charges, and she's started keeping rare breeds of chickens in the orchard. She has some pretty feather-footed bantams and some speckled Sussex hens, and some others with peculiar names which I can't remember. She's thinking of showing some of them, and she also sells their eggs.

'But we don't need the money,' Dad objects.

'That's not the point,' says Mum.

'Then you might as well give the eggs away.'

'That's not the point, either.'

Mum has discovered that having a saleable skill has its own value, which has nothing to do with making money and everything to do with self-esteem. Dad, who has enough of both, wouldn't understand.

My father still struggles with the whole baby thing. On the one hand, I know he's proud that he was one of the first people to see Malachi, but on the other, he's still upset at my unmarried state. However, he finds an increasing number of excuses to visit us (he's 'just passing', he's returning something I lent him, he's planning a surprise for Mum's birthday), and may even eventually forgive me for having a child out of wedlock. Sometimes, I hear him singing the baby tuneless little ditties when he thinks I'm not listening, and Malachi, who's a forgiving soul, gives every appearance of enjoying them.

Other things have been happening, too. Mikey and Gavin have had their union legalised, and have bought a tiny cottage together. They appear to be blissfully happy, and Mikey still finds time to visit his new godchild. Meanwhile, Kaz and Kent appear to have sorted out their differences and seem very settled and happy, living together in the caravan. Kaz has given up pole dancing at Kent's request, and has joined a local taxi firm, which she says she enjoys enormously ('I get great tips, Ruth!' I'll bet). She hasn't told Kent about her fling with Gary ('you were right, Ruth'), and they have no immediate plans for the future, but I hope and believe that they'll stay together, not least because I'm deeply fond of them both.

We keep in close touch with Applegarth, and have paid my uncles several visits. On these occasions, Blossom, who appears to consider that she's back in charge, is almost friendly, although I suspect that she's always relieved to see us go. Silas is fully restored to health and has recently stuffed a tortoise ('so hard to get hold of, Ruth, a dead tortoise. And so generous of the zoo'). Eric has almost finished his work on the Ark and is already looking around for another project to take its place. But I'm glad Kent and Kaz are around to keep an eye on things, especially as my uncles aren't getting any younger. They deserve a bit of looking after, and who better to do it than a newly-discovered son? Lazzo goes round most days to help. He loves Applegarth and the animals, and seems to ask for nothing more (although I'm still planning the promised visit to London Zoo).

And the Virgin of the hen house? I'm afraid the news there isn't so good, due to a recent incident involving a new initiative and a wild boar.

Eric, inspired by his researches into pig varieties, took it into his head to put Sarah to a wild boar instead of her usual mate.

'Nice gamey meat,' he explained. 'And the piglets will be so *interesting*.'

Now, Sarah has many idiosyncrasies, one of which is a refusal to conduct her couplings anywhere other than on her own territory, so the boar, kindly (and, I suspect, illicitly) loaned by a contact at the safari park, was duly delivered to do the business. So far, so good.

Unfortunately, before the happy couple could consummate their union, Sarah's visitor escaped, and came barrelling down between the outhouses and across a field 'like the wrath of God' (Silas's words), scattering sundry chickens and piglets in his wake. Upon being challenged by Lazzo with a broom handle, he made an about turn, and charged straight into the side of the hen house, impaling himself by his tusks and instantly demolishing all traces of the Virgin.

As Eric said afterwards, it is as though she had never been there at all.

A NOTE TO THE READER

Dear Reader,

Thank you for choosing to read *Ruth Robinson's Year of Miracles*. The idea for this novel arose out of all sorts of things: among others, my love of motherhood, music, and the countryside, and my affection for quirky eccentric people (my own family is full of them). The idea for the apparition of the Virgin came from markings which resemble a figure in the grain of an old blanket chest we use as a coffee table. The image is still clearly visible, stars and all (to me if to no-one else!).

If you have enjoyed reading *Ruth Robinson's Year of Miracles*, I would be really grateful if you could write a review either on **Amazon** or **Goodreads**.

In the meantime, I love hearing from readers, and your comments are always welcome. I can be contacted via my website at

http://www.francesgarrood.com/contact-me/

You can also follow me on Facebook at

FrancesGarroodAuthor.

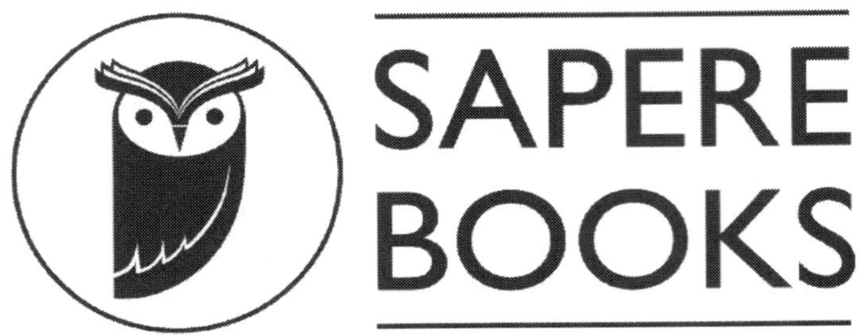
SAPERE
BOOKS

Printed in Great Britain
by Amazon

G000089383

david lange

my life.

david lange

my life.

VIKING

VIKING
Published by the Penguin Group
Penguin Group (NZ), cnr Airborne and Rosedale Roads, Albany,
Auckland 1310, New Zealand (a division of Pearson New Zealand Ltd)
Penguin Group (USA) Inc., 375 Hudson Street,
New York, New York 10014, USA
Penguin Group (Canada), 90 Eglinton Avenue East, Suite 700, Toronto,
Ontario, M4P 2Y3, Canada (a division of Pearson Penguin Canada Inc.)
Penguin Books Ltd, 80 Strand, London, WC2R 0RL, England
Penguin Ireland, 25 St Stephen's Green,
Dublin 2, Ireland (a division of Penguin Books Ltd)
Penguin Group (Australia), 250 Camberwell Road, Camberwell,
Victoria 3124, Australia (a division of Pearson Australia Group Pty Ltd)
Penguin Books India Pvt Ltd, 11, Community Centre,
Panchsheel Park, New Delhi – 110 017, India
Penguin Books (South Africa) (Pty) Ltd, 24 Sturdee Avenue,
Rosebank, Johannesburg 2196, South Africa

Penguin Books Ltd, Registered Offices: 80 Strand, London, WC2R 0RL, England

First published in 2005
1 3 5 7 9 10 8 6 4 2

Editorial services by Michael Gifkins & Associates
Designed by Mary Egan
Typeset by Egan Reid Ltd
Printed in Australia by McPherson's Printing Group

ISBN 0 67 004556 X
A catalogue record for this book is available
from the National Library of New Zealand.

www.penguin.co.nz

CONTENTS

PREFACE

This book has been a long time in the making. I wrote it because I thought it was time to say something for myself about my political career instead of having other people make it up. I wrote about my upbringing because my parliamentary career cannot be understood apart from it, and having done that I found myself writing about a lot else in my life as well.

I am grateful to the publishers and in particular to Finlay Macdonald of Penguin for encouraging me to write this book. Most of it has actually been dictated; Jan Young put it into type for me so that I could wrestle with it. I am indebted to Michael Gifkins for his editing, and to many others for their efforts in the book's production. Since it became known that I was writing this book, many people have reminded me of events I had forgotten, and I am very thankful to some of them.

David Lange

CHAPTER ONE

There is a beauty about the Bay of Islands which 175 years of somewhat ill-considered settlement has failed to destroy. On one side of the bay is Waitangi, which has come to be regarded, in the metaphysical way we construct our view of ourselves, as the cradle of the nation. From the grounds of the property where the first subscribers to the Treaty of Waitangi camped is a view of the sea beyond. A peninsula runs from the south, shielding the bay, and nestled at the foot of its hills is the township of Russell.

It was an accident of war that I was conceived in Russell. My father was a doctor and joined the army at the end of 1941, serving with the 3rd Auckland (Countess of Ranfurly's Own) Regiment, deployed to defend the Bay of Islands from enemy assault. It was doing so by planning and building a road from Cape Brett, at the northern tip of the peninsula, towards the south; the better, it was said, to get men and armaments to the point of possible invasion. My father had a somewhat cynical view of the war effort in the north and was sure that the road would simply allow the Japanese to get to Auckland faster. While work was in progress he was quartered in Russell at Pompallier House, once the residence of a bishop who came to New Zealand well before the Treaty of Waitangi was thought of. My father shared the bishop's house with a Salvation Army officer who served as a padre and was, like my father, a non-combatant.

Although he wore a uniform, my father remained very much the general practitioner. He delivered babies and tended to accident victims while looking after the health of the troops. The officers' issue of the day was a lemon-squeezer hat and he took the view that the lemon-squeezer would offer no protection at all should the enemy suddenly appear, and so he used to wear his combat helmet – on medical advice, as he put it. When my father decided to stop saluting and merely doffed his tin helmet when accosted by his fellow soldiers, his helmet-wearing was banned by his superiors on the grounds that it was causing ill-discipline.

My father was recently married when he joined the army. When I was in kindergarten he told me that my middle name, Russell, was given in tribute to the place of my conception. I have no idea why my first name is David since there is no forebear so called.

The surname Lange is German. In the general election campaign of 1984 my principal opponent tried and failed to make an issue out of my German ancestry. The name did however cause the family trouble during the First World War. My father's parents and their two boys went off in a horse and trap for a picnic at Thornton's Bay, near Thames, with a family by the name of Ziegler. All of the group were enthusiastic members of the Primitive Methodist church and none of them had ever been out of New Zealand. While they enjoyed themselves on the beach on a fine summer's day, my grandfather's tailor's shop was ransacked and burned. The friends had unknowingly chosen to have their picnic on the day of the Kaiser's birthday, which inflamed the wrath of the folk of Thames to the point of their destroying my grandfather's livelihood.

Even then the family had been in New Zealand for so long that the original German pronunciation of the name *(lung-ah)* had all but been forgotten. My grandfather, John Henry Lange, who was always called Jack, was born in Thames in 1872 but beyond that I do not know much about my ancestors on my father's side. My great-grandfather Hermann was a tailor, and my father used to tell me that the family had been tailors for 400 years. Having come to New Zealand, my great-grandfather practised his trade among the gold-miners. It is hard otherwise to explain why he should have ended up in Thames. My great-grandmother, who was a Nottinghamshire woman, somehow came into property and left my grandfather a share in a house in Mt Pleasant Road in Balmoral, Auckland, and twenty-six sections at what was called Beachlands garden suburb in Maraetai. The economic pressures of the times militated against the family's keeping any of these properties.

My grandfather Jack was one of five children. Two of his three brothers went to Australia. Hermann was a talented musician and is the ancestor of many Australian cousins. Carl was described by my father as a hypochondriac but lived to be nearly 100 and had three wives who died looking after him. Brother Will had a shop in Victoria Street West in Auckland where he carried on the family tailoring business. He settled in Orakei where in the early 1950s the community hall was called the William Lange Hall, but like many weatherboard monuments to temporal fame it has since been demolished. 'Uncle Will' had a son, Byron, who was lost on his flight home from war service in the Pacific and never saw the son born to him while he was away. I met this son on only the one occasion: I happened to be in court when he was charged with being involved in the management of a brothel. He clearly found it wise to go to Australia. The only sister in my grandfather's family was Violet. She married Howard Wilfred Danby, a Thames shoe retailer who was active in community affairs and was on the local hospital board for many years.

Grandfather Jack died before I was born but my grandmother used to talk about him with considerable affection. They were both actively involved in the local church: grandfather was the choirmaster and grandmother the organist. They were married in 1898 by the Reverend Hardie Boys whose son Reginald became a judge of the High Court and whose grandson Michael was our governor-general. My grandfather was also the superintendent of the Sunday school and a lay preacher in the church. Apparently he fell out with the church from time to time; my grandmother used to tell me of the occasion when he felt unable to carry on preaching but, being scheduled to do so, stood in the pulpit and announced four hymns and a benediction before leaving the building.

Grandfather's life in Thames seemed to move between his house in Sealey Street and the shop in Pollen Street where he did a busy trade. Like his brother-in-law he was a member of the hospital board and his only disappointment in public life was his membership of the Thames Harbour Board. The board was not a success. It borrowed a great deal of money, the harbour silted up, its revenue ceased and the board went broke. The members of the board were sacked and a commissioner was appointed. All this was a considerable blow to my grandfather. Keith Sinclair in his biography of Walter Nash was intrigued by the presence of papers relating to the Thames Harbour Board among Nash's collection. I like to think it is explained by Nash's sympathy for my grandfather. They were in contact with each other for many years when Nash was a travelling salesman for a haberdashery and stayed with my grandparents in Sealey Street.

The Labour Party was formed in 1916 and my grandfather joined its branch in Thames a year later. His connection with Walter Nash aside, his reasons for joining are hard to determine. He was, after all, a small-time businessman. But he was also a Primitive Methodist and there was in that church much empathy with what had come to be called the working class. My grandmother told me that he was deeply affected by the Waihi labour troubles of 1913 and felt that many people, some of whom were known to him, had been unjustly treated. His membership of the Labour Party may have been his response to that feeling.

My grandfather's life continued in its quiet way until the day in 1932 when he came home for lunch as was his wont, complained of feeling unwell, and died.

My grandmother rented out the house in Sealey Street and the shop in Pollen Street and moved to Auckland to live with my father. Mary Walker was born in the Kauaeranga Valley near Thames and had a hard upbringing in a tough farming environment. She told me about a flood which washed away all the family's cows when she was seven years old, and she remembered a day when the skies went dark because Mount Tarawera had erupted and spread its ashes far and wide.

Granma when I knew her was a person of tidy appearance with her hair in a bun. Neat to the point of obsession, she was a careful housekeeper. She used to urge me to save money and was certain that the pension would not last because she did not trust the government to keep paying it. She spread sacking on the floor across the front room carpet during the week; on Saturday nights it was removed so that on Sunday, and Sunday only, the carpet might be seen. When she left Thames in 1932 she brought with her the household stock of preserved fruits. It was in 1955 that we ate the last jar of preserved peaches and it was in perfect order.

There was something extremely regular about my grandmother. Every morning of every weekday she would have a cup of tea and listen to *Dr Paul* on the radio. Every Friday she would buy the *Listener* and the *Free Lance*. On Saturday she would make creamed rice puddings. You always knew exactly what she had in her cupboards.

She was heavily involved in the life of the church and the Women's Christian Temperance Union. The only secular organisation she belonged to was a group which went by the name of the Old Thames Girls' Association. This remarkable body met twice a year in the Lewis Eady hall in Queen Street in Auckland. Granma used to take me along to the afternoon's festivities. We caught the bus into town and took the tram up Queen Street to the hall where, because my grandmother had a bad hip, we would take the lift to the first floor. Here tables were set in orderly fashion with plates of cakes and savouries. The old women all wore hats. Cups of tea were drunk. There was entertainment, which was invariably the same. A man sang 'La bella Marguerita', there would be a recitation of poetry by two or three of the old Thames girls, and then it was time to gather up the crumbs, put the leftovers in a bag and make our way home. You could not drag a child anywhere near such an occasion today, but when I was eight it seemed exciting to me.

Granma looked after herself for years. She lived around the corner from us in the house that she bought after my father started his family. Her funeral service was held on the day of her wedding anniversary. Her friends and family saw her body to the crematorium for committal and my father left instructions with the undertaker to send the ashes to Thames to be buried next to her husband. Older readers will not be surprised to learn that New Zealand Road Services lost the ashes. The bus arrived in Thames without them and we never learned the fate of what was left of my grandmother.

Jack and Mary Lange had two children. My father, born in 1899, was the elder of their boys. His given names were Eric Roy, but he was never called anything but Roy. I was reminded of this oddity of nomenclature in the 1970s when I was practising law in Auckland. I went out to a secure psychiatric ward in the hospital at Avondale to see a client. When I got there I was accosted by two men in early middle age. They were two of the vast number of babies delivered by my father in his practice at Otahuhu. In the days before social security he frequently delivered them for little or no charge; one family which, unwisely as it turned out, kept on having children, decided in reward for my father's efforts to name a son after him.

The boy was given the name of Eric but before the next son arrived the family discovered that my father was not actually called Eric, so the new arrival was named Roy. The two who approached me in the secure wing were Eric and Roy, both of them in custody, both of them probably to die there, a tragic couple but each touchingly grateful to have my father's names between the pair of them.

My father must have had a happy childhood: a secure household, a good home and an understanding family. He also had good friends. He certainly enjoyed his school life and I was proud to visit his high school in Thames and see his name on the board as dux of the school, so many years before. He was a determined student and it was resolved fairly early on in his life that the family would send him to medical school.

He arrived in Dunedin to begin his medical studies in a brand-new suit which his father had crafted for him. My grandfather had pictured my father in the dashing style of the new undergraduate, but my father told me how uncomfortable he felt in what he described as knickerbockers and he soon put the outfit away. He became a resident of Knox College, a Presbyterian theological hall of residence which took in students who were enrolled at the University of Otago. He was joined after two years by his brother Harold, who also came to live at Knox College and study medicine but was spared the knickerbockers.

There were some interesting characters among my father's contemporaries. Arthur Porritt was one. He later went to Oxford and won a bronze medal in the 100-metres sprint at the 1924 Olympic Games before becoming a medical advisor to the royal household and later still governor-general of New Zealand.

Douglas Robb, who became one of the country's most eminent surgeons and chancellor of Auckland University, was a fellow student both in Otago and later in the United Kingdom. My father and he remained close for years. I still remember them in my old home at Otahuhu when they sat and debated whether the *British Medical Journal*, which was delivered as a tightly rolled package, burned better as kindling unwrapped or wrapped.

My father went through medical school in an uneventful fashion. He travelled home to Thames after each term, a journey which meant taking the train up the South Island, across Cook Strait in the ferry, the train up the North Island, changing trains to go to Thames, and then back again after the holidays. There was nothing exceptional about his academic career. When he graduated, he did his postgraduate work in Thames Hospital and then became superintendent at Coromandel Hospital. This was a small establishment a long way from other medical services and somewhat cut off. My father had to undertake the full gambit of emergency procedures as well as being a sort of general physician for quite a large district. He moved to general medical practice at Turua on the Hauraki Plains and then elected to go to Edinburgh for further study.

He worked his passage to Edinburgh, sailing as ship's surgeon on the SS *Port Fairy*. The pay was a shilling a month. He rounded Cape Horn working in a surgery above the propeller. In Scotland he studied surgery and became a fellow of the Royal College of Surgeons before engaging briefly in general practice around Edinburgh. One of the delights of his later years was to watch *Dr Finlay's Casebook* on television. He said it recaptured almost perfectly the circumstances of his country practice in Scotland.

Following this he cut a different course, proceeding to Vienna where he did a diploma in obstetrics, a specialty which in time came to occupy him far more than surgery. At the end of the 1920s he was back in New Zealand seeking work. He started by doing locums in the north and was for a short time the medical superintendent of Whangaroa Hospital in Kaeo. His housekeeper was a woman who became the mother of Clem Simich, my National Party opponent in the Mangere by-election in 1977. Following this he took on a six-month position at Rawene Hospital.

Remoteness was the lot of Rawene in those days. In later years I had a part-time legal practice down by the wharf and it seemed quite a way to get there from Kaikohe on the gravel road. In my father's time the hospital was the hub of the town. The regular medical superintendent was a man of fertile mind called G M Smith. In the early days of the depression of the 1930s he turned his thoughts to politics and brought out to New Zealand one Major Clifford H Douglas. Major Douglas was a Canadian who had certain advanced, and certainly untested, theories about money supply. What he also offered was a view of the world which was appealing to those who struggled for a living but who had no sympathy with the goals of the organised labour movement. He spoke of honest toil and how that toil should be handsomely rewarded. There was no place for idlers in his scheme of things. Starting with a convention under canvas on a beach in the Hokianga, Dr Smith made use of his six months' leave of absence from the hospital to take Major Douglas around the country and generally be an evangelist for what eventually became the Social Credit Political League. It was a remarkably persistent political movement which struggled on until it reached the height of its parliamentary influence in the 1970s and early 1980s, when its presence was a factor in my becoming leader of the Labour Party.

My grandfather died while my father was in Rawene. This may have encouraged my father in his desire to settle down. His brother Harold had not chosen to stay in New Zealand; having furthered his medical studies in Europe he came back home but left shortly afterwards to become medical superintendent on the island of Niue. Years later on Niue I saw the white wall he built outside the hospital, a wall which was demolished only in 2003 by a hurricane which devastated the island. After a number of years on Niue he went to Tonga where he became Queen Salote's physician, attending the royal family and working in the outlying islands. When Harold's first son was born, Queen Salote gave him the name of Lasike, a name which John, the son, has chosen to avoid using in his retirement in the English gentry belt.

Harold next went to Samoa and worked in the hospital in Apia where his wife, Rita, died in tragic circumstances. She was it seems unwell and, struggling out to the toilet at night, had drunk what she may have thought was water but was instead a caustic cleaning fluid. She is buried in the cemetery at Apia. She used to write long letters to my grandmother about her life in the islands with Harold and their son. More than fifty years after her death I tried to find her grave in Apia but, although the custodian had a number for it, I could not tell which little heap of stones was hers.

I have a long connection with Samoa. I first went there in 1978, when an old lawyer asked to see me. I met him in his dusty office where he said that he wanted me to know that my mother did not kill herself. I was able to assure him that this was indeed the fact because she had just seen me off at the airport. He was far from the last in the Pacific to mistake Uncle Harold for my father. It was on my visit in 1978 that I was presented, as was the custom, with a number of roasted pigs. A reporter from the *New Zealand Herald* asked me what I did with them. I told him I gave them to the Little Sisters of the Poor, a statement which was reported in the *Herald* as 'member for Mangere gives pork to needy young women'.

Following Rita's death, Uncle Harold joined the army and had an arduous war in Greece, Crete and Egypt, marrying again in Alexandria to a nurse from Waipukurau. After the war he started a practice in Pahiatua.

My father's ambition was to set himself up in general practice in Auckland. The place he chose was Otahuhu. He made his choice carefully. Otahuhu when he went there in 1932 had three medical practitioners. One, remarkably enough for the times, was a woman who had been at university with my father. Another of the three was a friend of my father. My father set up in the south of the town. Pickings were lean and the patients were impecunious, but there was no rivalry among the doctors.

Otahuhu was I guess not a romantic choice. It was a small industrial town, long since swallowed up by Auckland but then a place with a borough council and its own distinctive character. The area had a long history of Maori occupation, as it took in the narrow crossing between the Manukau and Waitemata harbours. Europeans had been there since the 1840s. The district became a soldier settlement when there were disturbances further south. The

British decided to secure Auckland by bringing out soldiers who pledged themselves to the colony's defence in exchange for land and a home for their families.

It was never a town of architectural merit; its most distinctive form of building was the railway house. These houses were not designed for comfort. If you stood at the front door of a railway house you could see the back door and if you walked through, you would pass the kitchen. On the left was the coal range, on the mantelpiece was the Edmonds baking-powder tin with the money for the newspaper in it, and on the wall there was invariably a portrait of Michael Joseph Savage, patron saint of the working people of Otahuhu. The railway houses were followed in later times by state houses. There were also quite a number of departmental houses in those days when the post office, the police and the like used to be responsible for housing their staff.

I did not know Otahuhu during its hard times in the 1930s. I was born in 1942 and when I knew it, it had prospered. In my young days it was an orderly town where convention was respected: every man had a job and every woman stayed at home unless she was a schoolteacher or a nurse. The men were employed at the railway workshops or the brewery or the abattoir or one of the three freezing works. Whatever difficulties my father had in his early days of practice in the town, Otahuhu proved to be a good place for a professional man to make a comfortable living.

My father rented a house in Princes Street in Otahuhu on the site of what was once the District Court and is now a misguided housing development. Then he built a house for himself, close to the medical facilities which were for him among the attractions of the town and next door to the little maternity hospital where I was born. There were two more maternity hospitals just over the road, and the largest of them all, St Mary's, was within easy walking distance.

It was its location as much as its size which made the new house remarkable. Where Mangere Road joined the Great South Road, a V-shaped junction was formed, at the point of which was a reserve. At the front of the reserve was a casting of a man on a horse, put there by a local philanthropist as a memorial to the Otahuhu men who had died in the Great War. Behind it there had long stood an obelisk fashioned in memory of Colonel Marmaduke Nixon, who died in what was described as the defence of the settlement during the Maori Wars. Our house sat squarely behind the two memorials. Its formal address was 10 Mangere Road, but letters addressed to The Monument, Otahuhu, always reached us.

It was a two-storeyed house in what I think is called the neo-Georgian style. On each end there was a single-storey annex like some sort of wing. There was a large tiled roof, four bedrooms upstairs, a kitchen, a dining room and a lounge. Half the ground floor was devoted to a suite of rooms for the practice of medicine. Each room had a bell for summoning a maid. On the ground floor there was a closet for the maid in which a device displayed different colours to show which room was calling for service. The absurdity of it was that my father never employed a maid. He pulled the system out when he got sick of his children playing with it. The house, it has to be said, was completely out of character with its surroundings. It is hard to imagine what effect it might have had on the people who lived around it, but it did not seem to put them off and they flocked to my father's practice.

My parents lived in the house until 1969. It was never a home again after that and was almost immediately converted to offices. It has since been much altered. The stone wall which surrounded it has been demolished. The washhouse and the workshop have vanished. The front entrance with its two colonnades has been torn down and replaced by an outside staircase behind a glass frontage. It is disfigured by commercial artwork. Oddly enough I can pass it now without the sadness I used to feel when I saw what had happened to it. Trees have grown up in front of it and a road has been built behind it. It no longer looks like the house I knew.

The new road runs over the site of the Huia maternity home. It was in the sluice room of the Huia home that my father met my mother for the first time.

CHAPTER TWO

My mother was born in Tasmania in 1909. Her name was Phoebe Fysh Reid and she was the daughter of Samuel Berjew Fookes Reid, a flour miller of Deloraine, and Edith Caroline Fysh, who came from a prosperous Launceston family. My grandmother's uncle was twice premier of Tasmania and a member of the federal cabinet at the formation of the Commonwealth of Australia. He must have been versatile because he represented sequentially the Free Trade Party, the Protectionist Party and the Anti-socialist Party in the House of Representatives. Grandmother's nephew Hudson Fysh was a founder of Qantas.

Samuel Reid's parents came from Scotland, where they were recruited by a Launceston migration association to supplement the supply of artisans and labourers in the colony, given the end of penal settlement and the movement of the able-bodied to the Victorian goldfields. The family settled in the Tasmanian north-west. Samuel Reid was a sportsman who loved fishing and who played football.

He was not the best choice of husband, preoccupied as he was with his own interests.

The marriage produced five children. My grandmother was determined to provide some security and education for the family while my grandfather gambled and drank away the little he got from flour milling. There were periods when there was no money in the house. My mother told me tearfully of the strain on her mother when the family was, more than once, evicted. After they moved to Hobart, my grandmother used to buy flowers at the markets and sell them at the ferry terminal to support her children. This state of affairs could not continue and the Fysh family intervened. Some of the five children were farmed out to relatives. Bargains were made with my grandfather which he did not honour, and in about 1928 he left his family in Hobart and went to Launceston. For most of my life I did not know what happened to him there – there were dark mutterings by my mother and occasionally she would hint at some disgrace, but nothing was disclosed to me.

I was at home in Mangere Bridge one day in 1995 when a woman came to the door. She looked like Dame Edna Everage. She said, 'Hello, David. I'm your Aunty Dawn.' She was the daughter of my grandfather and a Launceston boarding-house proprietor. Born in 1928 and adopted at birth, she took many years to discover her origins; turning up as she did, after the death of my mother and all my mother's siblings, she was most welcome.

Her birth must have pushed the Fysh family to one last effort. It was, I hope, as much in the interest of my grandparents and their children that a deal was struck as it was for the protection of the respectability of the Fysh family. My grandfather gave pledges of abstinence from women, gambling and alcohol. In return, the Fysh family paid for my grandparents to make a new start in New Zealand.

They arrived in New Zealand in 1929 and settled in Temuka so that grandfather could work at the Aero flour mill. As far as I know, he was true to his pledges for the rest of his life. Two of the five children chose to stay in Tasmania, while my uncle Don worked in a grocery shop at Clandeboye near Temuka and my aunt Betty went to Dunedin. My mother went nursing.

She qualified as a nurse before she left Tasmania and came to New Zealand to be close to her parents. Nursing offered security of residence and income, but she also enjoyed her job, reminding her family of the time she nursed Errol Flynn before he became famous. She trained at the Royal Hobart Hospital and kept in touch with the nursing friends she met there for the rest of their lives. In 1949, Dr Shoebridge, who was a consultant at the Royal Hobart and latterly a minister in the state government, came on a surprise visit to our family home. Having survived many a caution on the sin of smoking, I was surprised to be sent to the dairy to buy a packet of First Lord cigarettes.

After she arrived in New Zealand, my mother worked in Timaru and Dunedin before moving to Auckland where she became a midwife in Devonport. Then she went to Otahuhu and married my father shortly after meeting him. Her parents were by then well settled in a large old home they rented near the flour mill in Temuka. Mum and Pop were married in the Methodist church in Temuka and had their reception at Caroline Bay in Timaru.

They were ten years apart in age, but it was not that which

made them in many ways an odd couple. They were so different in character and habit.

My father was a tidy, careful man, much given to order. He used to tell me that there was no excuse for untidiness, but that lesson did not stick. He also used to say that punctuality was the courtesy of princes, an odd thing to suggest to a seven year old, as I was when I first heard him say it, but I came to agree with him. Pop had endless patience. His hobby was woodwork and he took no end of trouble over his cabinetmaking. There was an unassuming air about him: his only extravagance was to have the detachable collars of his shirts washed, starched and pressed by the Chinese laundry in Victoria Street East in Auckland. He suffered when he had to speak in public, but was saved from being trapped in his limitations by his wry sense of humour and his fine sense of the ridiculous.

He was a connoisseur of sporting disaster and, thanks to him, I was present at an infamous moment in our country's sporting history. Pop liked cricket, and when New Zealand played a test against England at Eden Park in 1955, he checked on the score between patients at afternoon surgery. When the New Zealand innings started to collapse he could not carry on. He saw the last patient out and bundled his children into the Dodge. We got to Eden Park in time to watch Appleyard and Statham take the last of the home side's wickets to see it all out for twenty-six, which remains New Zealand cricket's nadir to this day. My father contained himself at the ground, which was just as well because the crowd showed its displeasure by ripping off the pickets from the boundary fence and hurling them about. Once in the safety of the car he started laughing. The thought of it made him laugh for a long time afterwards.

Mum rarely saw the humour in anything. When she and Pop sold the old home in Otahuhu they moved to Kohimarama, where they lived in a block of four units. Each unit had a basement garage. Their neighbour below was from the Japanese consulate in Auckland. He had a Mercedes-Benz which he stored in the garage. One morning I had just arrived to visit Mum and Pop when their Japanese neighbour reversed out of his garage with some vigour. Unfortunately he had forgotten to open it first, smashing the door and inflicting considerable damage on the Mercedes. I got out of my car in time to see my father, who was then quite ill, standing in his pyjamas and dressing gown at the top of the steps, beside himself with laughter. The neighbour looked crestfallen. My mother came out and shouted at Pop, loudly enough to be heard well down the street, 'Don't laugh, Roy! He'll lose face!'

Pop had a pattern in his working life which was largely determined by the needs of his job, but on Sunday he followed a ritual of his own devising. Every Sunday morning he would vacuum the downstairs carpets. Then he would wind the grandfather clock before he went to church. It was as well that he did the vacuuming since my mother just did not get on with housework. She was not a person to do things as a matter of routine. Cleaning was the province of Mrs McHardy who came from the railway settlement two mornings a week and restored some order, but it was always a matter of real concern to my father that there was no rhythm to the house. One practice of my mother's drove him to despair. Mum had a lot of pots and pans; there were too many for the space available under the sink and there was certainly no place for each individual pot. They were simply jammed in wherever a niche could be found for them. Removal of one pot would cause an avalanche of the other pots, spilling on to the floor amid a tremendous cacophony. My father agonised while the noise continued. After the first swell abated there would be a second landslide and then usually Mum could get on with cooking the dinner.

My mother was never less than dogmatic and her assertions brooked no argument. She was jolly and enjoyed her life as long as she was on the move. Full of enthusiasm, she did nothing by halves, whatever it was, and could never be dissuaded from her course. She learned to drive, but never understood the principles of it. She was quite sure that if a car was labouring in second gear it would do better in a higher gear. Once the higher gear was engaged, the car would gradually stagger in a series of alarmingly expensive lurches to a stop. My father suffered in silence. When I was six years old I could see the error, but it was unwise to comment if I was in the front seat as Mum's inevitable response was to cuff me around the ears.

When Mum left the house and drove off down Mangere Road, it was some relief to hear the crashing of the gears without first hearing a bang as the right rear fender hit the telegraph pole behind the garage. This happened only too often. My father, who was usually meticulous about keeping the car in order, gave up completely in the end and simply did not restore the fender.

Mum did things in a big way. Everything was bought in bulk. The groceries were delivered twice a week. She kept bins of flour and sugar. Toilet paper and soap were bought in twelve-dozen lots from the medical-supplies retailer. When eggs were rationed, she used to buy twelve dozen of them informally from a farmer at Redoubt Road in Manurewa. She stored them for later use in baking in kerosene tins filled with water-glass. One of the jobs I most loathed in my boyhood was being sent to the washhouse to bring in some eggs. I had to plunge my hands into the muck in the tins to get them and this took the edge off my enjoyment of the cakes.

Mum's weekly laundry was a major operation. In winter it started before dawn when I could see from my bedroom the light struggling through the condensation on the windows of the washhouse. The gas-fired copper would be simmering. Mum stirred the washing with a long wooden pole, wrung it out, hung it out to dry and then waited for the woman to come on Tuesday to do the ironing.

My parents had four children. I was born in 1942 and twins were born in 1944, my brother Peter twenty minutes before my sister Margaret. I cannot remember anything about their arrival, but strangely enough I do remember being held by my father on my mother's back while she floated around a hot pool at Parakai before they were born. I have a memory of the twins when they were very young which is hard to forget. They were being breastfed and Mum fed them both at once. She believed that every nursing mother should eat peanuts to help bring on the milk, and would heap raw peanuts into a roasting dish and bake them before eating them by the handful. My sister Annette was born in 1947 in the Huia maternity home next door.

There was one other member of what should be counted as our

wider family. Sometime during 1943, the military authorities decided that my father's presence in the north was no longer essential to the war effort so he returned to his practice which had been, as it were, in limbo. To start with, my mother was the practice nurse, but she found it difficult to combine nursing and motherhood. At the end of 1943 my father employed Muriel Wilson for the purpose; she was always addressed by the family as Nurse, and I have never called her anything else.

Nurse lived in our house when she joined the practice. When the Huia maternity home was converted to a lodging house, she took a room there, but three times a year she would come and stay at our place to look after the children while my parents took a break for a weekend. For reasons known only to themselves, they always stayed at the Riverina hotel in Hamilton.

Nurse, who trained as a Karitane nurse, was brought up on a farm where the secondary school now stands, near Taihape. One of the joys of my childhood was to go to the farm for part of the Christmas holidays. Nurse took me with her on the overnight Limited Express. We arrived at Taihape in the dark and her father would pick us up for the drive to the farm. I remember making haystacks, carting the cream on a sledge to the gate and feeding the skim milk to the pigs. I also fed the chooks. We picnicked by the river beneath the towering limestone cliffs beyond. I was sorry to go home, but not long after I got back I was always sent a chocolate frog in the name of Rosy, the draughthorse.

In 1959 my father fell ill and had to give up his practice. Nurse, who had worked for him for sixteen years, moved back to the farm at Taihape, but a year later she brought her parents to live with her in Otahuhu while my parents went overseas. She announced that she intended to marry John Cruikshank, a widower who lived across the road from us. Her father died before the wedding and I was briefed to give her away if my parents could not get back from Europe in time. My father made it with a day to spare. Nurse and her husband bought my grandmother's house in Otahuhu. She lives there now, one of the few who remain of the people who lived in the Otahuhu of my boyhood. Nurse drove until she was ninety-three and still tends to her garden.

Our family life in the house at the monument revolved around my father's role as a doctor. The relentless discipline of single practice convinced me at a young age that I was not cut out to be a doctor. The demands on my father were seemingly endless. Pop was called out at all hours of the day and night in those days when doctors went to the homes of their patients. The police frequently rang to request his attendance at accidents or committals. And he was a maternity practitioner, which meant that many a family outing was cut short once advice had been received that a woman had gone into labour. He even went so far as to extract teeth. Once the root stayed firmly in place; Pop gave up and took the patient down to the dentist. I remember the dentist popping in to tell my father that everything was all right and to give him a ring if he had trouble with an appendix.

Pop held clinics two mornings a week at the Reidrubber factory, where he shared a room with Norman Douglas, who was the union secretary and later member of parliament for Auckland Central. On Thursday mornings he worked at a private hospital, either as surgeon or anaesthetist, removing tonsils. He did house calls on the other mornings, held a surgery in the afternoons and did more calls afterwards. Every evening before tea he put about two inches of cold water into the bath. He stood in the water to get undressed, shaking his clothes out so the fleas, which were the unavoidable consequence of his habit of sitting in the most comfortable chair in the houses he visited, fell into the water and drowned. At seven o'clock he held an evening surgery.

When I was old enough to go to kindergarten Pop started taking me with him on some of his afternoon calls. It was I think a way of getting me off Mum's hands. I was always made to feel welcome by his patients; at the surgery I was introduced to mothers with new babies and my father asked me to feel the fontanelle and estimate the age. When I was older I tested urine samples with potassium permanganate crystals over the Bunsen burner. If the power was off at the time of electricity rationing, I lit the Tilly lamp and the lanterns in the surgery.

From time to time I accompanied him to the scene of accidents. A dance at the country hall in Wiri was halted when the power failed and the electrician clambered into the ceiling to find the fault. He fell, plunging straight onto the piano, which had the lid raised to maximise the volume, ending up with one leg inside the piano and the other foot on the keyboard. Pop was kindness itself: he did not laugh until he had deposited the victim in Middlemore Hospital.

Then there was the night when two Anglican nursing nuns from St Mary's went into Auckland to view the coronation lights. One of them was run over by a bus as they crossed the road to the hospital on their way home. She was one of my father's midwives, and a policeman came to fetch Pop. We ran down the road to where the woman was lying motionless. My father asked the policeman for a torch and shone the beam into her eye. I can still hear him telling the policeman that the woman was dead.

He put his arm round my shoulder to comfort me. That was Pop: always affectionate, never indulgent. He contented himself when provoked with calling me a bally fool. It was Mum who, when she felt that discipline was called for, and she often felt that way when I was very young, used to slap me. What seem to me in retrospect to be small childish indiscretions were always violently punished. Mum demanded; she did not encourage. I do not want to make her out to be heartless, because I never thought of her as that, but she could be cavalier. One day my brother broke a bone in his foot. When he cried she shouted at him for disturbing the afternoon surgery. It was my father who came out and after a brief appraisal carried him off to Middlemore.

My mother approached the upbringing of her children in the way she did everything else. We were directed with great enthusiasm into useful projects and ended up cutting patterns, compiling booklets and writing letters to missionaries. We had to take swimming lessons and then enter swimming competitions. I was required to learn the piano and to play the church organ.

The wonder of it now is that none of us rebelled against this. If any day gave cause for rebellion it was Sunday. Sundays started with church at eleven o'clock. Sunday school began at two o'clock, or at least it did until the middle of the 1950s, when it was moved to the morning. When we were old enough to go to primary school, we had to go back to church at seven in the evening. When Sunday school was in recess, if we did not visit relatives we would go to Granma's for afternoon tea and hymn singing.

Our church activities were centred on the Otahuhu Methodist church, a few hundred yards from our house. Mum was not always a Methodist. Her father had no appetite for religion. Her mother was a devout Baptist; the Fysh family had a strong evangelical streak. Two of Mum's cousins came to visit us in 1947, both spinsters who served as missionaries in East Africa and were unused to living in an orderly community. My father had to go up a ladder and fasten the outside shutters on the windows of their room before they felt safe enough to sleep.

Mum slipped into Methodism with ease, although she could have settled for any number of churches. She was curiously catholic in her nonconformity. While the Methodist church was always her focus, any of the others were acceptable so long as they opposed drinking, gambling and acts of dancing on church premises, supported Sunday observance, and never challenged the literal interpretation of the scriptures. She had interests in missionary societies, the Bible Society and the Bible Training Institute in Henderson. We were often taken to Salvation Army services which I enjoyed for the robustness of the music and simply for the variety they offered. There were conventions to attend and evangelists to listen to. Sundays were of course off-limits to almost any secular activity – amusements like the pictures were off-limits on any day of the week, but Sunday's prohibitions were almost boundless. I made my first purchase at any sort of shop on a Sunday when I was seventeen and at university.

If she was nothing else, Mum was an exciting person to live with.

What she did not offer in affection, she made up in activity. She liked to toss picnics together, she barbecued heaps of meat bought from the freezing works, and she was a dab hand at a camping holiday. I think that she liked camping because it was in a way how she wanted to live: she was making do and enjoying herself.

She was wholehearted in her hospitality. On Sundays the home was awash with children from the poorer families of the town. Mum played host to a constant stream of workers from the Pacific who had taken seasonal jobs at the freezing works; on warm days they would settle on the lawn on fine mats given by previous waves of the grateful. The mix was topped up by nurses and doctors who came from Asia under the Colombo Plan and were adopted by my parents during their studies.

Outside of the church, my father had a limited circle of friends, closest of whom was a chemist, a Polish Jew whom I always called Uncle Harold. Pop kept a Homburg hat in the cupboard under the stairs for Jewish funerals. He was in the St John Ambulance movement, but his chief interest was in Rotary. Rotary meant luncheons every Tuesday at the Golden Glow restaurant in Otahuhu, until it burned down in 1956. Every so often the members' children were invited and we dutifully attended to eat the meal of luncheon sausage, beetroot and potatoes. Not long after the war, my father became convenor of a Rotary group which met regularly around a table in our front room. The members brought contributions of dripping which they wrapped for dispatch to the rationed British. Their efforts were apparently welcomed, although the toll of New Zealand's lavishing of sheep meat, butter and dripping on the British has never been quantified.

Every Christmas my father got a locum in and took three weeks off. We had what I remember as magnificent holidays. We went to Bethell's Beach and Pakatoa Island; we went camping on the east coast of the North Island and we journeyed through the far north. We took the car on the ferry to the South Island, staying in Temuka with my mother's parents in their old house down by the flour mill.

In the 1950s my grandparents kept reasonable health, although my grandmother was very stooped. My grandfather, for all that he had kept his vows of abstinence, was still not one to enjoy domesticity. The house was surrounded by long grass and weeds. Deprived of the camaraderie of the bar room, he consoled himself with a weekly haircut, offering up his place in the queue the longer to enjoy the company. My grandmother was deaf and rarely went out, but took great pleasure out of playing cribbage two nights a week.

After his retirement from the flour mill, my grandfather became caretaker at the Temuka motor camp. He and my grandmother lived in the cottage which went with the job. I went to stay with them over the summer holidays and got my first paid job as a worker in the employ of the Temuka Borough Council. The pay was £2 10s a week. I helped with the cleaning of the motor camp and my grandfather allowed me to keep the empty bottles I collected. The returns from these were more than my wages.

When my grandfather became too old to work, my grandparents had to leave their home at the motor camp. They had no money to buy a house, but my grandfather had his eye on a cottage on the north town belt. He called to ask my father if he would buy it. Pop demurred but said he would go down and see my grandparents and sort something out. He flew down to the South Island to find when he arrived in Temuka that my grandfather had already signed a contract to purchase the cottage. It is a measure of my father's patience that he paid and made no protest.

My grandparents lived in the house Pop paid for until my grandmother became ill in 1957. She suffered for a few days and then died with my mother at her side. My grandfather remained in the cottage until eventually it became too much for him to manage by himself; he went to Christchurch, where he lived under the eye of my mother's brother Don, before moving to a retirement home and then to hospital. Towards the end, my mother went down to Christchurch and sat with him in the ward. After two days, Mum found the restraints of the bedside overwhelming and when my cousin Christopher arrived to see his grandfather she seized upon him eagerly, urging him to look after the old man while she went shopping. She was away for only two hours, but when she got back grandfather was dead. Mum turned on Christopher and with passion demanded, 'Christopher, Christopher! What have you done to him?'

Whatever their differences, my parents brought me up in a happy household. Theirs was an enduring marriage and home to me meant security. There was never any excess and we did not flash money around, but there was always material assurance. In all the tides which ebbed and flowed through the household, there was one constant: every day started in the same way with porridge for breakfast. We ate it from surgical bowls placed on coir mats sent from the Pacific by my father's brother Harold. We always said grace and there was always a bible reading. As if to remind us of who we were and where we came from, we were seated on a bench in front of a map of the world on which the British Empire was coloured in a lurid red.

CHAPTER THREE

Childhood, before I went to primary school, was spent mostly in the company of adults. Our family home, being the place where my father practised, was as much a public as it was a private place. I was carried about a lot. My mother had a bicycle; its balloon tyres were orange because in wartime there were better uses for carbon than in bicycle tyres. My father fashioned a box which he anchored on the clip above the back wheel. Slotted into the box, I would cling behind my mother as she bowled along the roads of Otahuhu and Mangere to do her shopping, attend her piano lessons or pay social calls.

I liked to visit our neighbours. My childhood hero was a boy called George Kelly, who was some three years older than me and who lived two houses down the road. He had two sisters, Shirley and Beverley, who were active in the Girls' Brigade and Sunday school. Fred Kelly, their father, worked in the railway workshops. He was a skilful woodworker who was often invited to pass judgement on my father's cabinetmaking. The Kellys were largely self-sufficient in fruit and vegetables; their lawns and flowerbeds were carefully tended, and inside the house was immaculate. Everything was orderly. I loved that home and went there every day I could. On Sunday morning Fred Kelly would unlock the back door early and I would let myself in and sit in bed between Mr and Mrs Kelly until it was time to go home and get dressed for church.

One of my earliest memories, and one of the thrills of my young life, was the visit of Field Marshal Montgomery who commanded the New Zealand troops in the North African campaign and came to this country to thank those who had returned and honour those who had not. The twins and I were placed on the stone wall on the Great South Road frontage of our property, ready to wave as the field marshal went past and then to run behind the house to wave again from the Mangere Road side. A jeep pulled up and a drab khaki car stopped right in front of us, Montgomery barely visible in the back. He stepped out, a much-decorated figure in dress uniform. With a wave to us children, he climbed on to the jeep and stood upright in the back as it rounded the monument and drove off towards the old American military camp.

The camp, which was just past the railway crossing at Middlemore, was more than a camp; it was a small town with enormous storage sheds. Between the sheds and the main road a large number and variety of military vehicles were parked. This stockpile remained in place for years and I bought a gun tractor at auction there in 1962. The camp was once host to some 6000 American troops who were often to be seen in Otahuhu. They used to walk up the street, accosted by kids begging for sweets and I had my first taste of chewing-gum from a generous American soldier. My father was once reduced to laughter when a boy arrived at the surgery with a note from his mother. He kept the note and when I had learned to read he let me see it, if not understand it. 'Come quickly, Doctor,' it read, 'I think I have cort VD.'

The American camp was close to the site of Middlemore Hospital, which opened before I started school. The hospital was commissioned by the government as an urgent wartime project and when the war came to a close the property was passed on to the Auckland Hospital Board. On the day of the opening I stood among a great crowd of people in front of the hospital. The Otahuhu railway workshops band played the national anthem and provided musical entertainment. My uncle Wilf Danby from Thames was formally greeted as the representative of the Thames Hospital Board. I know from the record that the hospital was formally opened by the governor-general, Sir Bernard Freyberg, and I recall a tall, soldierly figure smoking a cigarette.

Middlemore stood at the south-western boundary of the Otahuhu borough. To get there from my house, you set off down Mangere Road, passing Otahuhu College and King's College before crossing the railway line and skirting the military camp. Here Mangere Road took the name of Massey Road and entered Mangere, which was a world apart from Otahuhu and mostly rural. There were some houses at Mangere East, which were the result of the spread of population from Otahuhu, and a long-established settlement at Mangere Central; Ihumatao, on the edge of the Manukau harbour, had a marae and a significant Maori population. Most of us in Otahuhu were largely unaware of its presence.

Mangere Bridge was a small village. For the rest, Mangere was an area of prosperous dairy farms with a smattering of Chinese families who earned their living on their market gardens, growing crops for the Auckland market.

Massey Road was named to salute the long-serving prime minister who farmed in the Mangere district. The family homestead, which was built as a hunting lodge in the 1860s and was occupied by members of the Massey family when I went to live in Mangere in 1977, is still standing on Massey Road. The Manukau City Council looks after it. It was a building unlike any in my home town and a conspicuous symbol of the divide which the railway line created between Otahuhu and Mangere. Mangere had the smell of the gentry about it; William Massey was a conservative politician and a stalwart of farming interests. His old electorate was the sort of place which offered a warm welcome among the faithful for a National Party leader.

Otahuhu was not such a place. A working town, it was surrounded by farmland, but there was little romance in the meeting of town and country. In the north of the borough on the narrow isthmus which led to Penrose there were large holding-paddocks for stock slated for slaughter at the Westfield freezing works. There were more holding-paddocks in the south-east, and saleyards next to the railway line. The saleyards were a wonderful place to visit on auction days, but the daily droving of incontinent cows and sheep along Mangere Road and the Great South Road left a mess behind. Added to that was the smell from the decaying remains of animals unfit for processing, which were dumped in the Manukau harbour. The fertiliser works used sulphuric acid to break down the phosphate rock, and the fumes of the process belched out around the clock. My father once explained to me how water reacted with sulphur dioxide to make an acid which could break down paint, a point which was demonstrated on foggy mornings when we would wake up to find the woodwork on the house gone black.

It was a town with few outward signs of wealth. The remarkable art deco town hall and municipal offices which graced the cover of the borough's 1948 centennial publication remained unbuilt. There was never the money for it. My father was one of a handful in Otahuhu who owned a motor-car. Because he was a doctor, and because he did a certain amount of his professional travelling on unsealed roads, he was allowed a ration of petrol and the privilege of buying a vehicle. Most of the townspeople relied for their motor transport on the fleet of yellow buses which were made in the local depot by grafting a wooden framework onto a Bedford truck chassis. Numbers of men at the railway workshops rode bicycles to work. In the afternoon they rode back with a load of firewood on the clip above the back wheel. This practice continued all year round and the wood was stored for the winter. At the brewery the employees were allowed to drink in the bar on the premises after work, while at the freezing works the workers pinched paper from the carton room and pilfered the best cuts of meat to carry home.

It was a tribal town, even in its sporting interests. Boys commonly took up the sport which ruled in their neighbourhood or at their father's place of work. Railway workers, and there were some 1600 of them at the workshops in the 1950s, were split between rugby and rugby league. Our neighbours the Kellys were league. Freezing workers were more often than not followers of the same code, and brewery workers almost to a man were also league supporters. The greatest concentration of them could be found close to our house, around St Mary's. Fred Kelly took me to watch rugby league at Carlaw Park. I used to go with George Kelly to Sturges Park, not far from our house, where the great Kiwi fullback Des White could be seen practising his goal-kicking for hours on end.

The working men of Otahuhu belonged to a union and supported the Labour Party. The town of my infancy had a council which was elected on a Labour ticket. A Labour member represented its people in parliament until 1949, when the National Party took the Otahuhu seat.

Otahuhu's Labour politics did not sit easily with my mother. She was not a Labour supporter and made no pretence about being one, maintaining her disdain for that side of politics even when I was prime minister. Her family on her mother's side were steeped in conservative politics. She liked what the National Party stood for: the idea of wealth and the people who had it. I went with her once on a visit to a house in Paratai Drive overlooking the harbour in Auckland. The house belonged to Howard Hunter, who was best man at my parents' wedding. I always called him Uncle Howard; he was a successful clothing manufacturer who married a daughter of the family which gave the Great War memorial to Otahuhu. Mum and I entered the living room of the Hunter house, where wealth and taste framed the view of the water. Overcome by its perfection, she burst into tears.

My father was Labour and was known to be sympathetic to the labour movement. The Labour government of 1935–1949 transformed medical practice in a way my father approved; he was labelled a socialist by some of his professional colleagues. The government paid doctors a fee of 7s 6d for every patient seen. My father thought that 5s was a fair return for his services and he gave the balance of 2s 6d to the patient. This happy scheme was brought to an end by the British Medical Association which deemed it unprofessional.

We talked about politics in a small way over family meals. My father never listened to parliament on the radio, but he enjoyed political meetings and he often took me with him. Most of them were in support of Labour candidates, but the one I most clearly remember was called by the National Party in 1954. The speaker was Sir Leon Gotz, minister of internal affairs, who was knighted for his services to the Queen on the royal visit. He had one arm and wore a black eye-patch over one eye; the National faithful may have assumed he was a victim of battle rather than of his own folly in blowing fish out of a lagoon in Samoa. The Gaiety theatre in the heart of Otahuhu was filled with Labour supporters and there was much heckling. Someone had a crack at the speaker's German ancestry: the minister said that his full name was Francis Leon Albert Gotz, and his initials stood for the flag. His boast that he was proud to stand by the flag was drowned out by a yell from a railwayman, 'Yeah, mate, and like all flags you're up the pole.'

I just loved politics after that and could not wait to take part. I started to listen to parliament on the radio. I listened every night it was on, all the way through secondary school, and was always on the Labour side. It was not because Pop voted Labour or because many of the families I knew supported Labour; it was because

Labour was for the underdog and I hated the National Party for its smugness and arrogance.

In a class talk at intermediate school, I announced my ambition to be prime minister, although I had a bob each way and spoke at the same time of my hankering to be an engine driver.

My formal education began when Mum enrolled me in the Otahuhu kindergarten on the corner of Princes Street and Great South Road. It occupied a large, ramshackle home which was refurbished and became the borough council's offices shortly after I left it. The house was mouse-infested, drab, with no playground and almost nothing by way of toys or amusements. We were made to sleep on ex-army camp stretchers and drank pink milk and ate apples. My mother flung herself into the Free Kindergarten Association and raised funds to expand the inventory of books and toys. My time there was saved for me by the dedication of the teacher, Miss Hamlin from a Mt Wellington family, who coped against the odds and delighted me by reading each day from a picture-book. Then, too, I had the excitement of catching a bus to the kindergarten and back. Mum put me on the bus with a note pinned to my shirt saying where I was going and the driver made sure I got off at the right place. She followed the same practice when the twins went to kindergarten at Papatoetoe; there was only ever one mishap when the driver overlooked them and Pop had to rescue them from Penrose.

At the beginning of the third term in 1947 I started at Fairburn Road School. It was a post-war school which had five permanent rooms, five prefabricated classrooms, and no hall. Its scale was daunting; no class had fewer than forty pupils. I knew about ten of them from my neighbourhood. The day I started was the first time I had been to the school and I did not enjoy it, though the passing years gave me some assurance. There was no school uniform and none of the boys wore shoes. My family could have afforded shoes, but like others in the same position I preferred not to wear them, whatever the weather. I wanted to fit in.

The teachers were a mixed bag. There were a number of well-meaning, pressure-cooker graduates, who on being demobbed from the armed forces trained as teachers for six months and were then set loose on us. Mrs Abel, the principal's wife, helped me to learn to read, and more wonderfully to read without saying the words out loud. Her next trick was to get me to read ahead and before I was in the senior classes I had set off on the path to speed-reading. Another good teacher was Bill Renwick, who was later director-general of education. In my later years at Fairburn Road we had a remarkable principal, Dr Bill Dale; while the rest of the staff got the bus or rode bikes to school, he drove around in a white Allard sports car. He wore bow ties and chain-smoked indoors and out. He was a Yale graduate although born in the United Kingdom: my father described him – and I had no idea what he meant – as a remittance man. Whatever he was, he was good at instilling enthusiasm and confidence in pupils. He would enter classes uninvited and take over the lesson, drawing faltering responses from the shrinking violets and praising their efforts to the limit.

Not even Dr Dale could get me to regard sport and physical training as anything other than abhorrent. I was fat and deeply conscious of it. I loved the cultivation of the school garden, but soon the allotments gave way to an unfiltered swimming pool and I loved its cloudy water just as much. Once I was in, I could wallow without thinking about how I looked.

In 1953 I started all over again at the newly opened Otara Intermediate School. Otara, like Mangere, was mostly farmland in those days. When like Mangere its name became a byword for state housing, the school changed its name to Papatoetoe. My anxiety about the new school was not reduced when after a fortnight I tripped and smashed my arm through the glass of a door. The woodwork teacher applied a tourniquet and I was whisked off to my father for extensive stitching. There are still the signs of his handiwork on my lower left arm today.

Ultimately I settled in at the school to the point of being made head boy in the second year. I found that verbal assurance was compensation for physical incompetence. It was at Otara Intermediate that I discovered that I could speak and hold an audience. I was never afraid to stand up and talk and I was seldom lost for a word. The subject hardly mattered. When I was speaking, I was light on my feet and I packed a punch.

My teacher in my second year was Bill Bestic. He seemed to have been given a licence not to teach us. He began the class each day by outlining a schedule of tasks, then he would leave us. An intercom system had been installed, by way of which he monitored his pupils at a distance. He checked on progress just before lunch and started us off again afterwards. On Friday afternoons we made speeches. The school had an adequate library and I read all I wanted. It was a splendid year, the best I ever had at school. It ended with our final assembly, and when it was over I was no longer a head boy. It happened that my bike was out of action and I had to borrow Mum's. The balloon tyres were now black but there was no escaping the fact that it was not a boy's bike. On my way home there was a cloudburst. I headed for shelter under the trees in the grounds of St Mary's, where I fell off the bike. Soaking wet, I sat on a bough and reflected on the transience of status.

My time at intermediate school is marked in my mind by two events, one of significance in public life, the other of profound importance in my own.

The public event was the visit to New Zealand of the Queen and the Duke of Edinburgh, the royal pair arriving here in December 1953. They were greeted by a frenzy which is hard to imagine today, given the indifference with which we mostly now view the institution of monarchy, although it is true that the royal extras of those days had not yet confused their roles with those of soap opera. The enthusiasm of the public was near-universal and certainly demonstrative. The arrival of the *Gothic* in Auckland brought countless craft onto the water, just as cheering admirers lined the streets wherever the royal motorcade travelled. The Queen journeyed throughout the country. Roads were sealed so she could drive along them, or in the case of the road from Kaikohe to Whangarei, the half she drove on was sealed and the other half finished many years afterwards. The prime minister of the day was Sidney Holland and he went everywhere the royal couple went. His constant presence may have grated: many years later I was accompanying the Queen and the Duke through a park in Christchurch when I spotted Eric Holland, son of Sidney and himself once a cabinet minister. I stopped and introduced him to the Duke, explaining his relationship to the former prime minister.

'Bloody old Sid,' said the Duke to the Queen.

For me, the high point of the royal tour was Christmas morning, 1953. It made such an impression on me that I have never let a Christmas since go by without mentioning that I sang to the Queen.

When I was nine my mother determined that I should learn to sing and so she enrolled me in the Friendly Road Choir. The choir was a relic of the time when C G Scrimgeour ran a broadcasting station which was later nationalised under the name of 1ZB. Certain rights to the programming were retained by the Scrimgeour interests, which were succeeded to by the Rev T T Garland. He conducted two services on a Sunday, and broadcast for twenty minutes at six o'clock on Friday evenings. I belonged to the choir which sang on Friday evenings in the radio theatre. Every broadcast began with the same ditty:

Love and laughter, other things were after
You can have your share we say
Come join our happy band
In spreading joy throughout the land
And be happy bright and gay.

When it was known that the Queen was coming to New Zealand it was resolved by the Royal Visit Office that the Friendly Road Choir should sing carols to the royal couple in front of Government House in Auckland. Much rehearsed, wearing our best white shirts, we were duly conveyed to the vice-regal grounds. Father Christmas drove up in a horse and sleigh. We sang our carols. The Queen and the Duke stood on the steps and listened to us and the

Queen called for a camera to film us. The Duke left to visit the site of the Tangiwai disaster and we in the choir went proudly home.

It may have been while the royal visit was still in progress, or perhaps it was not long afterwards, that it became clear to me that some matter of considerable upset had taken place. My father was distracted and went into Auckland more often than I had ever known him to. Finally I was taken into my parents' confidence: he had been charged with indecent assault. He had carried out a gynaecological examination at an evening clinic in his surgery and the woman concerned went to the police to complain about his conduct. I do not remember the woman's name, if I ever knew it, but the police laid charges and took my father through a depositions hearing. The matter then went before a grand jury, which led to a formal arraignment at which the case was sent for trial in the Supreme Court. Somehow or other Pop kept going. My brother and sisters were, I think, unaware of what was happening, but Nurse was a stalwart in support.

Shortly before the trial started, Howard Hunter came to our home. He drove out to Otahuhu in his Bentley, wearing his black Homburg hat. He said he would like to take me for a drive. We rode around the corner to Fort Richard Road where he stopped the car and told me that whatever happened in the next few days I was going to have to be the man of the house. He wanted me to know that if I needed support I could rely on him. I could call on him at any time and I was to make sure that Mum did too. He said he was sure that when the trial was over Pop would be coming home. Uncle Howard was kind and his words were meant to be encouraging, but that was not their effect. That my father might not come home was a thought that had not occurred to me. Now I had my first glimpse of what a trial really was, and what its result might mean to us.

My father duly surrendered himself for trial at the Supreme Court. In those days you did not get bail during the course of a trial. He stood in the old dock in the Number 1 courtroom and after his plea was taken he sat in the dock next to a prison officer. At the end of each session he was taken down the stairs behind the dock to the bowels of the court and at the end of each day he went by prison van to the remand section of Mt Eden Prison where he was locked in a cell.

He coped, but I do not know how. I have been in the cells of the Supreme Court and in the cells of the Mt Eden Prison on many occasions and I have never once entered either place without being haunted by the memory of my father being caged up there.

Pop was represented by a youngish lawyer who was brought up on the West Coast and was making a name for himself as an advocate in Auckland. The father of the present bishop of Auckland gave expert evidence for the defence on gynaecological procedures. My mother sat through every day of the trial. She went around the back of the court and gave cakes to the gaolers, hoping that my father might be treated better for the consideration she was showing. I could not bear to watch. Mum let me hover around outside and on the last day she came outside to tell me the jury had gone out to think about what they were going to do with Pop. Forty-five minutes later my father walked through the big door of the Supreme Court. I clung to him and sobbed.

I was brought close to tears again about twenty years later when

I was appearing for an accused in a jury trial. The presiding judge was Mr Justice Moller. It was he who had acted for my father. He called the prosecutor and me into his chambers. After dealing with the matter at issue, he asked the prosecutor to leave, assuring him that what he had to say to me was nothing to do with the trial in progress.

'You know, Lange,' he said, 'that not guilty doesn't always mean not guilty.' I knew that very well. 'I just want you to know,' Mr Justice Moller said, 'that your father was not guilty.'

I am not sure how much toll those experiences took on my father. I have a memory of his surgery being full again soon after his acquittal, but it may in fact have taken far longer than I recall for his practice to return to normal. He never again saw a woman patient without Nurse being present, and he never again allowed the police to call on his services. The effect on me was immediate. There was only one thing for me to do: I was going to be a lawyer.

CHAPTER FOUR

In 1955 I went to Otahuhu College. It had a huge roll, drawing on a catchment area all over south Auckland. The school population today is overwhelmingly from the Pacific but I can remember only one Pacific Islander among my contemporaries. This was Hugh Henry, the son of the first prime minister of the Cook Islands. He married Helen Nicholls, who lived down the road from us. The school was nominally co-educational but in practice an imaginary line was drawn from the administration block to the Mangere Road boundary, and at intervals and lunch-times the boys gathered on the western side of the line while the girls stayed on the east. There were no girls on the agricultural course, whose students kept sheep, tended beehives and grew citrus fruit on the open ground around the college. Nor were there girls on the industrial course, which operated like a school-within-a-school and prepared its pupils for life as apprentices to trades. On the commercial course, girls learned typing; on the home science course, they learned to cook and sew.

Only the so-called general courses allowed the mixing of the sexes, and then only in some classes. We took music classes separately and it was the same with art.

Boys were required to take part in military drill. The school had its own armoury with a great stock of .303 rifles, all in working order. It also had a rifle range. In the first month of school we had what was called barracks week, when every male pupil not classed as a conscientious objector was uniformed in khaki and issued with a rifle. While the girls carried on with their classes, the boys were formed into companies to engage in drill and exercise in mindless conformity. A whole week of academic life was lost at the beginning of each year for that and, lest we drop our guard, a full day a month thereafter. Teachers who had served in the armed forces turned up in full military rig with medals and a mindset to match.

I hated military drill. In my first year I was squeezed into an ill-fitting uniform and in great discomfort marched around the paddocks. In my second year a uniform could not be found to fit. It was decided that I should be treated as a conscientious objector and I was assigned to spend drill days in a prefabricated classroom with a teacher who may have been shell-shocked, such was his nervousness. Along with the Exclusive Brethren and the occasional genuine conscientious objector, I wasted every drill day in this pointless confinement.

I was also at odds with the school's obsession with sport, although I never fail to mention when occasion allows that I went to school with Mac Herewini and Waka Nathan, two great names from a time when being an All Black meant more than mere celebrity. I could not play rugby because I was overweight in every grade.

I played soccer instead, learning that as a back I could stop people getting past me without too much effort. Being in a team appealed. I played cricket for a local club rather than the school; I liked the game and could field in the slips without moving too much. The school steeplechase, however, was the cause of annual humiliation. No boy was excused and I was always at the back and stayed there until the field was far enough in front of me to allow me to hide until it was over.

Music I enjoyed at school. I learned to play the clarinet and joined the school orchestra. My teacher was an English military bandsman. And I liked some of the academic staff. My third-form English teacher, Joyce Pegler, was competent and inspiring. I warmly remember Miss Housby, a form teacher of broad education and striking appearance who was fluent in French and played hockey vigorously with the girls she coached.

The male teachers did not leave such a positive impression, although I was grateful to Mr Branch, the chemistry teacher who gave me a paying job as a laboratory assistant. One master was called Jock Leaming and was a veteran of the First World War. He taught Latin, always wearing a suit, a scarf and an overcoat, and pointed to the blackboard with a furled umbrella. He was demanding and brutal. Mr Leaming taught the poet Denis Glover at Auckland Grammar School and Glover made a telling reference to him in his autobiography, going so far as to say that he loathed and despised him and suggesting that Mt Eden Prison was to be preferred to Leaming's classroom. I saw some disparaging comment by Glover in the *Listener* one day and with a degree of hesitation drew it to Mr Leaming's attention. He thanked me very much and sent me off to the post office with 2s and a telegraph message. It was addressed to Denis Glover, care of the *Listener*, Auckland, and read, 'My head is bloody but unbowed. Leaming.' The post office refused to accept the telegram on the grounds that it contained a swear-word.

I survived Latin because I sat next to Rodney Fisher, a very able student who kept me out of trouble by whispering the answers to questions just ahead of Mr Leaming's demands. Rodney, who was brought up in the Otahuhu railway settlement, went on to Cambridge where he took a PhD on elements of the demonic in German literature of the twelfth century. I often used his achievements in my later speech-making as an example of what the welfare state could do for you.

My academic record was no more than adequate. I passed School Certificate with an average of sixty-three percent and was accredited with a pass in University Entrance, no great achievement given that one student in my year was reliably understood to have been accredited a pass only on promising the headmaster that she would not go to university. I have no doubt my parents, my father at least, were disappointed in my academic achievement at Otahuhu College. I did however win the speech competition four out of five years, but I won easily and became cocky. In my last year I made a speech which attacked the pretensions and practices of the professions, the medical profession included. The headmaster announced during the adjudication that he did not consider my speech worthy of being marked, so that was that.

By the end of my last year at secondary school, I could not wait to leave. The school had a depressing effect on me. In response I did what my mother would have done. Mum always met her troubles head on: she fronted up, sometimes recklessly, and made the best of a bad lot. I decided that nothing was going to get me down. I bluffed and blustered my way through school, gliding out of many difficulties. I learned how to adapt and make quick responses. Public speaking taught me verbal survival skills. These were the lessons I learned at school which lasted all my life.

An odd thing happened to me in my last year at school. I was ill, and spent a week at home with a fever. My father called in a specialist friend but the illness was never diagnosed. My vision was blurred. When I recovered from the fever my vision remained blurred and I never saw anything clearly again without the use of glasses.

My father always made it clear to me that he did not plan to support me through university. In 1959 he became ill with heart disease, at a time when the cure for angina was retirement. Pop could not carry on his practice and was without income for some time until he became a medical officer in the health department with responsibility for south Auckland schools.

In any case I was ready to go to work. In the third form I had a paper-round. I delivered 130 copies of the *New Zealand Herald* in Mangere East, starting at five in the morning. Later on I had the easier task of collecting the paper money. In the fourth form I delivered telegrams. In my last year at school I applied for a job at the Westfield freezing works. My application was accepted and the week before I left school I was kitted out in work boots and overalls and a little round hat. The day after I left, I reported to work at six o'clock in the morning and set about the business of life.

The pay was 5s 10d an hour, plus a cost-of-living allowance which was the management's way of avoiding proper payment of overtime. The job was hard work: Westfield processed up to 25,000 lambs a day when the season was at its peak. I was assigned to the fellmongery, where I put lambskins through washers and extractors and then flung them onto conveyor belts. Six hours into the task on my first day I was weak from exhaustion and sat down forlornly in the primitive dressing room. A man came and sat opposite me. He was dressed much like me and from underneath his hat he produced bundles of £5 notes. I asked a workmate who he was. When he told me he was the union secretary I resolved that I would become one too, but I learned in time that he moonlighted as a bookmaker's runner and spent all his time taking bets.

I went home every day worn out and got up and dragged myself to work early every morning. By the end of the year I was ready for the Christmas break. I remember the exhilaration of leaving the place, knowing that I did not have to come back for three days. That year a bonus was offered to all the workers to celebrate a record number of lambs shipped to the United Kingdom for the Christmas season: we each got a can of corned beef.

The next summer, and for several summers after that, I worked in the freezing chamber alongside John Buchanan from Papatoetoe who became the chief financial officer of BP and later sat on the boards of BHP Billiton and Vodafone. We wore sweaters and protective gloves and packed meat in cartons, then stacked the cartons in an ice cabin. The work was hard and constant. You could earn good money but it was a degrading way to do it. Conditions were dismal: we were entitled to a so-called 'warm' break for ten minutes every hour, but the only place to take it was in the lavatory. The management's interest in the place and the people who worked there was minimal. The works were run from a distance on behalf of the Vestey family of the United Kingdom and there was no effort to engage the workforce in the company's objectives. I resented the remoteness and incompetence of the management to the point that when Westfield collapsed some years later my first response was pleasure at the thought of the departure of the Vesteys from the New Zealand meat industry.

It was impossible in the appalling conditions at the works not to identify with my fellow workers, although the identification was not immutable. I deeply resented the piece-workers who went on strike knowing they would not suffer any loss of income. They simply went twice as fast when they came back on the job while the rest of us had to work like dogs to cope with their sudden enthusiastic output. There was little satisfaction to be had at the works: theft was rife and sabotage was commonplace. I would not steal but I enjoyed some of the minor acts of sabotage. Every year the manager came into the works and selected prime lamb which was set aside in the freezer for eventual presentation to the favoured, like the masters of the ships which carried the produce off to England. Every year the freezing-hands carefully took the lamb out of its bag and replaced it with some nasty old ewe which had been set aside for further processing.

Westfield gave me one happy legacy. I used to retrieve pig trotters which had been thrown aside and place them in steam pipes to cook. My liking for pig trotters has never left me. What Westfield also gave me was an abiding dislike of the law which obliged all workers to belong to a trade union. The union delegates matched the management in their arrogance and indifference. My distaste for compulsory unionism was carried into my career in parliament and coloured my view of the Labour Party's trade union associates.

In 1960 I went to university. Regulations for the LLB degree required candidates to start with arts subjects so I enrolled for English, French and history as well as the legal intermediate. Almost from the outset I took little interest in the academic side of university life. I more or less gave up on French and eventually abandoned English, given that I was obliged to study Icelandic as part of the course and I could not see the relevance of it. At the end of the year I passed only in history and legal studies. For all that, I felt it was a year of considerable accomplishment. I was no longer a schoolboy. I had my first pair of long corduroy trousers. Above all, it was a year of great freedom. My parents owned a property in the country at Redoubt Road in the hills above East Tamaki where we spent many holidays. Now they decided to sell it and use the proceeds to travel abroad for six months. My brother and sisters were boarded out with friends in Otahuhu and Papatoetoe and I arranged to live at Trinity College, a hall of residence for Methodist theological students which accepted other students as boarders.

Trinity College was wonderful. There was a wide range of students and I shared a room with a Fijian commerce student. There was also a good library. The hall provided three meals a day, seven days a week. The meals were the same every day but they sustained us and the total cost of board was £3 2s 6d a week. There was a group of us who kept company together because we were doing law and had lectures at the same times; I learned how to play billiards and snooker. I started smoking but I did not drink, only in part because I was brought up in a home in which drinking was held to be a moral failing and where my mother once took an axe to a crate of beer sent by a fellow member of Rotary as a Christmas gift to Pop. Drink simply did not appeal. I did not drink until I went to London, when I tried beer, which I did not like. I did not drink again after that until I entered parliament. I had a continuing association with the Methodist church and sang in the Pitt Street choir, to my great enjoyment. I met Bob Wynyard, who was to be a friend for many years.

Bob was from Whirinaki in the Hokianga in the far north. He was one of fourteen children who lived on a small farm and his father was a railway worker. He passed School Certificate at Rawene High School and then went to work to save the money to study for his University Entrance. Finally he did his degree so that he could be a schoolteacher. I went with Bob to the north several times that year. We hitchhiked to Cape Reinga and back, and he introduced me to his home, to the customs of his people and to an extraordinary part of New Zealand. I had a great regard for him and his reserved manner.

In following years at university Bob and I travelled a lot together. We hitchhiked around the South Island, walking from the end of the road below Franz Josef to the bridge at the Haast River. I was fat when I was a university student but I was fit. Apart from my labouring at the freezing works during the summer break, I kept active. I was a lieutenant in the Boys' Brigade and in 1962 I organised a three-week tour of the South Island for a group of twenty boys. I did the cooking. I bought the gun tractor I have already mentioned, a military-surplus vehicle which I used like a car; it carried up to ten people and I took it down to the Firth of Thames. I also drove it to the Kaipara hills where my brother Peter and friends from the Boys' Brigade took the tractor off-road. Bob and I canoed down the Wanganui River one year, and another time I helped him and others repair the old Methodist church at Whirinaki.

My parents came back to New Zealand before the end of 1960. After my examinations I went home and exhausted myself in the cause of the Vesteys and tried to get a job in a law office. A law degree in those days was a part-time business. Lectures were held early in the day and in the evening and the rest of the time you worked as a law clerk. I applied to a couple of distinguished firms, and at one major firm the principal asked if I had been to Grammar or to King's. My reply ended the interview. Giving up on the prospect of private-sector employment, I found a job in the legal division of the State Advances Corporation, an agency which owned the government's stock of houses and lent money to small borrowers.

The job meant an eight o'clock start in a bureaucratic organisation where you clocked in and out and where your performance was judged by things like signing on the dotted line rather than doing the work competently. It proved however to have one great attraction: the work involved searching titles in the Land Transfer Office. This gave me a licence to be away from the office for a good part of the day. I took the chance to go and sit in the Magistrates' Court. I spent so long there that I became familiar with its procedures and excited by the advocacy I heard.

I lived at home for all that year and the next, although I found Mum's demands that I justify myself to her more and more trying.

The next year I shared a flat in Gillies Avenue in Epsom with Bob Wynyard, and the two years after that I flatted in a house in Mt Eden with other students. That group broke up at the end of 1965 and I spent my last year of part-time study back at home.

At the end of 1961 I resigned from the State Advances Corporation and went to do my stint at Westfield. One night at a cinema in Otahuhu I chanced to see a man I recognised from the Magistrates' Court. I had watched him acting for a seaman who was alleged to have thrown a machine for scrubbing decks off his ship. It was apparent from the evidence that the man had no love of scrubbing decks; when asked by the ship's master to account for the missing appliance, the accused said that he wished he had thrown the other one over the side as well. But nobody had seen the deed and in the end the seaman was acquitted. I had no idea who his lawyer was, but when I saw him at the pictures I introduced myself to him and we chatted. His name was Jack Carthy. He asked me what I was doing and I said I was working at Westfield and hoping to get a job. He told me to come and see him. The result was that I ended up being employed by Haigh, Charters and Carthy. It was one of the greatest breaks of my life.

Jack Carthy was the junior partner in a firm which was established by Frank Haydn Haigh. Haigh was an extraordinary man, one of a set of Henderson Valley wine connoisseurs, art collectors and supporters of the literati. He was a protector of lost causes and defender of strange faiths and had a formidable reputation for acting for people others did not want to know, which he did with exemplary skill. His colleague Les Charters, an honours graduate from Victoria University, was imprisoned during the Second World

War as a conscientious objector and worked as a law clerk for many years after the war until he was well past the age of eligibility for military service, whereupon he took the oath of allegiance which was required of a barrister and solicitor and became a partner in the firm. Les specialised in civil claims for damages for personal injury and had one of the largest such practices in the country. He was also a superbly good draughtsman. Jack did whatever the other two did not do.

I started work at Haigh, Charters and Carthy with a man who is still a great friend. Thakor Parbhu came to New Zealand from Navsari in Gujurat in India when he was twelve years old. He was ten years older then me and was married to Shanti, who came from a Wellington family. Thakor was not the first Indian person I knew. My father had several Indian patients and as a child the only Sunday entertainment I was ever allowed was to watch Indian films in the hall at Pukekohe, thereby accounting for my life-long hatred of Hindi movies. It was Thakor and Shanti who led me to India, a country which has absorbed me since I first went there.

A meeting with a friend of Thakor and Shanti led to my first journey overseas. I travelled to Fiji in 1963 and stayed with the Haris, a merchant family which had a tailor's business. There I acquired my first properly fitted suit. Until then I had to make do with whatever could be made to fit: my mother used to alter shirts for me by putting gussets in the sides. Unfortunately the gussets were always of a different material from the shirt and on one shirt the gussets themselves did not match. To have a suit made for me by a tailor in Fiji was an uplifting experience. I wore the suit until I went into parliament, when it was shiny with age and use.

My work at Haigh, Charters and Carthy covered everything from land transfer donkey-work to process-serving to preparatory work on cases. Frank Haigh had a good reputation in defamation and won some big cases. As he required the attendance of a runner at court, I heard some brilliant advocacy.

The most interesting office work I undertook was done on behalf of the Communist Party. The party at that time was suffering from self-doubt and its members believed that they were under constant surveillance. To a point they were right. A Security Intelligence Service agent approached me in my first year with the firm and asked me if I would report on the party's activities, but I declined. Frank Haigh used to send me up Queen Street to the party's rather seedy office in Karangahape Road to collect pamphlets alerting their readers to the dangers of nuclear testing in the South Pacific. Knowing that the office was likely to be under observation, I never entered it without some loss of assurance. The party had various assets which its members were sure would be expropriated when the government made it an unlawful organisation; the memory of what was threatened during the waterfront strike of 1951 was fresh in the party's mind even then. As a result, I became quite an authority on trusts. I engineered a complex arrangement of trusts and bailments to protect the publication of the *People's Voice*, a weekly paper printed in a factory in Auckland which the party owned. Under the law of the day a printer as well as a publisher was liable in defamation and any successful action would have exhausted the party's assets in the absence of some legal shield. I used to muse from time to time about the propriety of assisting what was popularly held to be a subversive organisation, but I decided I need not be reluctant about arming the party with legal defences. The Communist Party in my time did nothing I could see to be illegal. Its conduct did not even border on the unethical. It was rather too inward-looking for anything like that.

My years as a law clerk at Haigh, Charters and Carthy went by easily. The university dropped Icelandic from the English course and I finally passed. My undergraduate degree I can only describe as undistinguished. My love for my work at the firm did not translate into enthusiasm for the academic side of the law, perhaps because the part-time nature of the study made it seem like a grind. At the end of 1966 I graduated with a great desire to start on the next part of my life. Mum and Pop bought me a wig and gown from a firm of legal outfitters in London and on 13 March 1967 I was admitted as a barrister and solicitor of the Supreme Court of New Zealand. My parents were present at the swearing-in and it was a happy morning.

I left the ceremony quickly because I had my first case in the Magistrates' Court. I was acting for a young man who had been found by the police under a pylon in Victoria Park. Some distance away from him was what remained of a money-box taken from a telephone booth. The man was arrested and charged with breaking and entering a building, namely the phone booth, with intent to commit a crime. He could not be physically linked with the shattered money-box and the police had no admission of guilt from him, but it looked bad enough. What saved my first client was the nature of the charge which was laid. No one can break and enter a telephone booth: it is designed to be opened and can be entered without breaking. Because of the deficiency in the charge, my client was acquitted. It was a triumph for the law at the expense of what was right.

I was so excited by my success I rang my father at his work at the health department in Papatoetoe. I told him what had happened. Pop laughed. 'Disgusting,' he said and put the phone down. At his funeral several years later a member of the staff at Papatoetoe told me how proud my father was of my first day in court: the next day he bought cakes all round to celebrate.

CHAPTER FIVE

After I was admitted my father surprised me by giving me £750, the proceeds of a life policy he took out on me when I was born. I bought a cheap return fare to London. It was not my intention to look for long-term employment overseas since I intended to practise law in New Zealand. I wanted to be a criminal lawyer because of what had happened to my father, because of the excitement and the cut-and-thrust of it, and because of the challenge of taking on the system on the side of the underdog. I thought that I could make money when I needed it by doing actions for damages for personal injury. The idea of political involvement was always in the back of my mind although I knew I was unfit for candidacy at that stage and had much to learn. I simply wanted to see the world. Through Thakor and Shanti Parbhu I met a wide circle of Gujurati acquaintances and I was keen to see the place they came from. I also hoped to catch up with some of the Colombo Plan students who had found a halfway house at my family home.

The cheap airfare was available for travel to people under twenty-six years old and offered enormous flexibility. In June 1967 it took me first to Tasmania to see my younger sister Annette, who had recently moved to Launceston. I went to Canberra to catch up with an old friend of the family who was a Plunket nurse at our home when the twins were young. The next stop was Brisbane. From there I caught the train to Gympie to see the New Zealand rugby league team play a Queensland Country XIII. The match did not take place because Gympie was under water, so I went back to Brisbane and took a flight to Manila.

The Philippines were my introduction to a new world for which Otahuhu had not prepared me. Every official and many who were not seemed to be armed. Cinemas had signs which asked patrons to deposit their firearms with the cashier. Three days were enough and I left for Hong Kong, which proved pleasantly chaotic. In a hotel in Kowloon I got a room with no windows and no air conditioning for £1 a night. I wandered the island and the New Territories. I made enquiries about getting a visa for Vietnam. At home I had applied to the South Vietnamese representatives in Wellington for a visa but had been declined without any reason being given. I had been a speaker at an early meeting held in the town hall at Otahuhu to protest about New Zealand's involvement in the Vietnam conflict and, although I took no part in street demonstrations, I helped Frank Haigh prepare the defence of several who were arrested for protesting during the visit to New Zealand of Air Vice Marshal Ky. In Hong Kong I discovered that I would have no trouble getting a visa, but by then I was tired of making do on my own.

In Bangkok I was the guest of a woman who had worked as a

cardiologist at Green Lane Hospital in Auckland. She lived with her parents in a pleasant, comfortable suburb far from the heart of the city. Life in the house was made easier by the presence of two servant girls who would, if they approached you, disconcertingly drop to their knees and shuffle along the floor towards you. Bangkok itself was a blur of temples overrun by American soldiers on leave from Vietnam. I was a pampered visitor until a Caravelle aircraft took me by way of Rangoon to Calcutta.

Dumdum airport in Calcutta was aptly named. It had a wonderful air of vigorous chaos about it, which was a portent of the city and the country it served. There were ten people wanting to carry your bag and another ten wanting to run away with it. I knew nobody in Calcutta and decided to make my way to the centre of the city on a bus said to be driven by disabled servicemen. For a very modest fare I ended up, after a long haul, in central Calcutta. I made my way through Chowringhee. In Sudder Street I spotted something called the Red Shield shelter. Here I got a bed in a dormitory for five rupees a night. That was about 40c in those days. I settled in and made myself known to the room attendant, the Salvation Army officer who ran the place and the American Peace Corps workers and draft dodgers who frequented it.

I wandered into the streets around the shelter. The pavements were lined with people seeking alms, the rubbish was piled high and prostitutes cried out for business. The noise was raucous. It was appalling and at the same time it was exhilarating. It was a challenge to walk the streets; along with the stench and the squalor there was a threat of violence. The Congress Party had recently lost control of the government of West Bengal to a coalition led by the Communist Party and there was revolution in the offing.

There was a Methodist church in Sudder Street and the minister invited me to supper, which turned out to be a full meal after the evening service. It was a very English house, and the minister, his wife and his two daughters were good company. After a pleasant evening with them, I decided to go the next day to the legislative assembly. I could not believe what I saw. What looked like a riot broke out on the floor in front of me: members attacked each other with microphone stands and tried to strangle each other with the leads. There were fist fights wherever I looked. I fled and made my way with some difficulty back to the Red Shield shelter. The Salvation Army officer advised me to get out of Calcutta and I took his advice seriously. There was mayhem in the streets and a real prospect of anarchy. I paid an extortionate taxi fare to get to the airport and after several hours found a place on a flight to Bombay. While I was in Bombay the government of India imposed presidential rule on West Bengal after extensive rioting and loss of life. It was a year later, when I was in London, that I found out that the minister's wife and two daughters were thrown by the mob into the path of a tram and killed.

I spent my first hours in Bombay asleep at the airport, but after that I was well looked after by members of the family which had been my hosts in Fiji. To get from Bombay to Delhi, I took the train. It was an eighteen-hour haul and I went third class, but it was that journey which convinced me that for all its calamities and crowding and chaos, India would always have a hold on me. The train carried its passengers through the country evening. As night came closer, the carts were driven home, children gathered the clinker from the railway line, fires were lit, the families gathered, and there was some degree of comfort to be gained in a tough life. In the morning I awoke to small paddy-fields and then the train carried me through industrial suburbs to Delhi.

I stayed in Delhi at the YMCA, which was really a secure and friendly tourist hotel. I saw the sights and made the journey to Agra to see the Taj Mahal, splendid in the squalor of its setting. Then it was back to Bombay. After a few hours on the train I felt hungry and, when a porter came past offering meals, for a small sum I bought a dish of mutton korma. After a few mouthfuls I could eat no more of it. By the time I got to Bombay I was in a state of considerable digestive upset. I rushed to the nearest cheap hotel and spent the night in the toilet. I called a doctor friend of Thakor and Shanti. His treatment allowed me to travel as far as Navsari in Gujurat where once again another arm of the family of my Fijian hosts took me in. I was desperately unwell, and had a slow recovery. There was something of a relapse when I read in the *Times of India* that two porters had been arrested for taking bodies from the Hooghly River and passing them off to Indian Railways as mutton.

It was in Navsari that I discharged an obligation undertaken in New Zealand. One of Shanti's brothers had married a woman from Surat. The groom had to return home before the immigration arrangements were complete and his New Zealand family had reached the limits of the amount of money the Reserve Bank would allow them to send to India for his wife's support. As a traveller I was allowed to take $400 in foreign currency out of the country and I gave half of it to the bride, who came from up-country and spoke no English. She shook with anxiety when she met me but was obviously grateful.

Air India carried me from Bombay to London. I well remember the sense of fulfilment I felt on landing in the United Kingdom. I was brought up in a world where Britain was paramount in my country's life: it was the home of the law I had studied and of much of our tradition. I was passing through customs when two well-dressed men asked me to come with them. I followed them into a room where they introduced themselves by saying they were from MI5. They asked me my reason for visiting the United Kingdom and a series of questions about my background. Then they said they wanted to search me and my luggage. I was staggered by this extraordinary turn of events; more so when I remembered there was a letter in my jacket pocket. I recall its wording to this day. It was a well-meant letter from the secretary of the Seamen's Union in New Zealand and was addressed to the secretary of the Combined Riverboat and Tugboat Workers' Union of the Soviet Union. It asked the comrades to treat as a fraternal delegate one who had rendered great service to the union and would be valuable in the work that they were doing. It advised that I would be coming to Moscow for the fiftieth anniversary of the revolution and concluded with the assurance that the struggle for world peace and socialism continued unabated.

I was wondering what was going to become of me when the officer searching my suitcase found a bible packed by my mother; he slammed the case shut and I was allowed to leave. I went by bus to Earls Court where I knew I had a friend with a room. The friend was out so I sat on the step all night. In the morning I went to New Zealand House, which in those days held mail for visitors to collect. I knew that family and friends had written to me at that address and was amazed to discover that my mail had been uplifted. Whoever signed for it had given my passport number.

When I became leader of the opposition more than fifteen years later, I received, as is the custom, a briefing from the head of the Security Intelligence Service. I said to the director that our meeting was not the first contact I had had with his organisation. 'I know,' he said, and turned up the concert programme even louder lest directional microphones pick up any of the conversation. I have never since assumed that anyone who suspects surveillance by the SIS, however unlikely the suspicion may seem, is inevitably paranoid.

I arrived in Britain with less than £50. I saw an advertisement for vacation accommodation in a student hall of residence in Mecklenburgh Square. This was a lucky break. I had a bedroom, a study and a bathroom, and it was a most attractive place in the summer. I ate at cheap cafés and spent my time trying to get work. London Transport refused me a job as a bus driver on the grounds that I was too fat. Law firms knocked me back. I finally got a job with a reinsurance company in the Minories in the East End. Here I was employed as an accounts clerk. The hours were leisurely, the work the same. The task was to reconcile the company's manual accounting system with the output of an early computer which could not calculate beyond nine digits. It was a maddeningly formal place where a man with brass buttons served morning tea to the staff. My take-home pay was £8 17s a week. I had to leave Mecklenburgh Square when the summer holiday ended and found a room in a house in West Cromwell Road, Earls Court, where I shared facilities with two friends from New Zealand. The rent was £5 10s a week. Feeding the gas meter to heat the place turned out to be a challenge; it was a big event when the mail arrived from home with 5s postal notes from my parents.

Even without much money I found a lot to enjoy. There was something wonderful about a Sunday in London, when I could listen to the speakers in Hyde Park and collect Sunday papers which their readers had discarded in the grounds. I savoured extraordinary journalism written to please every possible taste, something beyond my experience in New Zealand. I read *Private Eye*. I went to Central Hall, Westminster, one of the great Methodist citadels, and even sang in the choir there. When parliament was sitting, I found my way to the gallery of the House of Commons. One Sunday afternoon I came across Kingsway Hall, another place which had a certain name in Methodism. It was the preaching place of Donald Soper, who was superintendent of the West London mission.

Soper was a minister, a socialist and a great orator. He spoke at Hyde Park Corner and could hold his audience until he was well into his nineties. In church he dressed like an Anglican priest and everywhere else he wore a black cassock. When I first heard him that Sunday evening he was, as I remember it, talking about turning the other cheek. As always, he spoke without notes and with great authority and insight. After he finished I went with the rest of the gathering for a cup of tea in the hall.

A young woman was serving the tea. She was slightly built with dark hair and I liked her at once. She was friendly, she laughed a lot, she was loud and joyful and easy to talk to. She was full of life. Her name was Naomi; she came from Newark-on-Trent in Nottinghamshire and worked at one of the hostels run by the West London mission. I went back to Kingsway every Sunday after our first meeting and every time I went there she greeted me warmly.

I allowed myself to believe that Naomi liked me, but I thought nothing more than that. I had never had a girlfriend and always assumed that I was an unlikely candidate for marriage. Because I was overweight and ungainly, I simply wrote it off.

Towards Christmas 1967 many of us who met at Kingsway decided to go as a group to a performance of *The Messiah* in the Albert Hall. I went along and Naomi was there. She was going home to Newark for Christmas, and she and I arranged that we should meet on New Year's Eve in Trafalgar Square. We did meet, and in the bleak winter weather among the milling crowds and the mounting excitement as the New Year approached, the clock struck midnight and Naomi kissed me. I had never had such an experience in my life. She walked home to her flat in Holborn. Because the underground was not running, I walked all the way from Trafalgar Square to Earls Court and did not notice the distance.

After that we met every day except for Wednesday, when Naomi worked late at the hostel and I used to go to the House of Commons. We ate out at cheap restaurants, we went to the theatre when we could get half-price tickets, and in February we went twice to Newark at the weekend to visit Naomi's family. At the end of February we attended a wedding in Chepstow. The groom came from an Otahuhu family and I was best man. Naomi and I talked about marriage and early in March we were engaged. I could not believe my luck. Somehow, inexplicably, I had fallen on my feet.

I was not sure how Naomi's parents would respond to our engagement. Mr and Mrs Crampton lived in a pleasant part of Newark, which itself was an attractive old town with a castle and a weekly market. They attended the Barnby Gate church, a building very much in the Methodist tradition. The church organ was presented by W E Gladstone, who was for a time member of parliament for Newark, as was George Grey, later famous in New Zealand. Naomi's parents were kind and well-meaning. They were bicycle-clip people; nothing was done without intense preparation. They were guarded and careful. Like Naomi herself, they had never left England and now Naomi and I told them that we were going to be married and would live in New Zealand. They raised little objection, perhaps because Naomi had left home by the time she was eighteen and had already made a life for herself away from her family.

I felt oddly at home in Nottinghamshire. My family had long associations with the area: my paternal great-grandmother was born there and we had kept in touch with our English relatives. My father had visited several of them when he was a student in the United Kingdom and I visited their survivors. One cousin, who was then nearly 100, was still farming out at Melton Mowbray.

Everything was looking up for me as summer approached. I got a job in the National Provincial Bank and with it a considerable increase in income, followed not long after by a considerable increase in wealth when I realised that the bank's slow procedures allowed me to write large cheques to buy shares on a rising market and sell them at a profit long before I was called to account for their purchase price. I went with Naomi's father to Trent Bridge where I saw Gary Sobers score five sixes off the first five balls of an over, to the acclaim of the crowd, and block the sixth, to heartfelt booing. My sister Margaret flew over from New Zealand to be a bridesmaid. The marriage was fixed for 3 August 1968, the day before my twenty-sixth birthday and the day before my return air ticket would no longer be valid. I stayed before the wedding at the home of my cousins, the Millers.

I ordered a new suit for the wedding from Montague Burton, tailors. The first time I tried it on, it hardly fitted anywhere. Alterations were requested and the day before the wedding Naomi and I called into the shop in Newark to collect my new clothes. If anything, the fitting was worse than before. Naomi flew into a rage and screamed abuse at the tailor. It was shockingly sudden and unexpected. I took the bus down the A5 then got out and walked the miles over the rolling hills to the Miller house. I realised how little I knew the woman I was marrying and thought with some regret of the loss of independence which would necessarily follow marriage. The longer I walked, the less it seemed to matter and I chided myself for my self-indulgence. The choice was mine to make and I had made it.

The wedding was held at the Barnby Gate church. I wore the suit the Fijian tailor had made for me. There was a reception in the Robin Hood hotel in Newark, much enjoyed by a large number of guests, many of whom came with us to the railway station to wish us well as we boarded the train to London. We took another train to Heathrow and then flew to Munich, where we arrived exhausted. By way of Innsbruck, Rome, Delhi and Singapore we came home to New Zealand.

Mum and Pop met us at the airport. If they had any reservations about the marriage they certainly did not show them; they did all they could to make Naomi feel welcome. There was an intensive round of meetings and introductions as Naomi was flung into the family and the church community. A celebration of the marriage was held at the Methodist church hall in Otahuhu. The hall was full with family and community connections made over several lifetimes. It must have been bewildering, but Naomi responded robustly.

We were living for the time being on the ground floor of the family home at Otahuhu. I had no job and I was determined to find one well away from Auckland; it would have been too easy for me to slip back into my life there, leaving Naomi with all the burden of adjustment. We agreed that we should go somewhere away from my old associations to make a fresh start together. Very shortly after we arrived in New Zealand I heard of the death of a solicitor in Kaikohe and learned that his practice was available. Naomi and I went by bus to Kaikohe, found a room at a boarding house and talked to the widow of the former practitioner. I should perhaps have made more searching enquiries. It was agreed that I would take over the practice and lease the office for $10 a week.

Kaikohe was then a town of about 3000 people. The population was predominantly Maori. It was a service centre for a struggling rural economy. Farming in the hinterland was very hard work in those days. The town had a maternity unit but no hospital, and while it still had a railway line, it was rarely used by passengers.

We rented a house made of two army huts joined together and lived there in some discomfort. The work I inherited proved to be of no monetary value. Substantial clients had long since moved on; my predecessor had fallen into alcoholism and kept the office alive in Kaikohe through procrastination as much as anything. He had a branch office in Rawene which he used one day a week as a place of refuge. We bought a car for $180, which allowed me to travel once a week to the Rawene office. There were two large and long-established law practices in Kaikohe which served commercial and farming interests, and it very soon became clear that I would be host to the rest. If people had no money and wanted a lawyer, I was their choice. For all that, my time in Kaikohe was the best introduction to general legal practice I could have had.

One of my first clients was a man who came to complain about branches overhanging his property. I explained the ancient law to him and told him that he could cut down the branches on his side of the fence but that he must be careful to place them on his neighbour's property, lest he be accused of theft. Not long after I was accosted by the angry neighbour. 'Listen, mate,' he said, 'you won't be living in this town for long if you tell people to throw their rubbish over my fence.'

I appeared in the Magistrates' Court at its periodic sittings in Kaikohe, Rawene, Kaitaia, Kaeo, Kawakawa, Dargaville, Whangarei and Maungaturoto. I dealt with arrests in police cases, domestic hearings and civil actions. I also appeared in the Maori Land Court. I found that clients did not hesitate to call at awkward hours. Weekends for some of them seemed to mean the chance to grab the lawyer when he went to buy the paper. On New Year's Eve I went in a boat to Rangi Point opposite Opononi, then rode a horse three miles up into the sand dunes above the harbour to make a will for a very old Maori woman who lived there in isolation. I searched out people in remote communities to serve proceedings. I defended small-time criminals and errant publicans.

Naomi was pregnant when we arrived in Kaikohe. The baby was due in June 1969 and the early months of the pregnancy were a wonderful time for us. Then almost eight months into the pregnancy she became very sick. Her illness was not at first diagnosed and was only much later found to be salmonella. She was sure that something was wrong with the baby. The child had been active, but now activity had ceased. She went to the doctor. When she came home she stood and looked around at the things we had got together for the baby: the clothes, the pram, the cot. 'We won't need these,' she said. 'There's no baby.'

The doctor could not detect a foetal heartbeat and Naomi went to see a specialist in Whangarei. He offered no prospect that the baby might be born alive. She came back to Kaikohe and not long afterwards went into labour. An ambulance took her to the hospital in Whangarei and I followed as best I could, willing the old car to keep up. The child was stillborn. In the way they did things then, neither of us ever saw the baby. Her body was taken away in a bucket. We learned later that she was buried in a pauper's grave in the Whangarei cemetery. I still cannot read a notice of a stillbirth without feeling the grief of it.

Mum and Pop came up from Auckland to help and we went back to the routines of work, but the joy had gone out of it. By the end of 1969 it had all become too much. My practice was no great challenge intellectually and such minor triumphs as I enjoyed were not sufficient to engage me. I wanted to go back to the law in Auckland. My aim was to do a master's degree and I hoped to make up for the mediocre performances of the past. I was sure that my father was disappointed in my academic record and I wanted him to know that I could work hard and do well. The law school offered me a job as a tutor at a salary of $1200 for the eight months of the academic year. The decision was made. I was going to prove myself in Auckland.

CHAPTER SIX

On the day the truck came to take our household possessions to Auckland, I appeared for the last time in the Kawakawa Magistrates' Court. Naomi and I moved into a flat we rented on the third floor of a block of city council flats in Freeman's Bay. I became a full-time student and tutor to a few classes every week. In addition, I was supervisor of the law school library on Friday nights from seven o'clock to eleven. I doubted that any student would be in the library at that time, but to my annoyance a Fijian Indian student was there every night until eleven o'clock exactly. I must record that this student later became president of the Fiji Law Society and a very strong supporter of constitutional propriety at the time of the Rabuka coup in 1987.

Tutoring the undergraduates was undemanding. The academic work was more enjoyable, and in the end successful. I worked very hard at it, enrolling for six papers, four in criminal law and criminal behaviour, and two in medico-legal subjects. My supervisor for the criminal papers was the wonderful Bernard Brown. There was something dashing and intriguing about Bernard. He was funny, he wrote poetry, he had an edge to him which made him unlikely ever to be dean of the law school. He had a fascination with the forms of the law and its language, and the gift of sharing his enthusiasm. I owe a lot of my academic achievement that year to Bernard's scholarship and wisdom.

With my undergraduate experience in mind, I was diffident to begin with but I soon came to relish the freedom of postgraduate work. I liked the calculation and complexity of the civil law of liability for personal injury caused by accident. I immersed myself in the cases. I was especially interested in medical misadventure and I often used to call my father and ask him for his advice or comment. I enjoyed the intellectual exercise of the criminal law, but decided that its study was an indulgence.

The criminal law was irrelevant to the impulsive criminals I saw in court in Auckland and the north. It made no difference to them and had no influence on what they did. What happened in court was a charade and the law's elegant extrapolations were meaningless. The pomposity with which sentence was delivered was always in inverse proportion to its effectiveness. The law mattered only to a few of the most calculating criminals; it was a fraudulent construct afforded unwarranted majesty in the eyes of the public. Its practice made me more and more uneasy and I knew when I left it in 1977 that I would never go back.

Naomi was still not well when we arrived in Auckland. She was asthmatic, and not long after we left the north she suffered a bad bout and was admitted to the respiratory unit at Auckland

Hospital. For some days she was not conscious. My father talked to the medical staff and suggested I ring her parents to tell them that she might not recover. I made the call, waited and hoped. Two days later I was able to call again and say she would be all right. While Naomi was in hospital I was offered a job as a magistrate in Hong Kong. It was a three-year posting to an exciting city at a generous salary. I woke her one afternoon with the news. She must have been heartily sick of my ambitions. 'You can stuff that up your jumper,' she said in the broadest of Nottinghamshire accents.

Pop himself was ill and I went to see him one Friday evening in August. He had a rasping cough and I asked him what was wrong. He said that it was pneumonitis. I asked him what that was. 'The old man's friend,' he said. That night he wrote to Peter and Margaret and Annette, who were all overseas. The next morning Mum called to say he was dead. His death was not unexpected, but it was more sudden than I had dreamt and was a great wrench. The Methodist church in Otahuhu was closed for renovation and the funeral was held at the Anglican church in Station Road. Hundreds of Otahuhu people came to pay tribute in a great farewell to Pop.

I learned just before Christmas that I had been awarded a master's degree with first-class honours. I could not help but be disappointed that my father was not there to see my academic rehabilitation. As far as my mother was concerned, it might as well have been School Certificate. My new-found expertise in negligence and other aspects of liability for injury caused by accident was rendered somewhat valueless when the government decided to embrace the principles of the Woodhouse report on accident compensation. Soon after my degree was awarded it became unlawful to sue for damages for personal injury. My cash cow had left the paddock.

I set out once again to earn my living in practice. Towards the end of 1970, Allan Nixon, who was a sole practitioner in Auckland, decided to take up an appointment at the law school. His was an extraordinary life. At the age of nineteen he was sent to prison as a conscientious objector and served four years. He then took a master's degree in psychology, entering the law in later life, representing people for whom no other help was readily available. Allan had a shrewd grasp of human nature and was always an astute pleader, tailoring a submission to a magistrate's weaknesses. The advice he gave me when I took over his practice was very simple. 'As far as charging is concerned,' he said, 'charge $30 for a plea in mitigation, unless they've got a bible-class background. Charge them $60. They like to feel guilty.' I took over the practice at the beginning of 1971. It was an orderly transition: there was a great deal of work in progress and its volume increased markedly once I became better known around the court.

The income was needed. Naomi was pregnant and our excitement was coupled with apprehension. I went to antenatal classes, including a lecture on genetic selection which seemed rather pointless by that stage. The pregnancy was very carefully managed and proceeded without incident until some six weeks before the baby was due, when labour started. Naomi went to hospital where labour was suppressed by various medications. Roy, as it turned out, was born late rather than early in May 1971 and Naomi's mother flew out to New Zealand to be with her. Some time after Roy was born we moved from Freeman's Bay to a house we bought in New North Road in Kingsland, not far from Eden Park. We were living there when our son Byron was born in 1974 and did not leave until after I became a member of parliament in 1977.

My law office occupied a small space on the fourth floor of the Lister Building in Victoria Street East. The staff to begin with consisted of me and Marie McCaughan, my secretary. For a time I shared offices with a commercial lawyer named Charles St Clair Brown at his premises in the Grand Building next to the Northern Club. In that rather elegant atmosphere my clients looked distinctly out of place and eventually I moved to the basement of the Metropolitan Life Insurance Company's offices in Kitchener Street. It was handy to the Magistrates' Court and the probation service.

The workload soon became too much to deal with by myself. In 1973 I was joined by David Brown, who these days is a judge in the Family Court. When I first met him he was working as a probation officer. He was an Auckland law graduate with an accomplished academic record and had undertaken postgraduate work at Perugia in Italy. When Naomi and Roy and I visited England at Christmas 1972 we found him in a department store in Cambridge where he was working as possibly the world's slimmest Santa Claus. He had a good heart matched by sound judgement and we worked closely together as long as I was in practice.

Ours was predominantly a criminal practice, but it was not frequented by the kind of criminal who made the headlines. Professional criminals did not come near me since I could add no lustre to their image. I ended up with the people who found the system too big a challenge: I was the comforter of the confused. The great bulk of the work was done on legal aid, which in those days was paid at derisory rates. Ten pleas of mitigation in a morning at $4.40 each amounted however to a reasonable stipend and I did that and more. Every morning I started by seeing clients, went to the probation service to pick up reports, then down to the cells to interview clients waiting to come up in the dock, mastered the probation reports, looked at whatever else was available and relevant and then made my pleas. There were often briefs arising from my visits to the cells, many of them resulting in pleas of not guilty.

A large number of my clients were charged under a statute called the Police Offences Act, an antiquated piece of law with its roots in restraints on mediaeval tinkers and the like. There was one charge of being idle and disorderly with insufficient lawful means of support. The beauty of the charge from the point of view of the defence was that you could be as idle and disorderly as you liked but if you had sufficient lawful means of support you could not be convicted. Your means were those that were determined to exist at the time of your appearance in the court. I was approached in the cells one morning by a man whose only asset was a ticket on the fourth race at Whangarei that day. I had the case stood down under some pretext and waited until the race was run. When I heard that my client's horse had won I asked for the case to be called. The police orderly testified that he had heard the result on the radio. The ticket was worth $32 and the defendant was discharged.

Prostitution was a rich field, in interest if not in payment. I once defended a man who solicited custom while dressed in female clothing, and proved in the Supreme Court that a male could not be a common prostitute under New Zealand law. Thwarted, the police charged another soliciting male cross-dresser with attempted indecency; in other words, a sexual act between two males. The defendant was examined by the police doctor and his sex established. It was not of course the practice to have the doctor examine the accused's prospective client, and so I was able to show that the police could not prove that two males were involved in the attempted act. The charge was dismissed. I was not a popular figure in the police station for some while.

I had adventures in smart-alec advocacy. I could always get a sly-grogger off since the police never went to the trouble of proving the alcohol content of the liquor they seized because it was obvious to them that if they found thirty-six unopened bottles of Waitemata beer, there was liquor involved. The law said otherwise and the police had to put the bottles back where they had found them.

My practice brought me into contact with the run-of-the-mill human failings which arose from drunkenness, disorder and domestic disharmony. I spent most of my time in the Magistrates' Court. If a client was to be defended, I thought it best to offer the defence in the lowest possible forum. I knew it was quite improper to allow someone to give false evidence and I learned very early in the piece that it was unwise to allow a client to give evidence at all if there was any prospect that I could defeat the charge on the evidence of the police. I did comparatively few jury trials, partly because they went against the temper of the practice. Jury trials took a lot of time and they took precedence over other work. I earned less from a week in the Supreme Court than I could from a week of pleading. A jury trial meant the cross-examination of witnesses, most of whom were well-meaning members of the public. It was hard to make them out to be liars, but it was easy to make them look foolish. I did not care for it.

I did only two murder trials. A woman shot her husband with a rifle he had mounted on the wall next to the bed. Many of the jury were in tears when I finished her defence and I thought she might be acquitted, but she was found guilty of manslaughter. Another woman killed a baby, not her own, while she was in a psychiatric ward at Auckland Hospital. The question was whether she was insane or under the influence of drugs. If insane, she would be found not guilty of murder. If under the influence of drugs, she would be held responsible for her actions. Much turned on a urine sample given by the defendant shortly after she killed the child. The test did not indicate the presence of any hallucinogenic substance and the jury decided she was not guilty but insane. I went down to see her in the cells below the court to conclude my involvement in her case. She said, 'If I say something to you now, it won't be held against me, will it?' I told her that it would not, as the trial was over. She said, 'That wasn't my urine they tested.' A friend had given the sample for her. She escaped from the Oakley psychiatric hospital eighteen months later and went to Australia.

There was always something to keep me busy. One night about midnight I received a call from a man who told me that he had burgled an electrical goods store in Paeroa. He wanted to get rid of the booty and asked me if I would look after it for him until I could hand it over to the police. I agreed. About two in the morning a truck rolled up. Our front room was filled with electrical appliances worth far more than anything we owned. I did not know the driver and never found out who he was. I called the police early in the

The last of 400 years of tailors: my grandfather (far left) and great-grandfather outside the shop in Pollen Street, Thames.

My paternal grandparents, Mary Walker and Jack Lange.

My father and mother just before their marriage.

My mother, keeping me at a distance.

New Year's Day, 1946, at Long Beach.

On the front steps of our home in Otahuhu, about 1949: me, Pop, Margaret, Annette, Peter, Granma and Mum.

My maternal grandparents, Samuel Reid and Edith Fysh.

Among the prefects, Otahuhu College.

Try mine for size: with Pop on the front steps, about 1965.

Barnby Gate Methodist church, Newark, 3 August 1968.

Naomi and our three children: Emily, Roy and Byron.

Blood is thicker than water: with Mum, about 1990.

THE *DOMINION*.

Margaret, 1989.

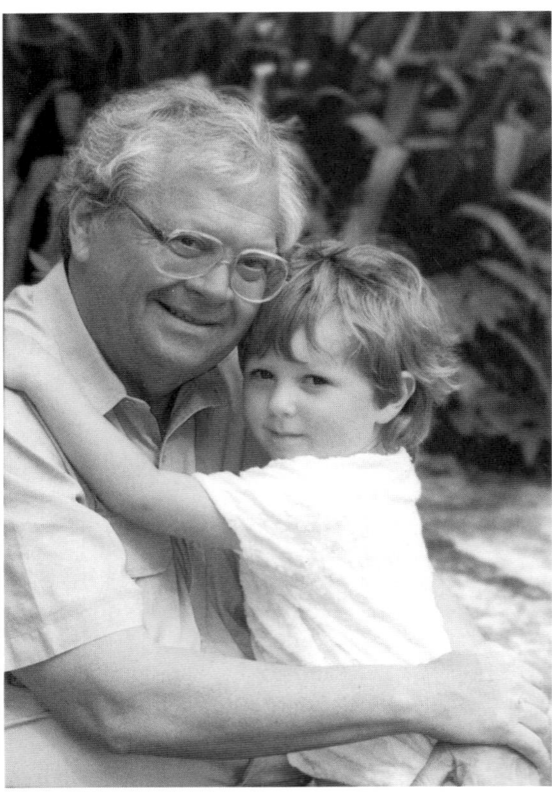

Edith and her Poppa.

morning and they came and took the goods away. It was that sort of life.

One day I was mowing the lawn when I slipped and the lawnmower sliced off most of two toes. I was coming out of the anaesthetic and vomiting into a bowl when a cop from the vice squad leaned over me and said, 'What do you know about a machine gun at Cassell's?' Cassell's was a motel on the Great South Road and I knew nothing about a machine gun. It turned out to be the property of a professional criminal called Trefor David 'Too Fat' Smith. I never acted for Too Fat. Peter Williams was his counsel and I was occasionally the solicitor of record. I did however act for Too Fat's wife when she wanted a divorce from him. Too Fat took exception to this and let me know I would be hearing from him. I walked into my office one day and found a pistol on my desk. It was a beautiful piece with a handle of carved ivory and I called Peter Williams and asked him if he wanted it but he declined. I walked up to the Auckland Central police station and handed it over. Ross Meurant, later a commander of the Red Squad during the Springbok tour of 1981 and a National Party member of parliament, was then doing time as lost-property officer and he took charge of the pistol.

Too Fat liked the grand gesture. He got a small-time criminal by the name of Rudi Alford to blow up the expensive car of a lawyer he disliked by putting dynamite in the petrol tank. I was in court when Too Fat was brought up from custody on a charge relating to the machine gun. 'Trefor,' I said, 'if you send Rudi after me, remember I drive a Hillman Imp and the petrol tank's in the front.' Luckily he roared with laughter.

I had interests outside advocacy. I was active in the Council of Civil Liberties and became its president in the mid-seventies. About the same time I became a talk-back host, under an assumed name because as a lawyer I was not supposed to tout for work. I called myself David Reid. It was easy work and I did it for the money. I broadcast with another lawyer who also used an assumed name, Bruce Christopher. This was Bruce Slane, who was later president of the Law Society and privacy commissioner. We worked on 1ZB of a night once a week.

The thought of politics never left me, although I was never in terms of party membership a political activist. I joined the Labour Party, if I remember rightly, in 1963, and worked for Phil Amos in the general election campaign that year. In 1966 I worked for Norman Douglas in the Auckland Central electorate. One of my duties in his office was to answer the telephone, and to do as much as I could to stop Norman from answering it himself. His usual response to inquirers was to bellow, 'Haven't you read the literature!' In 1969 I was returning officer in Kaikohe and took no part in politics. I do not recall any political involvement in the 1972 election, which was memorable because the National Party's time was obviously up and Labour won in a landslide.

In 1974 Michael Bassett asked me if I was interested in standing on the Labour ticket for the Auckland City Council. Bassett was a member of parliament and a cousin on my father's side of the family. My father had delivered him and it became plain in later days that he must have dropped him. My chances of success in the election were not great, as the council was dominated by conservative interests, but I went ahead with it. The ticket was led by Jim Anderton, a struggling businessman and party organiser who was Labour's mayoral candidate. Titewhai Harawira was on our ticket and enlived a candidates' meeting I went to with a fierce attack on the Labour government. Like the other candidates, I contributed $50 to pay for an advertisement in the *New Zealand Herald* in support of the Labour ticket. When I opened the paper to look at our advertisement I saw a photograph of Jim Anderton and no mention of the other candidates. Here was a warning of much to come. Jim Anderton and Catherine Tizard alone of the Labour candidates were duly voted on to the council: I came about halfway down the field but was not disillusioned or even disappointed. It was better than I had expected.

My involvement did publicise my interest in politics. At the end of 1974 my friend John Hislop, who farmed in the north, asked me if I was willing to contest the Labour candidacy for the Hobson electorate. It was an exciting prospect. Hobson was not a seat the Labour Party was likely to win at the following year's general election; the Labour candidate could expect to come third behind National and Social Credit. But my connections in the north made it worth the effort, so I went to a meeting in Kaikohe where I won selection ahead of the only other contender.

In February 1975 I travelled north to attend a meeting at a supporter's house. It was here that for the first time I met Bill Rowling, leader of the Labour Party and prime minister since the death of Norman Kirk the year before. He was well known in the north, having taught in the area as a young man, and was much liked by those who knew him. He was there to attend the ceremony at Waitangi which marked our national day, which was known then by the name of New Zealand Day. That year's ceremony was well attended, but it was to my mind a peculiar evocation of another place and time with a great deal of military pomp and no real feeling about what it meant to be a New Zealander. I have not been back to Waitangi on our national day since.

I made several journeys to keep in touch with the very few party faithful in the north. I then decided that I should be on the electoral roll in Hobson and to that end I had to establish a residence in the electorate. Naomi and I were the owners of a piece of land at Omapere on the south head of the Hokianga harbour (it has long since, to my lasting regret, been sold). We bought a shell home and had it put up on the property. The shell was literally that; it had no linings, no sewerage and no electricity. Naomi and the two boys moved there halfway through the year, while I commuted between the north and my practice in Auckland. I drove from the Hokianga through the unsealed roads of the Waipoua forest and down to Auckland to arrive in time for court, did my day's work and then went back north for the night. Looking back, I wonder how I did it, but even more I wonder how Naomi managed in such trying conditions. Roy was four and Byron was a toddler, yet she flung herself into it. We were lent a large caravan and travelled across the electorate, attending meetings in small settlements and doing all we could to raise support for Labour.

I had little contact with the wider Labour Party. What I could see of the organisation did not impress me. Every Labour candidate was invited to a meeting in Wellington and I had my first meal in Bellamy's, which was largely the feature of the day. Speakers scheduled to attend did not attend. Some were late. Some appeared but could not be heard. There was a session on publicity led by an advertising man called Bob Harvey, who told us that the detail of the campaign had not yet been settled; he was however able to provide each of us with a bumper-sticker. Few of the candidates were of my age. One who was a near-contemporary was Richard Prebble, whom I knew slightly in the law in Auckland and who was standing for the seat of Auckland Central on the retirement of Norman Douglas.

On the Sunday before the opening of the general election campaign, candidates from the upper North Island met in Auckland to receive copies of the party's election policy. It was an unhappy occasion. The government we all hoped to join had recently changed the system of social security payments in a way of which many of us candidates disapproved. The mood of the meeting was not positive. In the north we watched the formal opening of the campaign on television. There was a great deal of static. Bill Rowling spoke in the town hall in Christchurch. If he inspired the people in the hall, he did not inspire his television audience, or at least not those in the house I sat in. I remember that the mood was sombre and thinking that if ever I had the chance I could do better. I was in the front room of Bob and Maude Wynyard's home in Whirinaki and I said to them as we watched Bill Rowling, 'I'll be doing that in 1984.'

The Labour government was as doomed as my campaign in Hobson; what had started so positively three years before had petered out. On election day I did the rounds of Kaikohe and the east coast townships. I hoped at the least for the return of my deposit. I did get it back, but as expected, I came third. The only shred of consolation at a personal level was that the swing against Labour in Hobson was not as great as it was elsewhere in the country as the National Party swept into office.

Naomi and the boys and I went back to Auckland. She was again pregnant and we were again filled with a mixture of hope and anxiety. There were encouraging signs that the pregnancy was normal and our daughter Emily was born in May 1976. I was present at the birth, as I was at the births of my older children, and I was utterly shocked by what I saw. The baby had a hole in her face where her nose and mouth should have been. She had a cleft lip and palate. To me, who had never thought about such a thing, it looked absolutely unsurvivable. I saw no possibility of recovery, and yet of course a cleft lip and palate is treatable, and in Emily's case was treated wonderfully by the plastic surgery unit at Middlemore Hospital.

I felt deeply protective of this much-wanted baby daughter. The burden of the special care she needed, from infancy through surgery over many months and years, fell on Naomi. It was a hard time for her.

I was happy in my home. I loved our house in Kingsland and liked to work and potter about in it. I dug out the basement and helped build a flat under the house. I loved my family and could not bear to be away from them. I travelled miles to get home at night. I once spoke at a meeting in New Plymouth for the Council of Civil Liberties and drove home to Auckland after it finished, at the cost of the life of a cow and the destruction of most of the front left-hand side of my car. I had everything I hoped for in my personal life.

I could not say the same about my professional life. I had come to the end of the road as an advocate for lost and hopeless causes. I had advanced all the defences I could think of. I was more and more convinced that the answer for me was not in the law but in politics, but I had no idea where I might play a part in it.

Then the divine roulette wheel turned for me. In parliament late one night in November 1976, Prime Minister Muldoon, having described the Labour member of parliament for Mangere as effeminate and being in turn accused of belonging to a dishonest accounting firm, asked the speaker if it would be in order to accuse the member for Mangere of being picked up by the police for homosexual activity. What happened after that changed my life in almost every way possible.

CHAPTER SEVEN

The member of parliament for Mangere was Colin Moyle. He was picked up by the police late one night in Wellington and gave three different explanations for his presence on the street, thus opening himself to the charge that he had misled parliament. He resigned his seat and it was widely expected that he would seek vindication by contesting the seat at the following by-election.

I decided to put my name forward for the Labour nomination almost as soon as I heard of the resignation. I knew it was an opportunity made for me. I did not think that Moyle would win a contested nomination and that it was more than likely he would withdraw; in the short time before the by-election it would be difficult for anyone else to stitch up the seat. The electorate could not have been more familiar to me. In those days the Mangere electorate included my old home in Otahuhu, a large area of Papatoetoe and those parts of Mangere which did not belong to the Otahuhu electorate. I knew almost all of it. Many of the residents were once my father's patients. It was a reasonably safe Labour seat, although the majority fell to 1600 in the 1975 general election.

I knew nobody in the electorate organisation and I made no attempt to lobby. When nominations formally opened I presented myself at the Labour Party's headquarters in Papatoetoe, where my reception was not warm. When I produced my form and asked for seconders, the local party officials provided with some reluctance two people to endorse my nomination.

As long as it was thought that Moyle would contest the nomination, the better-known among the likely contenders held back. The exception was Mike Moore, who was recently a very young member of parliament. I met him at the candidates' conference in 1975 and when he lost his seat that year I helped him get a job as a social worker at Oakley Hospital. After Moore put his name forward, Moyle announced that he would not be in the field. The time for nominations was extended and when nominations finally closed there were sixteen candidates for the vacancy, of whom perhaps four had any real chance of success.

The selection meeting took place on the evening of 15 February 1977. Earlier that day I had appeared in court to defend two driving charges, one relating to blood alcohol and the other to speeding. I won them both. The police did not identify the testing instrument for the alcohol and did not provide a calibration certificate for the speed gauge. I was exasperated by the ease with which I could do bad things.

I did not write a speech for the selection meeting, although I thought for a long time about what I was going to say. The meeting was held in a local intermediate school hall. I drove there in my

Austin 1100, wearing the suit the Fijian tailor had made for me. The hall was packed. Given its circumstances, the by-election created a great amount of interest and there was a big news media presence. The selection panel consisted of four representatives of the Labour Party's national organisation, including Arthur Faulkner MP who chaired the meeting, and two locals I did not know. Every candidate was allowed seven minutes to speak and the order was determined by the drawing of marbles. I drew the last marble, number sixteen. It was wonderful luck. The audience was bored and restless by the time my turn arrived and desperate for relief; when Arthur Faulkner introduced me as the candidate who had the longest wait and I made the obvious response, there was a roar of laughter in the hall.

I made what I still think is the best speech of my political career. I talked about the electorate, about my hopes for the people who lived in it, and about the capacity of the Labour Party to revitalise itself. I ended by saying that we were going to kick the National Party in the polls.

This was the signal for the selection panel to retire. Given the audience response to my speech, I was hopeful. Inside the hall we waited, and waited. One of my fellow candidates, a Chinese man from Pukekohe, did not last the distance. Handing me a note which read, 'If my country needs me, ring Patumahoe 893,' he left. Close to midnight the panel decided on me and I was immediately introduced to the crowd as the Labour Party candidate for Mangere.

By the next morning I was a full-time politician. David Brown took over our law practice and kept it going and growing until he became a judge. Joe Walding, lately member of parliament for Palmerston North and one of the selection panel, gave me the money to buy a new suit. I found myself taken in hand by David Exel, an experienced journalist who had offered his services to the Labour Party and who guided me through radio broadcasts and press interviews. The news media were full of the by-election; it was presented as a measure of the Labour Party's ability to revive itself after the disaster of 1975. I tried to keep my mind not on the national significance of the contest but on the electorate.

Mangere was by the time I became its member of parliament vastly different from the district I knew in my boyhood. Gone were many of the market gardens and farms; in their place stood group housing. Amongst the housing was a poorly designed shopping centre, architecturally drab and commercially unattractive. The government was represented by the post office. There was no police station and no office of the Department of Social Welfare, nor were there any lawyers in practice. There was a large population of young people. Polynesians then were some way from forming the majority, but there was an uneasy pairing in the electorate between the established streets of Papatoetoe and the rapidly expanding state housing of Mangere. Great overcrowding in parts of Mangere Central spoke of the growing pressure of migration from the Pacific.

The National Party candidate was Clem Simich, the son of my father's one-time housekeeper. He was conservative and well presented. Likeable as he was, he did not seem to judge the flavour of the electorate very astutely. He had a motorcade which he led around the streets of Mangere in a Rolls-Royce, followed by several other glamorous cars. I was speaking on the corner of a street littered with motor wrecks and debris when he came past and I asked him if he would mind going around again. He and I spoke in a television debate which was broadcast nationwide. Most of the campaigning was done at local gatherings; if it was not the heyday of the public meeting it was close enough. There were rallies at which Bill Rowling and senior members of the parliamentary party spoke, workplace meetings (at one of which Mick Connelly MP chased a heckler across a paddock), street-corner meetings and cottage meetings.

Election day was tense for me, although everything was done which could be done to get out the vote and it was clear from the time the first returns came in that there was going to be a Labour victory. In the evening I went to a huge, empty old supermarket to await the outcome. Most of the gathering were party faithful. My mother was there; she may have been pleased at the result, but if she was, she gave no sign. Mum was a magnet for the news media. Asked by one journalist if she would vote for me if she lived in the electorate she was loath to commit herself. 'I'm a swinger,' she said. My sister Margaret asked her to leave before more could be adduced.

Naomi was certainly pleased, although the six-and-a-half weeks of the campaign gave us both some insight into what life was going to be like.

The margin of victory was somewhat higher than we had expected. It was a triumphant evening and I had in front of me all the possibilities the new life offered. I wanted to do something for the people of Mangere and I looked to the policies and programmes of the Labour Party to achieve that. I wanted to do something about the state of the law and stop the unnecessary harm being done to people by the legal process. Most of all, I was looking forward to taking part in the great political contest. I could not wait to get into it.

My first task was to get to know the members of my local party. There were numerous meetings. I was, as well, still the subject of media attention, but by this point I had mixed feelings about the extraordinary public interest in the by-election. It was undoubtedly uplifting to be the subject of so much attention but it was time-consuming and could be gruelling. There was so much to do and so much to learn that I felt overwhelmed. I had no formal introduction to parliamentary life; after a general election there are classes for the newcomers and some chance for them to learn the ropes, but because I came in at a by-election I had to find my own way. I knew what the pay was (it was more than double what I was earning from my law practice) but I had no idea that parliamentarians were entitled to other allowances and it was some time before I found out. I was surprised one day to find that Mangere was classified as a partly rural electorate and that I could claim twelve tax-free dollars a week, presumably to allow me to wave at the owners of the dairy herds on the road to the airport.

Parliament in those days followed the dairy farmer's seasons. It opened in May and sat every afternoon and every evening from Tuesday to Thursday and then again on Friday mornings. Until it opened, the routine for opposition members of parliament was to fly down to Wellington for caucus and committee meetings. This is what I did, although my first days as a parliamentarian were complicated by the holding of the Pahiatua by-election. It was a seat Labour had no chance at all of winning, but as a symbol of Labour's resurgence I was hauled all around the electorate.

The Beehive was not completed when I first went to Wellington. The cabinet and government members were housed in Parliament Buildings while opposition members were housed in the parliamentary library building. The offices were poor. I was assigned half an office in the library wing. I was also assigned half the time of a secretary. Jonathan Hunt, the MP for New Lynn, was kind enough to allow me a room in his house in Aro Street for a time until I could get accommodation. Hunt was also helpful on the subject of allowances and it was to him I expressed my disbelief that members of parliament could fly anywhere in the country for any reason at no cost to themselves. 'Oh yes,' he said, 'you can join the Invercargill public library and fly down there to change your books.' For a while I had a room in the Shamrock hotel in Molesworth Street where I lived for $2 a night. After that I shared a house in Brooklyn with Russell Marshall MP whom I knew from my time at Trinity College. We kept different hours and I saw little of him. For transport I bought an old Vauxhall which I left outside the parliamentary library when I went home to Auckland. Later still I rented a flat in Sydney Street East, just over the road from parliament, where I lived until I became prime minister.

Some things about parliament I found awkward. I was unaccustomed to being called 'sir' by uniformed messengers and having doors held open for me. I had never worked in a place where you could ring for tea and biscuits to be delivered to your office. When the session finally started, I took my place in the debating chamber with great excitement. As was the custom, I said nothing in the house until it was time to make my maiden speech. I wrestled with the speech for a long time; it was a statement about where I came from and where I wanted to go and it was full of reference to my electorate. I wrote nothing down. I was allowed half an hour to speak; as it happened I started ten minutes before the dinner adjournment and had to begin again in the evening. My speech was delivered in the courteous silence which is afforded the first effort of a new member. This was something to which I was quite unaccustomed. Interjection is the greatest spur there is to public speaking. In court I was subject to judicial intervention while at a public meeting there is heckling or abuse, and fluent speakers rely on such incidents as a prod to further effort. To speak for half an hour without such incentives was a challenge and it was with great relief that I finished without faltering. The speech was warmly received on both sides of the house.

My maiden speech was the most important parliamentary speech I ever made and was widely counted a success. It gave me a name as a parliamentary speaker and even led to my being talked about as a future party leader. I benefited from it for the rest of my time in politics.

I did little else in the debating chamber that year. As the least of the backbenchers, my speaking opportunities were limited. When the party leadership was away, I could risk the odd interjection. The major issue in the house that year was the Contraception, Sterilisation and Abortion Bill. It was a conscience issue which, as it happened, did more damage to personal and political relationships in the National Party than it did to the Labour Party. In part because of what had happened during Naomi's first pregnancy, I felt protective of the unborn child, and I said as much in my speech on the second reading. I said that I did not think the law could work unless the public accepted the principles of the legislation. I added that as a new member of parliament I was reluctant to impose my views on people who were far more knowledgeable than I was. With Marilyn Waring and about a dozen others I voted against the second reading of the bill and had as little as possible to do with it afterwards. The result of my thinking aloud was that I was hounded for some years afterwards by some of the more extreme pro-abortion activists. Another result was that Martyn Finlay, the Labour Party's venerable justice spokesman, took me aside and gave me a talk about the responsibilities of members of parliament. He did not succeed in changing my mind about conscience votes and I still think of them as an indulgence with the debate surrounding them an appalling ragbag of bigotry and sentimentality.

The caucus I joined in 1977 was a dispirited group with an air of the walking dead about some of them. Labour was a party of opposition and its defeat in 1975 was humiliating. Being a backbench member of parliament was a part-time occupation in those days, unless you were in demand as a speaker outside the house or determined to keep yourself busy. The foreign affairs select committee, for instance, met once a year to approve the estimates. It was not hard, if you wanted, to escape responsibility, and some of the caucus had long since surrendered.

I said nothing at my first four caucus meetings but I was alarmed by what I heard. The debates dwelt on matters of members' comforts. There was a discussion which raged for weeks over the provision of towels and cleaning services in the old library block. At one meeting, members talked at great length about superannuation: the subject was a proposal that widows of members be entitled to two-thirds of the pension, and telephone concessions for life. Before long I was heartily sick of it and expressed my concern at the fifth meeting I went to, but succeeded only in inspiring ill-feeling among some of the older members. I remember little or nothing which was done to prepare a strategy to take on the government once the pomp and ceremony of the formal opening of parliament was over and the hard graft of the session started.

Bill Rowling was the undoubted leader of the parliamentary Labour Party. He dealt well with individuals, but he could not chair the caucus effectively or guide it towards an outcome. He could not build a team. Although he was always civil to me, our relationship was never easy. Rowling had no reason to like me and in time I came to resent the bloody-mindedness with which he clung to the leadership.

The deputy leader was Bob Tizard, who was briefly finance minister when Rowling was prime minister. He was acute, fearless and never one to avoid a stoush. Arthur Faulkner was greatly influential in the caucus. Martyn Finlay, who was close to retirement, had an intellectual capacity which outstripped most of his colleagues and caused some resentment amongst those who could not understand what he was talking about. Warren Freer was a senior parliamentarian and an effective debater, but time had passed him by.

There were characters like Mick Connelly, who worked all the time and tended his electorate to the limit. Letters flowed from his desk. He wrote constantly in the house and handed the envelopes, barely decipherable, to the messengers for posting. He sent everything to constituents including parliamentary order papers and newsletters, and on one occasion, just as he rose to speak, Arthur Faulkner, his benchmate, realised that Mick had just posted his notes to a constituent. There was Gerard Wall, who could be astute and penetrating and then fall out with every member of the caucus in turn. Paddy Blanchfield, MP for the West Coast, was an invalid and local icon. In the days before I got my allowances I could not afford to eat at Bellamy's and I used to go to the members' bar where there was always a side table of leftovers from the day's meals. Here I could eat for the price of a soft drink. Paddy went there every evening after the house rose for dinner to reflect on the day and gather strength for the night. One evening I smelt smoke; soon I could actually see smoke. The fire alarm sounded but Paddy just sat there. The alarm became more insistent and I urged Paddy to leave. He did not move. I told him I was going and asked him one last time to come with me. 'Oh, no,' he said, 'bury me between the mountains and the sea!'

Among the younger members of the caucus, John Kirk, son of the late prime minister, was the problem-child. He invited me to lunch one day and drank, unaided, two bottles of wine before ordering a third to take back to the office. He had a gradual meltdown in the job until, having been detached from the Labour Party, he locked himself in his office to protect his assets from the bailiffs.

In the house I sat beside Richard Prebble, the most junior member next to myself. He was always combative and a vigorous debater. He seemed to carry a considerable domestic burden. He would often fling himself into the parliamentary contest to the point where the speaker called on him to withdraw and apologise. In the end he would have to comply. Invariably a messenger would appear to tell him that there was a call for him in the lobby: it was his wife wanting to know why he had given up the fight.

It happened the first four weeks I spent in Wellington that the airport was closed when it was time to go home. I drove up to Auckland with Prebble, Jonathan Hunt and Roger Douglas. Douglas was the grandson of W T Anderton, who was a minister in the first Labour government and the founder of the family firm which specialised in herbal remedies and which Douglas turned into a major success on the back of export subsidies. W T Anderton, a tall man in a black Homburg hat, came into the office at Haigh, Charters and Carthy one day when I was working there and Les Charters bowed in greeting. A few minutes after he left, Les came running out to me. 'Get that lying bastard back!' he shouted. I must have met Roger Douglas for the first time during the 1960s, since his brother Malcolm was a law clerk at Haigh, Charters and Carthy. I did not know Roger well when I went into parliament, but he was no stranger and was affable. He was always somewhat diffident in front of an audience and the effort of public speaking could tell on him. When he was relaxed and happy he was good company.

The goal of my journeys north was our new house in Mangere, bought towards the end of 1977. It was in Massey Road in Mangere East, close to the site of the old army camp and less than a mile from my former home in Otahuhu. It was not a particularly comfortable house, but it was what we could afford. The rooms were small and awkwardly shaped. Over time it was adapted to suit the family needs: some of the rooms were remodelled, and in due course an office and accommodation for the couple who looked after the children when Naomi and I were away were added to the garage. I was sorry to leave our home in Kingsland but I could look forward to voting for myself in 1978. As it turned out, the boundaries were redrawn before the 1978 election and I found myself living just outside the Mangere electorate. I did not get the chance to vote for myself until 1993, when I lived in Mangere Bridge.

Naomi thrived in Mangere. She ran the household and her first recourse outside the home was always the church. She was active in the little Methodist church in Mangere East and also took a strong interest in the Labour Party and was a stalwart of the Mangere women's branch.

I did all I could to avoid being away from home at the weekend. On Saturdays I worked in my electorate office which I set up in a community house in Mangere Central. Seeing constituents was demanding work; the greatest number of people I saw on a single Saturday was seventy-eight. Later I enlisted the help of the law school, which allowed students to count work in the office as part of their practical training. On Saturday night I went to social functions or speaking engagements. On Sunday I went to church and with luck the afternoon was free. The Labour electorate committee met monthly on Sunday evenings, and there were branch meetings on the other Sundays. On Monday I went to my office in the garage and wrote telegrams on behalf of constituents and then drove to the Otahuhu post office to have them sent to the relevant agencies. When the house was sitting I went down to Wellington on Tuesday, and when it was not sitting I would usually go on Wednesday. In any event I was always in Wellington on Thursday for the weekly meeting of caucus.

I was still active in the Council for Civil Liberties and I had more invitations to speak than I could possibly accept. It was a busy life and I was not entirely fit for it. At the end of 1977 I was thirty-five years old and weighed about twenty-six stone. It amazes me that I am alive to write this. I smoked up to twenty cigarettes a day but I can at least say that I drank very rarely. In those days members of parliament were showered with gifts of liquor and I used to drink some of it at Christmas and on other special occasions.

As a result of my activities, or the comparative failure of a large number of my colleagues to be noticed, I began to rise in the opinion polls. When asked by journalists to comment I used to say that it was the attraction of mass, but privately I did not at all welcome this development. The only effect of the publicity was to excite envy among some of my colleagues. In hope of diminishing the interest, I refused for a while to give interviews. In November I took Roy to Melbourne for a week, and before I left I spoke to Bill Rowling, telling him that I had no right to expect an overseas trip so early in my career but that it would help lower my profile if I could get out of the country for a while. The result was that I was chosen to take part in the speaker's tour of India and Japan in January 1978.

I went to India with much optimism since the country had never left my mind. There were three National MPs and two Labour members in the tour group. My second arrival in India was somewhat different from the first. We were met by the New Zealand high commissioner at Delhi and taken to a very good hotel. After briefings and official calls in Delhi we set off in a motorcade to tour India. We went through Haryana and the Punjab until we came to Amritsar, where we viewed the extraordinary Golden Temple. We visited the Gujurati parliament at Ahmedabad before travelling to Bombay and back to Delhi. After a hectic ten days in India we went to Japan by way of Hong Kong. Having worked out how to make the business-class fare go further, I flew to Alaska and then to London, and after a while there came home.

I was away for six-and-a-half weeks. The next poll showed that in my absence my rating had doubled.

CHAPTER EIGHT

It was my good fortune to come into parliament at a by-election. Simply being chosen as the Labour candidate for Mangere made me a nationally known figure. I was also lucky enough to enter politics when television was increasingly decisive in the contest between parties.

I first appeared on television in 1970 when I acted for a man who had decamped from Oakley Hospital and was charged with escaping from custody. I won his acquittal on a technical point which made even my client ask exactly who was mad. As there was some interest in the case, Judy Lessing interviewed me in a little studio in Durham Lane in Auckland. The result was broadcast on the evening news and I received a number of congratulatory responses even though not one of the writers understood what I had said and all had converted my observations to their own purposes. The experience gave me some insight into the nature of television: what you say may matter on radio and in print, but on television it is almost immaterial. I learned from watching Norman Kirk how important image is in politics. A gesture seen on television made far more impact than any number of words in the paper. I also learned early in the piece that it was pointless being part of the crowd. On television, one-on-one was what counted.

Television was good to me. I was large. I was confident. I was reassuring. I was a teddy bear.

Bill Rowling was for the most part ineffective on television. He looked small and he moved around too much. However well he knew his subject, he always sounded diffident. He was no match for his principal opponent: Muldoon too was small in person, but somehow he got bigger on television. He just filled the screen. He paid no attention to the conventional wisdom which holds that you should look at your interviewer; he looked at the camera and spoke directly to his audience and it worked for him.

Muldoon was also Rowling's master in the debating chamber. That did not matter outside the house, but it mattered a lot in parliament. Muldoon had an extraordinary capacity to intimidate; he also had a long memory. Given the number of people in the parliamentary opposition who had baggage from times past, and given what had happened to Colin Moyle, a number of Labour members were genuinely afraid of him and he often had a free run. His stare alone could quell some on our front bench into inertia. He was not in any sense a talented speaker and his unscripted speeches were a matter of constant repetition. He would have a point to make and he would make it three or four times and then move on to the next. He was easy to interject on and not particularly quick in response.

There were times when he was at risk and the game was enjoyable. Thursday nights after ten o'clock were remarkably frank. Muldoon would pass most of the evening in his room in the company of a couple of trusted lieutenants and when he came into the house he would pause by the bar of the chamber. Gordon Christie, Labour MP for Napier, greeted him by saying, 'Whoops, whoops, who's been having drinkies?' Muldoon walked a further three or four steps and peered ominously around the opposition ranks as if to invite further contributions before going to his seat and plonking himself down. Christie then made noises which indicated a certain degree of intoxication on the part of the prime minister, to which Muldoon's invariable response was to turn to his bald-headed accuser and slur, 'I hear they're selling toupees with brains attached.' He then lapsed into the occasional interjection, to the great concern of his senior whip, until the house rose and he left.

He was a man who could not be thanked for anything and it was unwise to pay him a compliment. It was hardly prudent to hold open a door for him. In later times I made a point when I saw him of holding open the doors in the parliamentary corridors because I knew he would scurry off and go the long way around.

When I became leader of the opposition I often found myself on the same flight as Muldoon, travelling with his private secretary, Ken Richardson, whom I knew from Ken's time in the high commission in London. I did not speak to Muldoon, or he to me, but I did say good morning to Ken. After a few weeks I was surprised when Ken asked to see me in my office. 'Mr Lange,' he said, 'it would make my life more tolerable if you could just ignore me.'

In 1979 when I went on a parliamentary tour to Europe I was the victim of Muldoon's malice. My fare was paid, but I met my own expenses with a view to later reimbursement from the travel allowance. It came to a substantial amount of money and I had an overdraft at the bank. I expected the money to be paid as soon as I got back, but it was not. The authority for payment of such allowances rested in those days with the prime minister and Muldoon did not give his approval before leaving the country on some long journey. I was in financial difficulty and I asked Duncan MacIntyre, a senior member of the National government, for his help. He called Muldoon and Muldoon told him not to pay. I got my money a long time later in accordance with Muldoon's idea of how much I should be inconvenienced.

He was a formidable opponent, the more so because the Labour Party could not make the right response to him. The parliamentary opposition had no idea of when or how to disengage from the contest. The government would put down bills or estimates and some instinct drove the Labour Party to speak against them at almost interminable length. The speeches might be of no substance and the speakers of no ability but nothing could stop them. My first full year as a parliamentarian was one of frustration: Labour seemed in a terminal drift and there was so much more that could be done.

The year started badly with a by-election in Rangitikei. The Labour vote collapsed and on election night Rangitikei returned not the favoured National Party candidate but the Social Credit aspirant, Bruce Beetham. It was a result which gave new impetus to the Social Credit Political League. Beetham was an appealing character who worked hard to evangelise for his cause. He was attractive enough to make many who were casting about for a home for their vote overlook the oddities of Social Credit's monetary policy, and his party's rise was a continuing blow to the morale of Labour's old guard.

When parliament opened in May 1978, anticipating the retirement of Martyn Finlay, Bill Rowling made me the party's justice spokesman and gave me a seat in the second row of the debating chamber. It was a substantial jump. I relished being higher in the pecking order as it meant the chance to ask more questions and I was much better placed to make interjections. I was also assigned to assist our social welfare spokesman, Mick Connelly. He was a determined man with rigid views and was impossible to work with. One evening he informed me that we were going to write the social welfare policy for the general election. I went to his room in the old parliamentary library building after the house rose that night and made suggestions to which he invariably responded, 'Yes, but this is how we're going to do it.' He would then write more and more in his extraordinary handwriting. I remember looking at my watch at one o' clock in the morning and realising that I was crying; not sobbing, but crying tears of frustration from the endless paralysing tedium of it.

Around the middle of 1978 some of the caucus gave thought to removing Bob Tizard from the deputy leadership. It came to nothing. If I knew about the effort before I read about it in the newspapers I have long since forgotten. Tizard, in spite of his experience and sharp intellect, was understandably a focus for caucus discontent. He had no time for fools and his relationships with caucus members were conditional upon whether you were a fool or not. There was no halfway house and some members could not cope with being told exactly what their limitations were and what their prospects might prove. Perhaps unfairly he became something of a symbol of the old guard.

I did not then want to displace Bob Tizard. I was anxious to become an established member of parliament without being seen as mounting any kind of challenge. My continuing rise in the polls was more awkward for me than not, causing envy in some quarters of the caucus and hope in others. The effect on Rowling's leadership was corrosive. I pledged my loyalty and more to the point I tried to demonstrate it. I travelled endlessly and spoke in support of the leadership to party members. When I spoke in public I was careful to keep within my areas of expertise so as not to present myself as an alternative to the existing leadership. I was well aware that my attraction was that of novelty and not experience or ability, and I had no wish to inflame the speculation which had followed me since I entered parliament.

During the 1978 general election campaign I formed part of a group called the demolition squad by the Labour Party. The other members were Basil Arthur, John Kirk and Richard Prebble, all members of parliament, and Joe Walding, who was candidate for the Palmerston North seat he had lost in 1975. We posed outside Parliament Buildings wearing hard-hats and wielding sledge-hammers. When we travelled the country we attracted large numbers of the public to hear our attacks on the government. It was in retrospect an unproductive approach and only too typical of a party conditioned to opposition. The very name we used was inherently negative and our tactics focused attention on the government and its policies rather than asserting Labour's own proposals. For all of that, the tour was a lot of fun. I enjoyed travelling with Joe Walding, who was as close to a mentor as I ever had in politics. Joe built a successful business before he ever went into parliament and I admired his ability to appeal to a broad cross-section of the general public.

Labour got a majority of the popular vote in 1978, a wasted effort given that we still lost the election. We did not make the necessary impact in the seats which were needed to win a parliamentary majority. The election did however produce a significant change in the membership of the caucus. Several members who were defeated in 1975 were restored; they included Michael Bassett, Mike Moore and Joe Walding. Mike Moore, sadly, became ill and played a limited part in politics in 1979. David Caygill, Ann Hercus and Stan Rodger were among the new members. (Geoffrey Palmer, who was a protégé of Bill Rowling, came into parliament at a by-election in 1979.) There was no doubting the talent of many of the arrivals: they represented a shift in age and outlook which put the caucus at risk of being more fractious than ever.

In 1979 I was chosen by caucus as its representative at the Interparliamentary Union conference in Prague. I followed that with a United Kingdom study tour conducted by the Commonwealth Parliamentary Association. What I learned from the experience was never again to put myself forward for any such activity. I travelled to Europe with Leo Schulz, the National MP for Coromandel. After a briefing in Rome we moved on to Prague for the conference, which was a disgraceful piece of extravagance in a city where people were queuing to get bread and sausage. The meeting was without any value at all as a conference, being merely a celebration of the division between East and West. I went by train from Prague through Nuremberg to Strasbourg. It was late afternoon when I arrived and checked into my hotel in the Place de la Gare. I could not afford to eat dinner at the hotel, though not far from it I found a little bistro. A sign offered, among other things, *jambon sandwich*. That seemed clear enough. I ordered three of them and ended up with three metres of ham roll. I carried my purchase back to the hotel, looking as though I was about to feed an orphanage, and almost the first person I met when I got there was Bill Rowling. I hung the ham rolls outside my window for refrigeration. They lasted me three days.

Then it was on to London. It is a matter of some doubt as to whether the Commonwealth Parliamentary Association has any point, but on that particular occasion there was no point at all. A general election made any useful business impracticable and I found myself on a holiday tour of the more scenic parts of the United Kingdom. The lasting benefit for me was my meeting with the incomparable Barry Jones, an Australian Labor Party member of parliament, a great scholar and wit and later a fount of sharp observation on the workings of the Hawke government. It was a pleasure to travel with Barry. On a dismal day in Stratford-upon-Avon we took pity on a fellow from Malawi who seemed out of sorts. We asked him if he would like to come with us to see *The Merry Wives of Windsor*. His face brightened at once. After about five minutes of the performance the man got up to leave and I asked him what was wrong.

He said, 'This is not blue movie! This is not movie at all!'

At the end of 1979 there was a move to rejuvenate the caucus by deposing Bob Tizard from the deputy leadership. This matched an earlier move to revive the party organisation outside parliament by electing Jim Anderton to the post of party president.

Michael Bassett was among Anderton's proponents. Anderton, Bassett and Roger Douglas were thick as thieves in the early 1970s. They were all political activists from an early age, but their activism was not an interest I shared. I was never a member of the Princes Street branch or any other set of university activists. I did not want to be, even if I had the time for it. I found legal practice far more compelling than any amount of fretting about what was going on inside the Labour Party. When I went to parliament I found that I had still less time for the endless rehearsal of grievance, speculation and anticipation which was the norm of caucus activism. I could not stand it; when the house rose at night I did not want to drink or gossip, I wanted to go home to sleep.

I knew that Bassett and Douglas were scheming to remove Bob Tizard and that I would be the beneficiary of his removal. I did nothing at all to stop them because towards the end of 1979 I was far more confident about my ability to do the job. I was thankful for their effort and would not have become deputy leader without it. But I did no canvassing and I did not solicit any vote. I never had the temperament for that side of politics; I did not ask any caucus colleague for a vote as long as I was in parliament.

The vote which removed Bob Tizard and put me in his place as deputy leader was largely a measure of the gap between the old and the new in caucus. One or two of the older brigade whom Tizard had offended once too often took my side. Tizard marked his defeat by a wonderful florid fighting speech in which the words 'bastard' and 'bastards' were used quite often and in which he told me that he would never vote for me for anything as long as my arse pointed downwards. I said nothing; it was not a statement which required a response.

I was elated by my elevation but I was not unguarded. I hoped to work with Bill Rowling as best I could. He had his own group of confidants and I was never close to his inner circle. I knew that one day he would go, as all leaders must, and I intended to replace him if I could but I did not wish to hurry his retirement. The problem for me was that my election as deputy leader added to the attention I already attracted and inevitably increased the distance between me and Rowling. What it also did was create friction between me and the party president, Jim Anderton.

Anderton was a determined, tireless organiser. As party president he rebuilt the party structure, put its finances on a sounder footing and turned a mess into an effective organisation. He always insisted that his later differences with his Labour Party colleagues were differences of principle. My difficulty with that is that I could never separate his principles from his ambition. Advancement of the principle inevitably demanded the advancement of Anderton. He was protective of Rowling but I did not see this as support for Rowling personally or for anything Rowling stood for. He wanted to keep Rowling in place because it suited him to have Rowling there while he built up his own position in the party and, through the party, the caucus. He had a Greek chorus of followers, Helen Clark among them, which kept up a dispiriting commentary on the activities of the party's parliamentary wing.

As deputy leader of the parliamentary party it was my duty to attend meetings of various party committees chaired by Anderton. It made no difference if he was running the annual conference or a meeting of the party executive; every contribution from the floor was matched by a monologue from the chair. It was mind-numbing.

It was also my duty to attend meetings of the Joint Council of Labour, at which trade unionists and the political wing of the labour movement met. Labour's close association with the unions was an inevitable consequence of the party's history, but it was not an electoral advantage by the late 1970s. The association of many leading trade unionists with the Communist Party and the Socialist Unity Party was a continuing joy to Muldoon. Industrial problems on several major sites were a perennial gift to the National Party. Meetings of the Joint Council of Labour were no place to resolve any such difficulties. The president of the Federation of Labour was Jim Knox. He was not in command of any lucid view and he could not follow a line of argument. Our meetings did not change my mind about the union movement; the entitlements which once gave unions assurance in times of difficulty had been milked to a pulp by a generation of leaders who owed their position to the state and not their membership.

My elevation to the deputy leadership offered no increase in salary but I did get a pleasant office on the third floor of Parliament Buildings. I also had a seat in the front row of the debating chamber. There were more speaking engagements and my attendance was required more often at party functions. I found myself cursed by the air travel which was the entitlement of a member of parliament; it made me a slave to invitations to the remotest places and I became very familiar with the take-it-or-leave-it attitude of the national carrier when it came to serving the provinces. I tried to spend as much time at home as I possibly could, but as my commitments mounted I felt more and more like a visitor to a household which took on a life of its own in my absence.

I was sometimes called on to deputise for Rowling. Not long after I got the job he was invited to dinner at the United States embassy and could not go, so I went in his place – the only time in my career I was asked to dinner there. We were having the soup when the ambassador was called out on a matter of urgency and the dinner was abandoned. The emergency was the loss of an Air New Zealand flight over Antarctica.

There were a number of Japanese passengers on the flight and there was publicity in Japan which suggested that their bodies had been handled less than respectfully. Our government gave various assurances to the Japanese government and to ensure fair play asked the leader of the opposition to nominate a member of parliament to report on what was being done. Rowling asked me to go. I spent most of a day in the morgue in Auckland, and if I had ever had any doubt what high-velocity impact might do to the human body I have none now.

I remember 1980 as a year in which the caucus was restless and out of sorts. Mat Rata, MP for Northern Maori, resigned from parliament to found the Mana Motuhake Party. Roger Douglas, who was not then the finance spokesman, issued an alternative budget and was sacked by Rowling from the shadow cabinet. There was concern about Labour's performance in the polls which came to a head after Social Credit's extraordinary victory in the East Coast Bays by-election. As had happened in Rangitikei, the Labour vote collapsed and helped put the Social Credit candidate into what had been a reasonably safe National seat. By the end of the year Labour and Social Credit were contesting second place in the polling, some way behind the National government.

A number in caucus then resolved to put Rowling's leadership to the test. The most active in the campaign against him were Bassett, Douglas and Moore. This time my instincts about their efforts were less clear-cut. I wanted to be leader and I was certain that Labour could not be elected with Rowling in office. My difficulty was that I did not want to be seen to push him out while I was officially his deputy. In the end I did nothing to discourage the coup, chiefly because I did not want to disappoint those who had put me into the deputy leadership.

The vehicle for the coup was a motion of no confidence in Rowling. If it was carried in the caucus it would be open to me to contest the leadership. Canvassing showed opinion to be close to evenly divided. The nature of the division is hard to describe. It was not new against old, as it had been a year before. Nor was it Auckland against the others, although there was some of that in it. There was nothing obviously ideological about it. It was a mixture of loyalty, distrust, calculation, idealism and opportunism which decided the vote. With a general election only a year away the stakes were high and the closeness of the contest left bitterness behind it. There was no question of my soliciting support for the motion of no confidence. I went out of my way to avoid contact with caucus colleagues, and as the vote came nearer I stayed one night in a hotel and another in Joe Walding's flat.

The critical caucus meeting was delayed when Rowling decided that an appointment outside Wellington was for him a matter of higher priority. It was now widely known that the motion would be put and hundreds of telegrams from Labour Party members flooded into parliament in support of Rowling. Rowling and his supporters insisted that these messages were unsolicited, but from what I heard about the activities of Anderton and Clark I believed they were far from spontaneous. I was told before the meeting that the motion was likely to be carried but by then I had been around long enough not to place any trust in such assurances.

When caucus met, the motion of no confidence was moved and a vote was taken which was tied. Rowling announced this result and then, remembering that he too had a vote, declared it lost. I was far from despondent. Even before I heard Rowling say 'I'm against it too' I knew he was finished. There was a lunch of fish and chips in Douglas's office and I relished every bite of it.

Rowling told the news media that he was happy to have me as his deputy while I told the media that I did not seek a job which was not vacant. Given the tottering balance of power in the caucus, neither of us could say anything else. It was Anderton who decided it was time for a punch-up. To the accompaniment of torrid statements about what might happen to those in caucus who had challenged the leadership, he called a special meeting of the New Zealand council of the Labour Party.

The council was the party's governing body. Its membership

included activists of the Anderton following, a scattering of the hard left and a larger number of provincial representatives. It was hard to be a Labour Party activist in the provinces then: I recall one schoolteacher from a small town in the north who endured many years of social ostracism because of his party membership. To him the Labour cause was noble precisely because it was hopeless and there were many others like him.

The council passed resolutions censoring caucus members who had supported the motion of no confidence and threatening disciplinary action against anyone in caucus who tried to displace a leader favoured by the party outside parliament. It was an unprecedented challenge to the right of caucus to decide its own leadership. Bill Rowling and I went to the council meeting. There must have been more than thirty in the room and much colourful rhetoric on the theme of treachery. There was no point in engaging in it and I let it wash over me, saying only at one point that if the leader of the party wanted me to go, then I would go immediately. There was a careful silence from Rowling.

I left the council meeting and went home to Auckland in sombre mood. It was not the abuse from council members which caused me to reflect; I could stand any amount of rain-dancing in those days. The problem was the great divide between the party at large and many of us in caucus. Labour had to contest a general election in less than twelve months and we were showing far more enthusiasm for fighting each other than for fighting the government. I had no obvious answer to the questions the council meeting raised about the relationship between me and the party at large and told myself that if I continued to do well as a parliamentarian and public figure the party would one day get me as its leader, no matter what its members thought. As it turned out, by the end of 1981 I was not even sure of that.

CHAPTER NINE

There were certain constants in my life at this time. Almost every Saturday I went to my electorate office where I employed a part-time electorate secretary, whose salary I paid from my own income. When I had time at home I did what I could to make the house more comfortable. I enjoyed putting up wallpaper but my efforts were thwarted by a malicious burglary. We were away on holiday and whoever broke into the house stole very little but threw paint over the piano and the walls, making a terrible mess of the place. The police investigated and tried to get in touch to tell me what had happened. It turned out that my mother was their only contact. A sergeant called her and later told me of her response. 'That's all right,' she said, 'he's got nothing worth stealing anyhow.'

Mum was still living in Kohimarama, but after she broke her hip and had a long spell in hospital she moved to a unit in a retirement village in Takapuna. It was from here that, when sought out by reporters, she launched her frank characterisations of my career, two of which I remember as 'I didn't know he had it in him' and 'How long can this last?' I could not help but think of Jimmy Carter, whose presidency was enlivened by the commentaries of his mother and the feckless behaviour of his ne'er-do-well brother. My brother at least was blameless.

At the end of 1980 Naomi and I went with the children to Britain. While I was there I took advantage of a grant from the British government to see people and places of interest. Part of the time was spent in Belfast where I stayed in the Hotel Europa, barricaded behind ranks of barbed wire. I saw the Lear aircraft factory, into which the British government was pouring assistance, and the De Lorean car plant, which consumed similarly large sums of taxpayers' money. Both enterprises failed. I was at Queen's University in Belfast when I heard an explosion, looked out the window and saw a mushroom cloud rising above the street. That was the last I saw of Northern Ireland. I went home with the family by way of Hong Kong and Canton, where we were the guests of the Chinese government. The very large cars in which we were transported had seats which moved forwards and back at the touch of a button, an emetic experience if you are travelling with young children.

Two issues dominated the political agenda in 1981. It was the year of Think Big, and the year of the Springbok tour. Think Big was the name popularly attached to the National government's scheme to secure New Zealand's economic future by building several major energy projects. The Springbok tour went ahead in the interest of shoring up National Party support in provincial electorates. The impact of both issues on the Labour Party was telling.

Labour showed remarkable solidarity in its opposition to the tour, notwithstanding the potential cost to the party in votes in the provinces. What happened is hard to believe today. Town and country were torn apart by the tour and family ties were ruptured. I flew one day to New Plymouth, where the aircraft could not land because of crosswinds, and was diverted to Wanganui. There I saw Hercules aircraft parked by the runway, soldiers in great numbers and police all over the place. It looked like a civil war, but the forces were gathered to allow a football match to proceed. My brother Peter was active in his opposition to the tour and among a group which at considerable risk invaded the pitch at Hamilton to stop a match taking place. He was frogmarched off the field and held under the grandstand by a zealous policeman who twisted his arm and bent his fingers back. The pain was great and Peter pleaded for relief. In a last desperate gasp he cried, 'My brother is the deputy leader of the opposition!' The constable broke his finger.

The tour led to a shift in the political ground. The Labour Party had always attracted liberal thinkers and social activists; it was a place for members of the women's movement and campaigners against nuclear testing and the visits of nuclear-powered ships. Before 1981 these issues did not much influence the popular vote and Labour was surfing well ahead of the wave. After the tour, the tide caught up.

The party's branch membership was swelled by the supporters of liberal causes. The most energetic among them could be met at the party's annual conference and at meetings of the party's New Zealand council or its policy council. Many were the children of Vietnam, who joined the Labour Party to carry on protest politics. Some of the most prominent were essentially single-issue advocates, fundamentalist in their inability to compromise. Smug self-righteousness made a number of them unbearable: it was easier to deal with the hard left, which being used to disappointment was often more realistic.

I did not find it particularly easy either to deal with the feminists who joined the party in increasing numbers. They were shock-troops, out to claim new ground, and they had no reason to be polite to me. The Labour women's council grew in influence in the 1980s and, although I had few direct dealings with it, it was never far from my mind. In 1984 I went to a South Pacific Forum meeting in Tuvalu where the delegates were treated to a fiafia, a kind of ceremonial feast. To my horror it became clear to me that the young woman in front of me intended to spoon the food into my mouth. I insisted that she desist, not so much from a sense of the dignity of labour as from fear of what would happen to me if the Labour women's council ever saw it.

Labour was less sure about its opposition to Think Big than it was about the Springbok tour. Some in caucus thought it was a good idea, given that the projects were supposedly rich in employment. A number of Labour's affiliated unions were enthusiasts for schemes like the high dam at Clyde and were insistent that the caucus should support the legislation needed to allow it to proceed. I was once on radio in Christchurch being somewhat derisory in my description of several of the Think Big projects when I was asked if my views were those of the Labour Party as a whole. Plucking an improbability out of the air, I said there could well be people in the party who believed that we should build a tunnel through the

Southern Alps. I was surprised to learn from the interviewer that one of my colleagues had proposed such a scheme the week before, without going so far as to suggest as I did that for the purposes of job enrichment it should be dug with knives and forks.

Our approach to Think Big was not something we could easily sort out. I remember desultory discussion in caucus followed by lacklustre performance in the house. It was generally assumed when I first went to parliament that Labour if restored to government would engage in targeted investment with a strong overlay of regional development. This must have been the context in which Roger Douglas once proposed the construction of fourteen carpet factories. The Think Big projects gave many caucus members pause for thought, but they did not lead the caucus as a whole into any deep consideration of the principles of economic management. As in so much else, we drifted.

It was often remarked that I had no education in economics. This is somewhat ironic. In the early 1980s, nobody was better qualified than a lawyer to understand the New Zealand economy. It was a legal construct. Only the law could allow farmers to earn an income by killing sheep and burying them, or allow manufacturers to profit from selling goods in Sydney they could not sell in Auckland. My association with a commercial law practice taught me only too well how business ordered its affairs to take advantage of regulatory intervention. There was a ramshackle wall of legal protection around the economy and its structures were creaking almost audibly. Muldoon's regulatory excesses were increasingly absurd. You did not need to be an economist to understand that; the question was what to replace them with.

One of the reasons I was drawn to Roger Douglas was his willingness to explore the possibilities. He liked ideas and was given to thinking aloud and to issuing publications which read as if they were written in capital letters. He could be obstinate, and having seized on an idea he could thrash it to death. He came early on under the influence of the market liberals, although he was a long way from the zealot he later became; around 1980 his thinking was eclectic and drew on Labour tradition as much as on those who questioned the traditional model. What I liked in him was his readiness to break with the past; he was not afraid to tackle the issues which had bedevilled the Labour Party in its recent history and kept it on the opposition benches. He had learned from Labour's unhappy experience in government between 1972 and 1975. I believed that Douglas alone of the caucus would enable Labour to reshape itself as a modernising party which could actually do something for the country. We needed fire and he provided it.

Douglas was a minister when Labour was last in government and he may have found opposition tedious. He spent part of his time building up the family business and had few prospects in the parliamentary Labour Party as long as Rowling held the leadership. As the general election of 1981 drew closer it seemed that he had had enough and I heard that he intended to step down. On the night that his electorate committee met to consider candidate nominations, I drove out to the hall in Manurewa where the meeting was in progress. The door was ajar and I could hear what was happening. It was a sombre gathering. There was a very gloomy address from Douglas in his characteristic monotone, ending with the announcement that he would not be standing again.

I pushed the door open and without waiting for an invitation spoke to the meeting. I said that Roger was important to the Labour Party. I said that because I was the deputy leader and not the leader I could not guarantee him the prominence he deserved, but if that were to change he would be our finance spokesman and he would have my support. There was a warm response from the electorate committee and a reluctant but not grudging agreement from Douglas to stand again.

It was a measure of my regard for Roger Douglas that I bothered. Politics was of less moment to me then. For much of 1981 I felt unwell. In the middle of the year I was diagnosed as diabetic; it was a condition which initially proved difficult to manage. The medication caused me considerable upset – I was always sick, and often being sick. For the first time in my life, my weight became a burden to me. I was close to twenty-eight stone and thought I was going to die. I had tried to diet but never succeeded. The only time in my adult life I ever lost weight was when I lived in London and was short of money. The idea of surgery to resection my stomach was put to me as early as 1975 and in August 1981 I revisited it. Although there was some risk attached, it seemed worth it: unless I did something about my weight, I saw no future in anything.

I played little part in the election campaign; this was calculation on the part of Rowling and his associates. I was happy enough to be consigned to speak in forlorn electorates and record a few radio commercials. Once again the Labour Party gained a majority of the popular vote and once again we managed not to win. After choosing a speaker, the National Party had a parliamentary majority of one. Social Credit had two members. There were some in the National

Party who were known to be restless under the Muldoon yoke, so it was always going to be a parliament full of opportunity.

Under the guidance of my medical advisor, Pat Frengley, I prepared myself for a gastric bypass. This is a procedure in which the stomach is reduced to a small pouch, making you physically limited in what you can eat. The first requirement was to give up smoking. I was sure that a different environment would help, so I went with my family to Launceston in Tasmania, where my sister Annette had a mixed business, what we would call a dairy. We lived in a caravan and I worked in the shop for a month. It was a wonderful break and I returned to New Zealand smoke-free and ready for surgery.

I went into the Adventist Hospital for the operation and woke some eight hours after the surgery. I wondered at first where I was. I could distinctly hear a Bach chorale. The singers proved to be real enough; they were in the hospital to entertain the patients. I needed no entertainment – I was euphoric. I was alive, I would be well, I was going to be transformed.

My stay in hospital lasted about a week. There was interest on the part of the news media, and the hospital staff were most helpful in keeping me away from them. A *Truth* photographer managed to get in, flinging open the door to the room which was marked with my name and taking a photograph of the large Pink Panther the staff had thoughtfully placed in the bed to represent me. I convalesced at home in Mangere. It was arduous enough and I was sick and sore. For some time I was limited to fluids and it was a real joy when I could finally eat some mashed potato. Two months after the surgery I made my first public appearance. I stood outside my house wearing a pair of my old trousers and let the photographers take pictures which showed how much weight I had lost. I went to Jaffe's menswear shop in Otahuhu and bought a new suit and other new clothes. I was full of a most extraordinary sense of well-being.

My weight fell to nineteen stone after the operation and was probably up to twenty by the time I became prime minister. The surgery had a peculiar effect on me. It seemed that anything I ate was rapidly absorbed. My heart sped up, my pulse raced to such an extent that to begin with I was apprehensive about eating. I found later on that alcohol acted even faster on me. But I hardly drank at all for a long time after the surgery.

Too much nonsense has been written about the change in my appearance which followed the surgery. I did not change my appearance in order to promote myself in politics – when I was a heap I did well enough in politics. I had the surgery because I wanted to live. I bought new clothes from Jaffe's because my old ones did not fit. I got my hair cut because almost every man in the country got his hair cut after the excesses of the seventies. It was cut by a barber until 1990. I got new glasses at the beginning of 1984 because I needed them.

I did this for myself and on my own account. The only advice on image which stayed with me was given to me by Brian Edwards in a talk before the 1984 election. He explained to me the relationship between action and image on television and in particular made me understand that what worked in front of a live audience in a hall did not work on television. The gestures and emphasis which were needed to communicate to a live audience were jarring on the small screen. On television something as close as possible to conversation was what was needed. This was particularly useful advice before an election campaign in which much of the television coverage was filmed at public meetings. While the camera was on me I had to remember that I was talking to one person. I could carry on in my usual way when the camera was gone.

I completed my convalescence after the stomach surgery by travelling to the United States. The American embassy offered me a month's visit to examine such aspects of the American way of life as I chose. My stated aim was to come to terms with a country which had elected Jimmy Carter in 1976 and replaced him with Ronald Reagan in 1980. This ambition may have been beyond the understanding of the State Department and I was not much the wiser when I returned. I came back to a country in which the prime minister put an end to inflation by making regulations which made it illegal to pay wage increases or put up prices. By now I was well and truly ready to get stuck into the government. I was ready to enjoy myself.

It was then that I found myself on the same side as the government. After hearing legal argument on behalf of a woman who was deported from New Zealand, the Privy Council in London found that something like 100,000 Western Samoans were in fact New Zealand citizens. This came as a considerable surprise to almost every Samoan and had a fairly blunt effect on the New Zealand public. The government decided to enlist the help of the parliamentary opposition: Muldoon met Bill Rowling and Bruce Beetham and asked for their support in passing urgent legislation to overturn the effect of the decision. Rowling did not consult the caucus before he agreed and then left for a month overseas.

Anderton meanwhile demanded that the government leave the Privy Council's decision unmolested, and in this he had the support of some Labour members of parliament.

There was a significant Samoan population in the Mangere electorate. Publicly many of them supported calls for the decision to be upheld while privately complaining that they could not cope with a wave of new arrivals. At the New Zealand government's invitation I went to Western Samoa, not to take part in consultations with the Samoan government but to get some feeling for the local response. I travelled with Jim McLay, the attorney-general, whom I had known since law school. I walked early one morning to a peculiar small wooden building in the middle of a clearing; it was the headquarters of the Mau, the Samoan independence movement. Its leaders had gathered there one day and had engaged in a confrontation with New Zealand soldiers which had led to several of them being killed and the rest taken away to forced labour on Nauru. I thought it ironic that those who had spilt their blood in the interests of their country's independence should have their achievements blessed with New Zealand citizenship by law lords in London. Samoan support for the Privy Council decision was shorthand for the wish for a humane and reasonable immigration policy in New Zealand. In the end the two governments made an agreement in which the citizenship bestowed by the Privy Council would be withdrawn and certain residential qualifications conceded to the 40,000 Samoans already living here.

Back in Wellington it proved reasonably easy to manage Labour's part in the passage of the legislation. I enjoyed telling Anderton in the confines of caucus that he had no right to speak publicly on matters which were the preserve of parliamentarians. As president he was responsible for the party's policy-making process; he had no licence to make policy himself or announce it. This point continued to escape him.

Anderton attended caucus in his capacity as party president. Most of those who played significant roles in the Labour government of 1984 onwards were present at caucus then. We met in a room on the third floor of parliament. On the walls were pictures of the party's former leaders. Rowling and I sat behind a table, the caucus secretary at one end of it. The members sat in a half-circle around the table. It is odd how the memory works. I am sure that every member sat in the same place each week, but I cannot remember now where anyone sat, except that those who were most inclined to be troublesome or aggressive sat at the back. Moore sat there, and Prebble. I do not recall members sitting in factional flying squads, although the caucus was certainly fractious. It was not a pleasant atmosphere. We were divided amongst ourselves and easily disheartened. Most of the time was spent discussing parliamentary business and the talk was often acrimonious.

There were six women members in the caucus: Mary Batchelor, who retired in 1984, Helen Clark, Ann Hercus, Margaret Shields, Whetu Tirikatene-Sullivan and Fran Wilde. They were very different personalities and did not obviously act in concert. Hercus was hard-working and seized with zeal, especially in her own interest. Clark was a silent attendant at caucus. She has spoken of the troubles she faced as a woman in the caucus of those days but she did not help herself by her association with Anderton and his cohort, which made her an object of suspicion and resentment and added to the difficulties routinely met by women members.

There were four Maori members: Koro Wetere was Tainui; Peter Tapsell, an orthopaedic surgeon, represented the home counties; Whetu Tirikatene-Sullivan was Ratana and Apostolic; and Bruce Gregory was a mystic from the north. I was never able to discover a Maori caucus, despite many efforts to do so. Anyone who wanted Maori support would court Koro Wetere on the assumption that he would bring the others with him, but this was almost always over-optimistic.

There were individuals who could be relied on to make a contribution. The soothing words of Fraser Colman, a former unionist and former cabinet minister, were listened to with respect. Frank O'Flynn QC often intervened effectively and could be cutting. Prebble had become an effective caucus advocate. David Caygill was reserved and astute. He was close to Geoffrey Palmer who was always busy and whose caucus speeches were usually reports on his various assignments.

When I looked at the caucus I saw many I liked and a few I distrusted. I saw supporters and opponents. Anderton's mutterings aside, I did not see enemies. Nor did I see friends. Joe Walding, whom I counted as a friend, left parliament in 1981. In every other part of my adult life I formed friendships which lasted, but apart from Joe there were none among my caucus colleagues. Friendship requires you to let down your guard. Perhaps because I rose so quickly to the leadership of the Labour Party I never was able to do that in politics.

In November 1982 Bill Rowling announced that he would step down from the leadership of the parliamentary Labour Party the following February. The delay was almost certainly meant to allow a fair chance for another contender to be drafted. Rowling probably favoured Russell Marshall as his successor; Marshall certainly favoured himself and put his name forward. He was a hand-wringing liberal with no obvious qualifications for the job and when it came to the vote he was easily seen off.

The vote for deputy leader was a far closer contest. Mike Moore was among my chief supporters. He was a life-long politician and showed great personal fortitude in recovering from illness. In those days I never had anything but goodwill from him. His opponent, Geoffrey Palmer, was close to Rowling. There may have been a feeling in caucus that one faction should not have all the prizes, but for whatever reason it happened, Palmer's victory turned out well for me. Moore was incurably ambitious which would not have made him a reassuring deputy. He was impulsive and in his enthusiasm not always comprehensible. We would, I think, have made a volatile combination.

Palmer was relatively new to parliament. Between the two of us we had just over a decade of parliamentary experience. We were both lawyers and our election was the height of what proved to be a passing ascendancy of the legal profession in the parliamentary Labour Party. Palmer had a career of considerable distinction as an academic lawyer. He was learned, he had an interest in constitutional matters and was appalled by the constitutional outrages of the Muldoon government. We had very little in common and I hardly knew him when he became my deputy, but I came to rely on him. He had a capacity for the detail of administration and a reputation for fairness. He was willing to attempt the rational resolution of the most intractable of issues. He loved procedure: this is not my characterisation, it was his own not-infrequent assertion. If the procedure was right, the result would be right. The reverse side of this, as it proved, was that he became distressed when things did not go according to process. He was a lawyer first and, some way behind, a politician.

I knew when I was elected leader that I had been given the greatest chance of my life. There would be an election in less than two years and I believed that this time Labour would not lose. It was a chance to make a different kind of country in New Zealand. I knew that this could be a country which had the assurance to stand up for itself and make its way confidently in the world. It was about more than money, although the money was important. We had to start, as I used to say in those days, getting a bit of joy back into the place.

I probably spoke to caucus about the likelihood of victory in 1984 – it is all a blur now. When it was over Palmer and I went out to face the news media. I doubt I said anything particularly coherent since I was far too excited.

CHAPTER TEN

On 3 February 1983, the day I was elected leader of the Labour Party, Malcolm Fraser called a general election and Bob Hawke was elected leader of the Australian Labor Party. Hardly six weeks later Hawke was sworn in as prime minister of Australia. One of my first actions as leader was to go to Sydney to meet Hawke. This was an unabashed quest for a photo opportunity. A one-day international cricket match was held to raise money for the victims of bushfires. I went with Roger Douglas and there was little time to make any arrangements. We paid our own way into the ground and talked ourselves into Hawke's enclosure. Hawke was gracious and our conversation more cordial than any we ever had afterwards; photographs were taken and duly published in the papers at home. New Zealand beat Australia by fourteen runs. We had some free time in Sydney and Douglas said, 'Come on and I'll show you something.' He took me into a shop in Centrepoint where he pointed to a display of a large number of products made in Mangere by his family company and selling profitably in Australia thanks to the export incentives offered by the New Zealand government.

Douglas was now the Labour Party's finance spokesman. I gave him no prescription and there was no doubt of my confidence in him: I expected him to prepare for the day when the Muldoon government would be gone. I knew his weaknesses as much as I valued his strengths – he would be at odds with some in the caucus and many more in the party outside parliament, but I thought him robust enough to stand up to moderation by the party's policy-making processes. I knew that his thinking was not always consistent, but what reassured me was the knowledge that as finance minister he would have the advice and the huge departmental resources of Treasury behind him. It was well known in Wellington that senior officials of Treasury and the Reserve Bank were at odds with Muldoon over economic policy and demoralised by his propensity to override their judgement. Officials might for that reason welcome the appointment of Douglas and would undoubtedly stop him from acting like a maverick. It was the practice in those days to second a middle-ranked Treasury officer to the staff of the parliamentary opposition and this officer was set to work with Douglas.

Much changed when I became leader of the opposition. Rowling as leader kept a stable of supporters while I was cosy in my dealings with those in the caucus who were clearly on my side. I knew this could not continue. I wanted to be approachable by everyone in the caucus and accountable to all the factions. I purposely set out to keep a greater distance between me and those who were once my closest colleagues. I found myself in a new relationship with members of the parliamentary press gallery and other journalists. As deputy to Rowling I went out of my way to avoid comment on matters which were his responsibility; now I was expected to comment on almost everything. It was hard work to keep myself briefed, but I liked the freedom of it, or at any rate freedom up to a point. There is nothing like knowing that every television interview could be your last to put some caution into your words.

I inherited an office on the third floor of Parliament Buildings. It was once the prime minister's office and it was comfortable enough, if somewhat shop-worn in the way the old buildings used to be before the rehabilitation of the 1990s. My salary rose very smartly to a level of a cabinet minister. If I remember rightly, I had a staff of five to begin with. Ross Vintiner became my press secretary. He was thoughtful and hard-working, and he needed to be. There was no end to the demands of the news media and he fielded them by himself. Margaret Pope was a private secretary. She was softly spoken and reserved and dealt with the correspondence which flooded into the office.

There was much to learn. One of the first visitors to my new office was Lin Smith, the director of the Security Intelligence Service. He came with the agreement of the prime minister to brief me on matters of national interest. I had some apprehension about his visit. Almost everyone involved in the civil liberties movement in the 1970s had concerns about the activities of the SIS. I used to be a frequent observer at sittings of an official inquiry into the SIS, which was established after it was learned that an SIS agent was spying on staff and students at Auckland University.

The head of the SIS in those earlier days was Brigadier Gilbert, a conservative figure; Lin Smith, too, was a former senior army officer and I doubted I would find him sympathetic. He proved when he arrived to be an unlikely spy, liberal enough in his views and invariably straightforward in his expression of them.

Smith told me about the UKUSA agreement, a longstanding arrangement between New Zealand, the United Kingdom and other Commonwealth countries and the United States to share intelligence. He went into some detail about its workings and briefed me on the relationships between the SIS and other government agencies. He described the Government Communications Security Bureau, which monitored telephone and radio communications. The nature of its activities is well enough known today, but almost all of what Smith told me then about the bureau was new to me. He emphasised that New Zealand's intelligence effort was aimed at China and the Soviet Union, although he appeared to doubt the intelligence capacity of the Chinese. He was more concerned about the covert potential of the Russians and their allies.

Smith was far from alone in his anxiety about the Soviet bloc. It was widespread in those Cold War days and background to the debate about the ANZUS alliance which caused so much difficulty in the Labour Party in the early 1980s.

The alliance was the product of an agreement made between Australia, New Zealand and the United States in 1951. It enjoyed strong public support in this country, where it was popularly seen as our defence against Soviet aggression. It was routinely described by diplomats and conservative politicians as the cornerstone of our international relations. Public attachment to ANZUS was so great that I did not believe that Labour could win a general election if a Labour victory was seen to threaten the alliance. The alliance was, however, disliked by many Labour activists: some distrusted the alliance itself, while many more objected to it because it meant the visits to New Zealand of American nuclear ships. The party's policy was to exclude both nuclear-armed and nuclear-powered vessels from New Zealand, but the problem was the American response. The United States could decide that the alliance was not worth its trouble if it could not bring its ships.

Bill Rowling, who was now the party's foreign affairs spokesman, believed that New Zealand could be nuclear-free without the Americans putting an end to ANZUS, if only because it would not be possible for them to make a new defence agreement with the Australians. My aim at the time was to reach an understanding with the United States which would allow New Zealand and the United States to have some kind of defence relationship which did not depend on nuclear weapons. It is odd to write that now, given how quickly we found that we could have an alliance with the United States only on American terms. But that was not something I knew in 1983.

The first task was to put discussion of the issue on a different footing. I believed that a nuclear-free policy should be based on the exclusion of nuclear weapons. I agreed with the prevailing opinion in the Labour Party about nuclear weapons; I went on ban-the-bomb marches in the 1960s and I have not changed my mind about nuclear deterrence since. But I found it hard to accept that the Labour Party's policy required the exclusion of nuclear-powered ships. Given that nuclear energy exists, it is the intention behind its use which matters. The weapons are made to destroy and we have to learn to live without them. The rest may be useful, if properly managed. The management is an environmental issue and the inevitable exclusion of nuclear-powered vessels was not an appropriate basis for our foreign policy. I still think this was a logical position to take. The difficulty was that the United States saw the ANZUS alliance as a means of projecting nuclear force. As we learned, it reserved the right to imply that every vessel in its fleet was nuclear-armed, from the oldest rust-bucket to the most sophisticated nuclear-powered vessels, which made the means of propulsion irrelevant.

I raised the question in public. Anderton of course objected and so did many party members. Some were simply concerned about the environmental dangers posed by nuclear-powered vessels. Others scented a back-down from the nuclear-free policy. By the time of the party's annual conference in September it seemed that delegates might well call for New Zealand's formal withdrawal from the ANZUS alliance.

The party's conference in those days was some distance from a stage-managed event. It was widely reported on television but it was not designed for the television audience. It started with meetings of special-interest groups on a Friday morning and finished at lunch-time on the Monday. What could roughly be described as the rank-and-file of the party met in great numbers. The delegates had their head: the conference gave them a chance to have their say and, if it came to it, vote. There was always substantial trade union representation on the floor of the conference; it was not always of a single mind, but it had the capacity to muster up a significant block of votes in support of any particular proposition.

Policy in those days was not discussed in secluded workshops: it was thrashed out on the floor of the conference. Delegates debated remits which would, if adopted, be referred to the party's policy council for further discussion and possible inclusion in the election manifesto. Long lines of delegates waited for a turn at the microphone if the issue was a contentious one. The atmosphere was sometimes rowdy and it could be angry and ill-tempered.

The 1983 conference was held in Auckland. I looked forward to it with a certain apprehension. There was strong support for Bill Rowling among the party's ordinary membership and I did not endear myself to the rank-and-file when I talked about the difference between nuclear weapons and nuclear propulsion. There was awkwardness in the relationship between me and Rowling, who as foreign affairs spokesman was responsible for steering discussion of ANZUS through the conference. There was also awkwardness in the relationship between me and Jim Anderton. When the president began the conference with a call for Labour to be the party of Robin Hood and not the party of the sheriff of Nottingham, I knew that my speech to the delegates would be critical.

I had had a lot of advice from colleagues about my speech, and I had some notes, but most of what I said was extempore. If I was nervous, and I probably was, it was the occasion which made me nervous, not the audience.

I rarely doubted my ability to speak. Over the years I had learned a lot about what worked and what did not. The first requirement was to look absolutely unfazed by anything that happened, and in particular by anything adverse. There was no fiddling with papers. The aim was to look in command. To break myself in, I almost always started with something unarguable and germane to the event. I had to be able to see the audience to be sure of its response. The sound of its reaction was not enough. It was often helpful to pick out a little patch of discord in the crowd and provoke its components into heckling or shouting and then allow its defeat by the majority of the audience. At events like party conferences, it was possible to flick from topic to topic, gauging the response and riding the ones which incited enthusiasm. If gravitas was wanted, I would read from a script, but that was not my practice while campaigning, when emotion was paramount. The great advantage of not relying on a script was that I could readily capitalise on what had gone before or what was happening in front of me in the hall. I did not know every word in advance before I spoke, but I certainly knew the effect I wanted to achieve. Whenever I spoke, I always had an aim in mind.

My aim in speaking to the delegates at the 1983 conference was simply to identify myself with them. I spoke of the goals we shared and the capacity we had collectively to make our country a better place. The response from the greater part of the audience was pleasantly warm and reassuring and I was relieved. It was a start.

Bill Rowling was able to persuade the conference that it should not reach any conclusion about ANZUS. It was agreed that there should be a review of the alliance when Labour became the government, the aim being to broaden the defence agreement into co-operation on economic and social issues. This aim, together with the exclusion of nuclear-armed and nuclear-powered vessels, was the basis of the policy the party took into the general election.

Parliament sat very little that year. Muldoon towards the end of 1983 was unable to capture the attention of his caucus colleagues in the way he once had. He was in the house less often and when he was there he appeared not to enjoy it. He was less decisive in debate, seeming to need the reassurance of his notes, and bits of paper fluttered around him when he spoke. None of this was good reason to take him lightly. The Labour caucus met for three days at Tatum Park, a scout camp near Levin, to discuss strategy for the election. We watched a television series about the Whitlam government and its collapse. There were seven hours in all, or it felt like it, and the lessons from it were obvious. Disunity led to electoral downfall. The Whitlam government's slide into disaster was marked by a failure of internal communications. Its members were unaware of its goals and were inconsistent in their response to issues. Having taken the counsel of perfection in government from the Whitlam example, we examined our conduct in opposition. We agreed that we would do more than react to events as they unfolded; we would put forward our own policy rather than engage in knee-jerk responses to that of the government. We would not attack Muldoon. We would in fact ignore him except when we had to join in set pieces in parliament. We resolved to look like a government in waiting.

This was wonderful advice to give ourselves, but like much else in life it was easier said than done. I could not always restrain myself from having a flick at Muldoon. When the New Year's honours list came out I was astonished, like almost everyone, to find that he had awarded himself a knighthood: convention demanded that he wait for a successor to recognise his achievements. I was at the Auckland Cup at Ellerslie on New Year's Day and was asked by a television journalist what I thought about the honours list. I said, 'After a very long year we've got a very short knight.' I should have been more statesmanlike – he would have found it harder to take.

I did start to hold regular press conferences in the little theatre on the ground floor of the Beehive. This was the place where Muldoon spoke to the news media and I wanted to be seen with the symbols of the office. His response was very quick: he gave up the Beehive theatrette and took to having his press conferences in his office.

It was hard for the Labour Party to reach unity or even the appearance of unity. Towards the end of 1983 two sitting members of parliament failed to be reselected as Labour candidates. John Kirk lost the nomination for Sydenham. He worked very hard to lose it and never overcame the burden of his father's legacy. His replacement was Jim Anderton. I consoled myself with the thought that he would be too far down the food chain to make much difference in parliament. Brian MacDonell was another who was not reselected. He was not a dynamic figure and he was simply bowled in the selection process. Kirk and MacDonell chose to sit in parliament as independents, which gave an impression of instability.

Policy proved a graver difficulty. Our differences over economic policy were not played out in public in the way we had argued about the nuclear-free policy. This argument took place in private. Towards the end of 1983 Douglas produced an economic policy package, the detail of which has long since been lost to my memory. It was not short but it was consistent. It was by any test a radical document. Douglas has proclaimed it the blueprint for what he achieved as finance minister; whether that is true or not, it probably gave the flavour of it. I remember being surprised but not in the least perturbed. I expected him to think outside the square. The package was a long way from becoming policy. It would go to caucus and policy council and it would be thrashed about at the party conference in the second half of 1984.

The Douglas proposals met a mixed reception in caucus and hostility in the policy council. A competing prescription appeared, which was promoted by several of the caucus as well as by members of the party hierarchy. The rival view acknowledged the need for adjustment but assumed that the government would continue to play a leading role in the direction of economic activity. I thought that unrealistic, given the continuing failure of government interventions in the previous decade. There seemed no meeting place between the two proposals. The argument went back and forth between caucus and policy council. Geoffrey Palmer finally undertook an attempt at reconciliation. He wrote a brief paper in terms broad enough to accommodate both sides of the argument, although I doubt it satisfied either of them. When a general election was unexpectedly called in June 1984, Palmer's paper became by default our economic policy.

The fact of it is that Labour went into the election without an agreed economic policy. I have often thought about this in light of the accusations of bad faith made against the Labour government. I did not regard the Douglas economic policy package as being the policy of the Labour Party: I favoured it over the opposing argument, but it was not my intention simply to see it put into practice. If I was asked about it, I said it was not our policy, which was the truth of it. Later assertions by Douglas that the package was always his charter are merely vainglorious. It was not mine. There is much that I did or failed to do which I have cause to regret, but I will not be held party to a charge of wilful deception in the 1984 general election. I did my best with what I had – and in the middle of 1984 what I had was an unfinished argument.

In some ways I found leadership of the opposition heavy going. I did not like hawking myself around interest groups and the like. I started out with an extraordinary boost in the opinion polls which put me above Muldoon. From there the only way to go was down, which was where I went. Naomi accompanied me to big set-piece occasions and seemed to enjoy her involvement in the Labour Party in Mangere, but the demands of the job put a distance between home life and working life that I had never before experienced.

In January 1984 Naomi and I went abroad, using the travel entitlement granted to the leader of the opposition. We went by way of Los Angeles to snow-bound Washington. I met George Bush Senior, who was then vice president, and was given a tour of the Pentagon. There was an extraordinary memorial to the military engagements in which armed forces from the United States and New Zealand had taken part together. It was hard not to note that it was based on a misrepresentation. The display proclaimed itself a monument to the ANZUS alliance, but the treaty was not invoked in any of the several conflicts it depicted.

The Labour Party was well enough placed in electoral terms when I came back to New Zealand in February. Polling in the early months of the year showed us only a few points behind the National Party, a deficit we would on past experience expect to make up easily when the general election campaign began in November. Labour was aided when Bob Jones, a property developer and controversialist, started a party of his own called the New Zealand Party. It was a party unashamedly to the right of the National Party, but most unusually for parties of that ilk it was always entertaining. It was a have-a-go-and-to-hell-with-the-consequences party, but it is wrong to suggest, as Jones has, that the presence of the New Zealand Party won the 1984 election for Labour. It was the legacy of that presence which was more influential in 1987, when many who had first been separated from their allegiance to National by the New Zealand Party gave their vote to Labour. Nonetheless the split in the conservative vote was certainly useful to Labour in 1984.

In parliament when the house sat Labour's problems with Kirk and MacDonell were more than matched by instability in the National Party. The chorus of dissent inside National was getting louder. Among the caucus rebels was Marilyn Waring. A Labour member promoted a bill which would make New Zealand nuclear-free and on 13 June 1984 Waring crossed the floor to support it. It was defeated thanks only to the votes of the Labour renegades. The next evening Parliament Buildings were alive with rumour and speculation. Geoffrey Palmer was at a formal dinner at Government House. So too was Jim McLay, who was deputy prime minister. It was Palmer who confirmed to me that the most unlikely of possibilities was actually the case. Muldoon, claiming himself unable because of Waring's actions to command a majority in the house, had asked the governor-general to dissolve parliament.

There was never a night like that night in all the time I was in politics. The air was electric. I could hardly believe it. Muldoon had thrown away his government. There would be an election and not for a moment did I doubt we would win it. Not for a moment did I doubt that whatever might happen to us in government we would be better, and do better, than what had gone before us.

Muldoon and I both made statements to the news media late that evening. His has become the stuff of political legend. Mine was certainly less memorable, but more purposeful. The point I remember making was that Muldoon had run away from his responsibilities. In whatever else I said I wanted to convey the buoyancy with which Labour was approaching government.

Nobody expected the snap election. It found the Labour Party with its manifesto unwritten and differences over economic policy a long way from settled. Planning for the campaign was well under way when the election was called. The party organisation under Anderton was in fair shape to fund and fight an election. I spent a large part of the night the election was called recording radio advertisements which urged potential voters to get on the electoral rolls before they closed.

The date of the general election was 14 July 1984. The Labour Party formally opened its campaign on 26 June, a day set also for the release of the party manifesto. Electioneering of course began almost at once, although it did not begin particularly well for me. Before the election was called I had accepted an invitation to attend a rugby test match between New Zealand and France at Lancaster Park in Christchurch. This was a matter of duty. I grew up with rugby league and always preferred it to the other football game, but my attendance was part of an effort to reconcile the Labour Party with opinion alienated in 1981. I went to the game with Mike Moore and we were greeted by officials who offered to conduct us to our seats. For whatever reason they led us in front of the stand and then back again. We were roundly jeered. As we left after the game I was punched by one of the crowd. That was the only time in my career in public life in which I was physically assaulted, even though I used as prime minister to get out and about on my own in a way that prime ministers might hesitate to do now. It certainly marked the end of my efforts to reach some kind of understanding with the rugby public and I have not seen a game of rugby since.

Much worse followed.

New Zealand at that time had a fixed exchange rate. It was widely thought by the government's economic advisors that the dollar was overvalued. Douglas certainly thought so. There was speculative selling of the dollar as soon as the election was announced, but given the cost to the country of such trading it was unthinkable that an opposition finance spokesman could invite profiteering by openly advocating a devaluation. That was in effect what happened. Douglas held a meeting in his electorate and distributed copies of a paper in which he urged a substantial devaluation. Almost inevitably the paper became public. It was the first time I had serious cause to doubt Douglas's discretion and judgement.

He was contrite when he came to see me, acknowledging the gravity of what he had done. He had no explanation for what had happened and offered his resignation. I did not accept it. I did not see how I could possibly replace him as finance spokesman so close to the election. We were lucky that Muldoon for whatever reason did not make as much of the incident as he might have done, and I decided to weather the storm. I did not know it was only the first of them.

CHAPTER ELEVEN

The Labour Party opened its election campaign in the Christchurch town hall. It was the best-looking venue in the country and for me it was a sentimental choice. Rowling had launched the 1975 campaign there and had moved me to declare to Bob and Maude Wynyard that I would be in his place in 1984.

My speech at the opening was a marathon in the preparation. Ross Vintiner usually wrote my speech notes but everyone wanted to have a go at this one. Brian Edwards made a contribution. Mike Moore wanted a say, as did his offsider, Mike Rann, later premier of South Australia. There were others too and I picked out what I thought would work. I needed a script because the timing was critical: the opening broadcast lasted thirty minutes, twenty-seven of which were given over to live coverage of my speech, leaving exactly three minutes at the end for the first screening of our campaign advertising.

The town hall could hold close to 3000 people and that evening it was full. I could hear the buzz of the crowd as I waited behind the stage. The plan was simple. I would walk on the stage, Geoffrey Palmer would shake my hand and I would speak for the allotted time. To guide me, as I could not be seen to glance at my wrist, there was a stopwatch on the lectern. It was Palmer's job to get the stopwatch ready. When the time came, Palmer greeted me, shaking hands vigorously and smiling broadly, and then unexpectedly he spoke. Nearly five years later, when things were going badly for me, Palmer met me at the airport on my return from overseas with the words, 'You haven't got the numbers!' but nothing he ever said to me was quite as startling as what was uttered in the town hall that evening. 'The stopwatch is broken!' Bearing in mind my first rule of public speaking, I tried to look confident.

I spoke not to the crowd in the hall but to a single unknown voter watching my image on a television screen. I paid no heed to the reaction of the audience, and simply talked without exaggeration of speech or gesture. Out of the corner of my eye I could see a television technician and after a while I saw the rolling motion of the arms which is the signal to wind up the performance. I brought my talk to a close then let rip at the audience. Half an hour of calm had made them ready for anything and the response was splendid. It was a wonderful start to the campaign.

The campaign was a mixture of the old and new in politics. I did the rounds of the marginal electorates and spoke at many public meetings. I went looking for photo opportunities. The programme as a whole was devised with the demands of television in mind. There were set pieces, among which were a television debate involving all the party leaders and, on Sunday, 8 July, the head-to-head confrontation between Muldoon and me. Ian Johnstone chaired the debate between us.

Muldoon was on the back foot before the debate even started. The National Party campaign was not particularly well managed, and as the incumbent the contest was his to lose. At the same time, I knew that I had to do more than survive. I wanted to see him off. My aim was to stay calm, whatever the provocation, and present Muldoon inferentially and sometimes expressly as yesterday's man. The question lines were reasonably easy to handle, and towards the end I sensed that Muldoon knew that he had done nowhere near enough and that it was close to the finish for him. I looked across at him and said that I hoped he understood that there was a part for him to play in our country's affairs after the election. It was a way of acknowledging his defeat without seeming ungenerous. I did not mean to be unkind, but it was too much for him to take. Tears came into his eyes and he said, 'I love you, Mr Lange.'

When the broadcast was over he turned on me with some savagery, accusing me of demeaning him and running a nasty and derogatory campaign. It was a curious ending for a man who was once the master of such occasions. He went home and, as I later discovered, had his favourite lilies dug up from the garden of Vogel House, his official residence.

I was back in Wellington often during the campaign and grateful to my staff for the hard work they did. Some of them were with me in Auckland on election day and I invited the rest to join us there. They accepted, except for Margaret. I felt a pang of regret, or resentment, which I put down to disappointment that all of the staff would not be present.

On the night before election day I spoke at one last meeting in Mt Eden. It was a joyful gathering. I knew Labour was going to win, but I did not think about the significance of the victory. The emotion I felt more than any other that evening was relief. It was over, it was done. Nothing anybody said or did could make any difference now. There was nothing left to surprise me.

I woke up tense on the day itself, Saturday, 14 July. I went around the Mangere polling booths and spent time at the local campaign headquarters. It was arranged that I would stay with Naomi and the family at the DB hotel in Mangere where all of the staff were staying. Early in the evening we went from there to the Metro theatre in Massey Road. The old Metro was part of my youth; I had seen many films at the Metro and taken part in a school play there. It occurred to me that on my last appearance on that stage I had been dressed as a block of cheese. I thought often of my father that evening. Everywhere around me had some association with him.

The hall filled with people. Naomi and I waited with staff and members of the electorate committee in the kitchen at the back. As the results came in over the radio, it was clear that there was a substantial swing to Labour, more than enough to carry the country.

I spoke to the crowd when the issue was beyond doubt. There was a scrum of some proportion in front of the stage and I had to struggle to reach the ticket office at the front of the building to take a telephone call. At the other end of the line was Bob Hawke, who offered his congratulations and said that he had a friend who wanted to speak to me. This was George Shultz, the American secretary of state, who was in Australia on his way to a meeting of the ANZUS council in Wellington on Monday. It was an entirely unexpected call and the exchange was somewhat stilted. Shortly afterwards I was called to the telephone again. This time it was Muldoon. He said, 'Congratulations, Mr Lange. I've got some bad news for you tomorrow.' Before I could reply, he hung up. The hardest task I had that evening was to keep my composure when I went back to face the crowd.

For a large part of my life I had thought about what it would be like to win a general election, but nothing I imagined came close to the elation I felt that evening. Nothing I imagined came close to the sense of responsibility which fell on me when I heard what Muldoon said.

We were followed back to the hotel by officers from the Auckland Central police station. Their presence was a tangible sign that nothing was going to be the same again. Given my record of opposition to the interests of the police I doubt that my protection was a favourite assignment, but I did get to know and like many of the officers of the diplomatic protection squad. It did not take long to reach an understanding about the limits of their presence. The commissioner of police became deeply concerned that I was living by myself at Vogel House and invited me to nominate the officer in whom I had the greatest confidence to share the living quarters. I named the only female officer in the squad (in her spare time she bred Alsatian dogs) and heard no more about it.

Muldoon did not call me on Sunday. I spent the morning with my family. Roy was thirteen, Byron was ten and Emily was eight at the time of the election. Roy was at Wesley College and the two younger children were at local schools. The three of them had grown up with my career in politics; they were not anxious, but they were uncertain about what the new job might mean to them. Naomi and I had told them before the campaign was over that, whatever happened, their year's schooling would not be disrupted. That was almost as much as I could do for them. I was always a distracted parent and what was to come meant that I would spend even less time with them. We went to church on Sunday morning, we called members of the family in New Zealand and abroad, and I spoke to several of my colleagues.

The rest of Sunday was spent in travel to and from Wellington. Almost unbelievably, the outgoing government did not cancel or postpone the annual meeting of foreign ministers of the three ANZUS signatories. The incoming government did not take office for another ten days and could not be represented at the meeting, but I thought it appropriate to greet Shultz and Bill Hayden, the Australian foreign minister, on their arrival in New Zealand. Because his aircraft was too big to land at Wellington, Shultz arrived in Palmerston North. I flew there in an RNZAF aircraft to greet him. We went on to Wellington together, saying nothing of moment. The weather was appalling and the landing more sudden than was comfortable. After I had delivered Shultz to the official welcoming party and spoken briefly to Hayden, I went back to Auckland.

The day which followed was perhaps the most extraordinary of my life in politics. Muldoon called me at half past ten on Monday morning. He told me that the selling of the dollar which began with the announcement of the general election had continued and even accelerated right up to the day itself. He said that officials believed they had no choice but to close the foreign exchange market. The governor of the Reserve Bank, Spencer Russell, and the secretary of the Treasury, Bernard Galvin, were coming to Auckland to brief me. They had advised Muldoon that there should be a devaluation of the currency; he said he was sure they would make the same recommendation to me. Muldoon disagreed with them. He put it to me that he and I should make a joint statement that there would be no devaluation, and said that this in itself would be sufficient to stop the run on the currency. I told him I would let him know after I had spoken to the officials.

He did not tell me that the run on the dollar had almost used up the Reserve Bank's stock of foreign currency. Nor did he tell me that the country was close to the point of defaulting on its international obligations. I learned this from the officials when I met them. His call was brief enough and he put forward no argument against devaluation. Muldoon certainly knew that a devaluation big enough to stop speculation in the currency and allow orderly trading to begin again would have a cathartic effect on the economy and put at risk the regulatory structures with which he had contrived to manage it.

I met Russell and Galvin in a lounge at Auckland airport. The odd venue was chosen only because it kept us out of sight of the public. I was accompanied by Roger Douglas and David Caygill. Caygill was originally part of the Rowling following and his involvement with Douglas in economic issues did much to bring the factions in caucus together.

In making the case for devaluation, the two officials emphasised what a default would mean for New Zealand's reputation and future trading position. They had gone so far as to ask diplomatic posts overseas to find out how much foreign currency could be borrowed on credit cards. We were close to the edge. All of us at the meeting agreed that a substantial devaluation was essential and that a joint statement by me and Muldoon would not be enough; I would write to Muldoon to tell him what action he should take on behalf of the incoming government.

I expected some response from Muldoon, but I did not get one; it was not until I read Barry Gustafson's biography of him that I learned that he was waiting for some response from me. Russell and Galvin, for whatever reason, chose not to tell him what we had agreed. When I got back to Wellington later in the afternoon I told a press gallery journalist that Muldoon was refusing to act on the advice of the incoming government and this view was duly broadcast. That night on television Muldoon gave a remarkably intemperate interview in which he insisted that there would be no devaluation as long as he was finance minister. I responded, saying that he was bent on economic sabotage and that he must either follow the instructions of the incoming government or resign in favour of someone who would.

Muldoon's intransigence was an extraordinary gift to the new government. What happened that Monday night was political drama played out in front of anyone who had a television set. It made me prime minister before I had taken the oath of office, putting the reality of the currency crisis squarely in front of the public and forever identifying the old regime with recklessness and irresponsibility.

Muldoon wrote to me on Tuesday to say that he would follow

the instructions of the incoming government, and after discussions with Douglas and Caygill, who themselves held long meetings with officials, I wrote to request a devaluation of twenty percent, the removal of controls on interest rates and a freeze on wages and prices which was to last for three months. This was all done by Muldoon on Wednesday.

On Tuesday afternoon I met George Shultz, fresh from the meeting of the ANZUS council and the subsequent release of a communiqué which emphasised the importance of ship visits to the alliance. Shultz arrived in my office on the third floor of Parliament Buildings with a large number of officials. He stated the American position. I stated the Labour Party's policy. We acknowledged there was a distance between them. We looked forward to further discussions when I was formally in office. We both knew that, in accordance with its usual practice, the United States government would not make a request for a naval vessel to call at a New Zealand port for another six months. Later in the day I met Bill Hayden. In Australia as in New Zealand there was strong support in the Labor Party for a nuclear-free policy. The Hawke government took office promising to review Australia's military ties to the United States and then abandoned any attempt to limit Australian involvement in the American nuclear deterrent. I am sure looking back on what happened that it was the Australian example which led the Americans to take it for granted that New Zealand too would recant.

The new caucus met to begin with in the old caucus room. The first business was the election by the caucus of the members of the cabinet. I remember only that I was not in any way surprised by the results. If there were disappointments in the election and the following allocation of portfolios, only two of the downhearted were moved to complain to me. Gerry Wall was distressed not to be in the cabinet and was not consoled until after the death of Sir Basil Arthur in 1985, when he was appointed speaker. He was a fair if idiosyncratic speaker; a kind of video referee in that he was always several minutes behind the play. Frank O'Flynn was elected to cabinet and wanted to be attorney-general, a position I gave to Geoffrey Palmer, at his insistence. I always thought that the office of attorney-general was worth more to Geoffrey than the office of prime minister.

Most of the portfolio allocations were obvious choices on the basis of aptitude, interest or experience. I was minister in charge of the Security Intelligence Service, because the prime minister always was, and I took the foreign affairs portfolio, because it interested me and because I knew it would be critical to the new government. Douglas of course was finance minister, and Caygill and Prebble were his associates. The only appointment which was out of the ordinary for those days was Ann Hercus's appointment as police minister; I thought it might be an education for both police and minister.

The new ministry was sworn into office on 26 July 1984. My colleagues and I made our way to Government House, where the governor-general's butler welcomed us. Sir David Beattie administered the oath, we made small talk with him and Lady Beattie, then we posed for photographs. Some days after we had assumed the responsibility of it, we were formally in office. We were the fourth Labour government; it is a name which prompts mixed feelings now, but I was so proud to hear it then. I believed in our capacity to do good. My own ambitions had not changed since I first stood for parliament in the Mangere electorate. I wanted to do something for the people who had voted for us. I wanted to make the law more humane. Having acquired an interest in foreign policy, I wanted New Zealand to be a voice for good in the world. When I drove back to parliament and saw for the first time the little flag which indicated ministerial office flying from the bonnet of the car, I believed that it was all possible.

The official residence of the prime minister was Vogel House in Lower Hutt, at what I found to be an inconvenient distance from the Beehive when the traffic was heavy. In spite of its name it had no connection with the nineteenth-century prime minister. It was a comparatively modern dwelling presented to the government in the Holyoake era, and it stood at the end of a long right-of-way in a suburban street. The lawn was large and the grounds impeccably kept. A small stream ran through them. It was very much a house designed for formal entertaining, and on a grand scale. Downstairs there were large sitting rooms and reception rooms, a dining room with a magnificent table, and what looked like a commercial kitchen. Upstairs there were a number of guest bedrooms. Behind a door on the first floor was a one-bedroom apartment which formed the comfortable if somewhat cramped living quarters. The bathroom had two of everything in it, which seemed to assume an extraordinary amount of togetherness. I felt like the caretaker when I first saw the huge house and the tiny living quarters. It was not a family home.

I moved into Vogel House by myself. Prime ministers in the past made Wellington their principal residence, but I was younger than other prime ministers and I had my children to think of. There was not much to be said for moving them all to Lower Hutt. Naomi and I talked about the difficulties of a move; I intended to be back in my electorate for as much of every weekend as I could, and, knowing some of the demands of the job, I thought that I might well see less of my children if they lived at Vogel House than I would if they stayed in Mangere. Naomi wanted to stay in Mangere and I agreed with her, so I camped in Vogel House.

On Monday after the swearing-in I went to my first cabinet meeting. It was somewhat daunting. I had never been in the cabinet room, let alone presided in it. It was on the tenth floor of the Beehive and was round and windowless. There were days later on when I would have given a lot for the distraction of some passing clouds. A few old hands among us – Fraser Colman, Roger Douglas, Colin Moyle and Bob Tizard – had been ministers in the third Labour government. For the rest of us it was a new experience. There was little on our first agenda and we spent our time reviewing what had happened since the election. It was really a chance for ministers to find the chair appropriate to their ranking in the cabinet and to meet the cabinet secretary, Patrick Millen. When the meeting was over we had a cabinet lunch which was, as I learned, the custom and was held in a small dining room in Bellamy's. Then it was back to the office.

My new office was on the ninth floor of the Beehive. I doubt I liked this disorienting round building more than anyone else who worked there, but I was certainly pleased to take possession. The office looked over the harbour across the railway yards. It was comfortably large but not particularly imposing – the inner walls were exposed roughcast concrete. Although the building was only a few years old the décor was already dowdy. Beyond the office was a dark sitting room, and beyond that a little dining room, a bathroom and a tiny kitchen. The back door of the suite opened into the press office, and then came the staff tea room, the reception area, the rooms which housed the private secretaries and then you were back at the front door of my office. The Cabinet Office staff worked on the tenth floor, and the eighth floor held committee rooms and other rooms occupied by staff of the Prime Minister's Office.

Many of the staff were public servants, permanent staff who worked for both Labour and National governments. The head of the Prime Minister's Office was Gerald Hensley, a senior public servant who had a distinguished career as a diplomat. He had extensive contacts in the international intelligence community and spent much of his time in oversight of the government's intelligence activities. Ken Richardson was another survivor of the Muldoon regime. He was a ten-pound immigrant from Liverpool whose tact and judgement led him to the top rank of the parliamentary private secretaries and whose droll sense of humour made him one of the best raconteurs I have ever met. After four weeks of being in government I asked Ken who the man was who occupied the third room on the right from the front of my office. Ken said, 'It's your principal private secretary, Prime Minister.' Some kind of employment grievance had led this man to keep to his room; Ken soon afterwards replaced him in name as well as in fact. At Ken's instigation, Lorna Best was employed as diary secretary. She kept track of the many demands on my time and put those which were to be met into an orderly itinerary. I came to value Lorna, who worked for me right until the end of my time in parliament. Marjorie McDonald was the principal typist and a good one in those days when almost everything was written out in longhand.

As well as these, and other public servants on the secretarial and clerical staff, there were a number of contracted employees. Most of them came with me from the leader of the opposition's office and others were recruited from the Labour Party's parliamentary research unit. Ross Vintiner became chief press secretary. Margaret was the speechwriter. The requirements of the job meant that my days of extemporising were largely over. Stephen Mills was recruited from the research unit in 1985 as a political analyst.

The resources of the Prime Minister's Office were small in comparison to the departmental resources available to some of my ministerial colleagues. At its heart was the prime ministerial advisory group. This group came into being when Muldoon was prime minister. He wanted a source of advice which was not bound by the conventions of the public service. Its members were individuals of some distinction, people who had risen in the ranks of the private sector or the voluntary sector or who had academic achievement to their credit. They were seconded to the Prime Minister's Office for two years or less, on the understanding that they would go back to their regular employment when the term was up. If they had political sympathies, they kept them to themselves. There were some remarkable people in the group in the five years I was prime minister, and I relied on their experience and judgement when I fell out with Douglas and other ministers. There were never more than eight or nine of them. It was not until

I was almost at the end of my time in government that the office was remodelled into the larger Department of Prime Minister and Cabinet.

My working life had a structure to it. There were many distractions and disruptions and I was frequently abroad, but there was much which hardly varied. On Sunday night, or early on Monday morning if I had some obligation in Auckland, I flew from Auckland to Wellington to prepare for the cabinet meeting. I read the cabinet briefing papers. I met officials and advisors on Monday morning. I chaired the cabinet. After lunch there was a press conference in the Beehive theatre at which the work of the cabinet was disclosed and a great deal of jousting took place. Cabinet often continued in the afternoon. On Tuesday if parliament was sitting I went to the house for question time. If there were set-piece debates or matters in which I had an interest, I went back to the house in the evening. Wednesday and Thursday were the same. The caucus met on Thursday morning. I was chairman of three or four cabinet committees and I went to their meetings when I could. I dealt with visitors to my office, I spoke to colleagues and I read reports and correspondence. I often travelled to engagements outside Wellington. I tried to be home on Friday evening, although that was not always possible. I carried correspondence home with me and signed it on the aircraft. If I could, I spent the best part of Saturday in my electorate office. On Sunday if I was in Mangere I went to church and on Sunday afternoon there was often a local Labour Party obligation to be met. Then it was back to Wellington.

I was forty-one years old when I became prime minister. I was fit and well. I had the largest state house in the country, I had a car with the number plate CR1, and I had any number of people running around after me. I wondered how I was going to keep my feet on the ground.

CHAPTER TWELVE

The problem with recording one's life is not that there is so much that escapes the memory, but that there is so much that does not. If I were to recreate in detail my life in government this book would be impossible to carry. When I look at my diary for the latter half of 1984 I wonder once again how I was ever well enough to do what I did. It records one day when I spoke at the manufacturers' conference in Wellington, flew in a small plane to Alexandra, went by helicopter to the high country, spoke to a meeting of farmers, opened a power station, and flew back the same way to Wellington, where the diary invited me to attend the house in the evening.

The diary entries were boldly made in Lorna's characteristic block lettering; there were notes too by Ken Richardson, of which the seemingly quirky were probably references to visitors from the world of intelligence, and names of journalists in Ross Vintiner's handwriting. Some names appeared repeatedly. They included departmental heads like Gerald Hensley and Lin Smith, and the secretary of foreign affairs, who was usually entered as 'Mr Norrish and officials'. When Margaret Wilson succeeded Anderton as president of the Labour Party not long after the change of government, I met her every week in an effort to break down the suspicion between me and the party organisation. I had first encountered her when I was teaching at the law school in the 1970s and I knew we at least had the law in common.

Other names were legion. I hardly realised when I became foreign affairs minister that the job carried many formal responsibilities. Courtesy calls were paid on me by every representative accredited to New Zealand. It was sometimes a strain to keep the courtesy in the call, given the innocence of some emissaries about the country to which they were accredited. Ministerial attendance was expected at the national day celebrations of countries with permanent posts in New Zealand, although in this I was enormously assisted by Frank O'Flynn, the deputy minister, and by the protocol which required me to be present only for the formal toasts.

It was part of the job to meet visitors of importance to New Zealand. In every case the visit was heralded by long briefing papers about the visitor's country and by security reports which were essentially biographies of the more colourful members of the travelling party. I would familiarise myself with trade, with the visitor's stance on multilateral issues, the history of any offence which might have been taken and the possibilities of co-operation between the visitor's country and New Zealand. Some visitors I found superb, like Rajiv Gandhi, who was here in 1986, and some hard to take, like the African visitor who made a boring lunch more tedious by reading the second page of his speech notes twice. There was always a dinner, and these too could be a delight or a grim duty. I had little in common with Mahatir, the prime minister of Malaysia, who was almost my first official visitor, but I knew enough about Malaysia and he knew enough about New Zealand for us to get by for an evening.

Another recurrent obligation was the weekly press conference. They were usually well attended and it was important to prepare for them. The idea, not always achieved, was to set the agenda at the press conference and make it look like those who wriggled away from reporting it were somehow letting down the profession of journalism. I learned a few tricks over the years. If things were proving difficult it was always helpful to pick out the representative of the *Australian Financial Review*, who could be relied on to ask questions of not the slightest interest to the local news media. I took satisfaction later on from having the press conferences broadcast live on Radio Pacific. It was some insurance against the reporting of words I had not actually uttered and it was an incentive to journalists to avoid obviously stupid questions.

In my early days in government there is no doubt that I had the advantage at my press conferences of simply not being Muldoon. The press gallery was bruised by its encounters with him and I must have come as some relief to its members.

I was determined to set myself apart from Muldoon in another way. I never had the least interest, even had I the aptitude for it, in standing over cabinet colleagues. There were many among my cabinet colleagues whose abilities I respected, and within the limits imposed by the conventions of cabinet government I let them get on with it. There were also some I had to keep an eye on. One minister was unreliable in effort and even attendance at cabinet. Another once complained to me that the news media would not publish his press statements, not knowing that I had told the press office to make sure they were not distributed. A third was earnest and able but too easily unsettled by question time in parliament. These were matters which could be remedied. I did not treat the cabinet like an echo chamber; I valued its collective judgement and I willingly accepted the responsibility as prime minister of acting on it.

An enormous amount of material was distributed in advance of the cabinet meeting. For those for whom the papers were a novelty at half past ten on Monday morning there was the assurance of silence. Some ministers chose not to concern themselves with papers outside their own area of interest but the rest had no excuse to get it wrong. The quality of discussion was well ahead of debates in caucus, which by their nature were less well informed. My job as chairman was to steer the discussion so that all were able to make a contribution, none felt aggrieved or unheeded and we arrived at what was clearly the appropriate result. We were able in this way to reach agreement in a surprising number of contentious cases.

It was my birthday very soon after the government took office. A huge party was held in the Metro theatre in Mangere but I did not enjoy it – I was in some distress and I felt feverish. The evening's close was a relief but the next day I was worse. This was Sunday and on Monday I was due to travel to Papua New Guinea. Tests disclosed a form of pneumonia. My succumbing to it was simply bad luck, but I did not believe that I could afford to have questions raised about my health and my capacity to handle the job. I decided to go on the journey and do my best to conceal the illness. The official party travelled in an air-force aircraft accompanied by a number of journalists; I spent the flight in a bed behind a curtain at the front of the aircraft and hid there when we refuelled in Sydney. I was sick and sweating when we got to Port Moresby, but the climate there is such that many of the travelling party were in the same state after a few moments on the tarmac.

The occasion was a Commonwealth heads of government regional meeting. It was convened because Papua New Guinea had built an alarmingly expensive and very large parliament house constructed by a New Zealand company. The Prince of Wales flew out to open it and there was a state dinner on the day I arrived. We were entertained by a squad of bare-breasted women performing traditional dances. The prince seemed too tired to notice much, an observation confirmed when the soup arrived and he fell asleep with his head in it. The formalities were followed by meetings of no moment, although Bob Hawke did spend one breakfast-time telling me why I would be well advised to back off from the nuclear-free policy. This was the journey on which Ken Richardson, who was in constant communication by two-way radio with Jock Munro, the head of the diplomatic protection squad, left his radio in a suitcase in my room, so that when Jock's broad Scots tones were suddenly heard from inside the suitcase saying loudly, 'Jock to Ken, Jock to Ken, can you read me Ken?' the president of Bangladesh cried, 'Oh, my God!' and fled from our talks.

Hawke was also present at the South Pacific Forum meeting in Tuvalu which took place little more than two weeks after I got back from Papua New Guinea. Tuvalu is a beautiful place. It is only a couple of metres above sea level and was once host to Charles Darwin, who dug holes to prove his theory of the formation of coral atolls. I liked the forum meetings. There was a quality to Pacific dialogue which was unlike anything in Australia or New Zealand – a great deal of grunting and long periods of silence while Hawke's patience frayed and his temper simmered not far below boiling point. Hawke and I always had a strained relationship. His language was frequently obscene and he was steeped in the culture of mateship, which for me was never a good starting point. He saw his success in overcoming his own party's support for a nuclear-free policy as a tribute to his statesmanship. There was no end to his vanity.

When I got back from Tuvalu I met Sir Edmund Hillary at my home in Massey Road to ask him if he would become New Zealand's high commissioner to India. Muldoon had closed down our post in New Delhi and we were fortunate that the government of India chose to keep its post here. I was sure that we should have a mission in the most populous country in the Commonwealth, and knowing that Ed Hillary was revered in India I believed he would be a powerful symbol of New Zealand. He seemed surprised by the invitation and said he would let me know. In due course I received a letter from him in which he said he was willing to give up his commercial activities, which would be a condition of the appointment, but that he would find it difficult driving himself in Indian traffic. He wondered if there was any prospect of a driver. I called him at once and said there would be more drivers than he could manage and more cars than he could possibly sit in. He and

June Mulgrew did finally accept the invitation, to my everlasting satisfaction. The other posts I filled from outside the ranks of career diplomacy were London, where I sent my friend Joe Walding, and Washington, where Bill Rowling bore the indignation of the State Department equably enough.

It was about this time that the cabinet agreed in principle to adopt the form of indirect taxation which became known, at my suggestion, as the goods and services tax. We were well aware that it was a radical proposition. The case was put to us that it would simplify the tax system and make it more efficient, and would reduce what was obviously widespread tax avoidance. I was very much in support of it. It was agreed to by cabinet on the understanding that it would not be introduced without the accompanying protection of the position of those less able to afford the shift towards indirect taxation.

Our discussion took place entirely inside the cabinet. The new tax was determined to be a budget matter and in those days budget matters were held to be secret until the moment they were revealed by the finance minister. That was not an inevitable course, but I thought it was the wiser one. Like Douglas, I wanted it done, and done before the general election of 1987 when the electorate would pass judgement on us. It was not so much the advocacy of Douglas which moved me in this respect as my wish to see the government free of the dead weight of the conservatism of the union movement. During the election campaign Jim Knox of the Federation of Labour infuriated me by making a clumsy intervention in which he pledged industrial anarchy if Labour were not elected. The union movement in its turn was angered by the temporary continuation of the freeze on wages. Mike Moore was an enthusiast for the kind of economic management in which unions and employers sat down with the government and decided what would happen next. I met union leaders at his instigation very early on in our first term in office and found them sour and uncommunicative. There was no place there for a more co-operative style of decision-making.

The goods and services tax was to begin with a Treasury initiative, although it hardly matters at this remove whether the idea came from Treasury or from Douglas. Theirs was a perfect marriage. If they had differences in our first term in office I was not aware of them. They were always hand in glove. Douglas gave Treasury the opportunities which had eluded it when Muldoon was minister; Treasury brought discipline and consistency to the partnership. The intellectual weight was obviously Treasury's. Parts of Douglas's flat tax package of 1987, like the scheme for a guaranteed minimum family income, were developed in his office rather than in Treasury and showed nothing like the same robustness.

It was after the 1984 budget that I first heard the words 'new right' flung at the government. I wrote it off as abuse from the old left, although I was not particularly happy to have the budget defended by the Featherston Street evangelists or have the government puffed by right-wing publications like *The Economist*. I thought that what Douglas and Treasury recommended in our first two years in office was demanded by the circumstances, when we faced a huge deficit in the current account and what looked like an intractable budget deficit, and we owed billions of dollars to foreign lenders. It was only towards the latter part of 1986 that I formed the opinion, confirmed beyond all doubt the following year, that there was an

A gift to the 20-inch screen, 1977.

THE NEW ZEALAND HERALD

ELECTION SPECIAL

LANGE GRABS MANGERE!

A JUBILANT David Lange gives the victory sign last night after his sweeping victory over National's Clem Simich in the Mangere by-election. The big margin for Lange eclipsed Colin Moyle's in the 1975 General Election.

Sunday News, 1977.

THE *NEW ZEALAND HERALD*

Still scope to shrink, 1982.

Two lapsed lawyers: with Geoffrey Palmer in 1983.

THE NEW ZEALAND HERALD

Jubilation in the Metro theatre, Massey Road, Mangere, 14 July 1984.

Margaret Thatcher in a composed moment.

AP WIRE

Jerry Falwell, the president of the Oxford Union, and me, 1 March 1985.

Ronald Reagan not speaking to me, 1985.

Rajiv Gandhi in Auckland, October 1986.

The New Zealand Herald

At the fortieth anniversary of the founding of the United Nations.

The New Zealand Herald

THE NEW ZEALAND HERALD

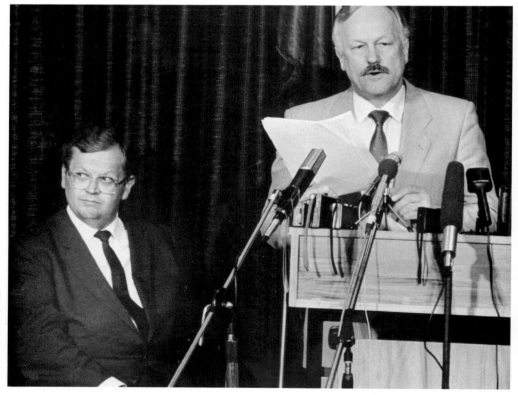

Election night, 1987.

THE NEW ZEALAND HERALD

Full throttle on flat tax, 17 December 1987.

Jane Ussher/The *Listener*

Team man.

The *New Zealand Herald*

He who laughs last: handover to Geoffrey Palmer, 1989.

The New Zealand Herald

The Queen at Government House, Wellington, 1990.

Katherine Cottier

On the road with Gary McCormick, election night, 2002.

unbending element in the views of Treasury and its minister which was more like religious belief than professional practice.

When I chaired the economic summit conference which the government convened in September 1984, it seemed to me that Treasury thinking was close enough to the feeling of most of those who took part in the conference. The conference revealed widespread disillusionment with economic management as practised in this country in the 1970s and dissatisfaction with its results. It acknowledged the urgency of the case for change. Its participants were tired of the Muldoon-style of economic management. The Treasury prescription fitted the mood as well as the need. I saw it then as a break with the past and a chance to start again.

Almost as soon as the economic summit conference was over I left with Naomi for New York, accompanied by Ken Richardson, secretary of foreign affairs Mervyn Norrish, and a note-taker from his staff. At the United Nations I heard Ronald Reagan open the new session of the general assembly. I met numerous foreign ministers, of whom the most impressive was Andrei Gromyko, who became the Soviet Union's foreign minister when I was fifteen years old. He spoke in Russian, occasionally pausing to correct the translator.

I also met George Shultz. He said that New Zealand could not have a working military alliance with the United States unless we accepted visits by American naval vessels. I said that the vessels were welcome if they conformed to our nuclear-free policy. We agreed that officials would continue to look for a formula which satisfied us both.

Shultz was well aware of my personal reservations about the ban on nuclear-powered ships, but I gave him no reason to think that I would concede him the nuclear-free policy for the sake of keeping alive the ANZUS alliance. He may well have assumed that I would, but I am not accountable for that. It has been tiresome over the years to have a legend of my concession regurgitated. I understand why the State Department might find it comforting to repeat it, but nobody in New Zealand with an interest outside the malicious or the meretricious should. I am grateful to Merv Norrish, who owes me nothing and who was in the room during my meetings with Shultz in 1984, for telling a conference in Wellington in 2004 that he did not interpret what I said as an undertaking to abandon the policy. Norrish himself saw the nuclear-free policy as something which might in the interests of the relationship with the United States be better observed in name only.

After leaving New York I made my first official visit to the United Kingdom and met Margaret Thatcher at Downing Street. She came to the front door carrying her handbag and we stood in front of a false fireplace to have our photograph taken. She looked as though she was swallowing a lemon. We had talks, but we did not have a conversation. She expressed forthright opposition to the nuclear-free policy and had no interest in anything short of our capitulation. I enjoyed meeting her; whatever else she was, she was her own woman.

We next went to New Delhi. The presidential palace, where we stayed, was a long way from the Red Shield shelter in Chowringhee. Its protocol was demanding and its décor imposing. Even the cupboard doors looked like grand entrances, so much so that Ken opened one and walked through to find himself in darkness. We had a wonderful welcome from the government of India and lunched at Hyderabad House with Indira Gandhi. The same afternoon she invited us to accompany her and her two grandchildren to a gathering which celebrated the festival of Dussehra. We sat on a stage in front of an enormous crowd, so large that I could not see the end of it. The numbers were in the hundreds of thousands. Mrs Gandhi spoke and then quite unexpectedly called on me to do the same. I have never made a speech like it. The noise of the crowd was extraordinary. The response to what I said charged me to greater effort until I finished by saying, 'Jai Hind!' and a shock wave of approval broke over us. Giant effigies stuffed with firecrackers exploded all around. That remarkable afternoon marked the end of our tour: Ken gave the staff of the presidential palace the tips which are required in such a place and carefully wrote their amount in the notebook in which he kept the record of our expenses.

I very much liked Indira Gandhi. She had a remarkable air of command and authority and was in her way as formidable a woman as Margaret Thatcher, but it was possible to carry on a conversation with her. I was shocked only a few weeks after I met her to learn of her assassination. I went to her funeral, a journey made possible only by the assistance of the air force. As Naomi and I were leaving home for the airport we found on the back doorstep a big bunch of flowers left by a local Indian shopkeeper so we took them with us. Our party arrived in Delhi late at night and it was a disturbing sight, with shops ablaze on the road between the airport and the Ashok hotel. There were soldiers and military vehicles everywhere. At the Ashok, Naomi and I found ourselves in a room next to Yasser Arafat whom I met, pistol on his hip, in the corridor. The toilet in his suite flushed noisily all through the night. I told Jock Munro in the morning that I wanted to move. Jock said, 'There's no need for that, he's left.' The security arrangements did not meet with Arafat's approval.

Early in the morning we went to pay our respects to Indira Gandhi at her father's house, Teen Murti, where her body was lying in state. The high commission had with great difficulty procured a wreath made of fibreglass, which was as close to flowers as could be found in the city. Naomi fortunately thought to bring along the flowers from the Mangere shopkeeper and we placed them and the wreath by the body and respectfully made our way out. The cremation took place the same day. The official guests made their way to the cremation ground in buses and Mother Teresa of Calcutta was on our bus. When we got to our destination, Middle Eastern potentates pushed out with great vigour and knocked her to the ground. I did my best to see she was all right.

The funeral pyre was a great pile of wood. Priests poured ghee from five-gallon buckets over wood and body and Rajiv Gandhi stepped forward to light the fire which consumed his mother.

City and airport were in chaos. So many aircraft had arrived in Delhi that fuel was not available from the usual suppliers. It was then I learned that the air force was indeed ready for any emergency. There was a substantial sum in US dollars on the aircraft, and magically it became possible for us to leave for Singapore.

Roger Douglas delivered his first budget only a few days after I came back from the funeral. Three of its measures attracted particular attention.

The cost of the superannuation scheme devised and implemented by Muldoon was disproportionate to spending on other forms of social welfare and generous beyond the country's means. Its beneficiaries were numerous, and the Labour Party's manifesto pledged that the substance of the scheme would be preserved. The budget kept to the letter of the manifesto promise by putting a surtax on the other income of superannuitants; this was rightly seen as a lawyer's subterfuge. My mother was among its sternest critics. She spoke at some length to a journalist about the surtax and the character of those who had imposed it. I first knew of this when I saw the billboard on my way to work one morning. The irony is that my mother never paid the surcharge, as her income apart from superannuation did not reach the threshold at which it was payable. It took me some time to persuade her that she was not being victimised but her reaction was by no means untypical. Whether or not they lost income, many of my mother's generation came to distrust the Labour government, and in some cases cast aside years of political allegiance, because of the surtax.

The other features of the budget were the announcement of the government's intention to impose a comprehensive tax on expenditure, and the elimination of a wide range of farm subsidies.

The content of the budget was put before caucus not long before it was delivered. There was little discussion of the surtax and the question of indirect taxation was put to one side. Some crowing was heard over the removal of the farm subsidies, and I thought it appropriate to remind caucus that we would not always be in government and that benefits on which Labour supporters relied could as easily be slashed by our political opponents.

Not long after the budget an invitation arrived in my office, one of many hundreds I received that year. As soon as I read it I made up my mind to accept it. It was from the Oxford Union, a venerable and much renowned student debating society. It invited me to Oxford in March the following year to debate nuclear deterrence with Jerry Falwell, whose name I knew only slightly as an evangelist and sometime associate of Ronald Reagan. I was thrilled by the union's letter. I had been a debater at university and, although I doubted the standard here was anywhere near as high as at Oxford, I backed myself. I was pleased that the debate would let me make the case for what I always saw as the essential part of New Zealand's nuclear-free policy, which was our refusal to allow ourselves to be defended by nuclear weapons.

My diplomatic advisors were dismayed. Merv Norrish, who consistently warned me that the nuclear-free policy put New Zealand's relationship with the United States at risk, said that my taking part in the debate would do no good. The visit to the United Kingdom I eventually made to speak in the debate was regarded by the British government as unofficial, and officials of the Ministry of Foreign Affairs in New Zealand declined to have anything to do with it. They may have thought that they could explain it away if they took no part in it. I was paid a call by Terence O'Leary, who once in my hearing described himself as Her Britannic Majesty's representative in New Zealand. He said that my taking part in the debate was very unwise. 'Margaret won't like it,' he added. I took seriously what my officials said to me but the invocation of Mrs Thatcher was close to incitement to make the journey. As it turned out, I had no reason to regret my acceptance of the invitation.

On the last Friday before Christmas 1984 I held a function at

Vogel House for staff members and their families. Naomi and the children came down from Auckland. There was a barbecue and a satisfactory lot of food and drink was consumed on a splendid sunny afternoon. My brother Peter made large numbers of pottery mugs inscribed with commemorative words and I presented them to the guests. I thoroughly enjoyed myself, but once again I did not feel at my best. I stayed with the family at Vogel House on Friday night and on Saturday morning I knew why I felt unwell: I had chickenpox. Naomi and the children left by car for Auckland. It was my plan to follow them not too long afterwards, but the staff of the national carrier were on strike and I was stranded in Wellington. I thought for a moment about asking the air force to fly me home, but resisted the abuse of privilege. The best I could do was arrange for the air force to fly negotiators to Wellington in hope of an early resolution of the dispute.

I spent Saturday and part of Sunday at Vogel House, alone and feeling sick and sorry for myself. I wanted to call Margaret but I did not know what to say to her.

CHAPTER THIRTEEN

I always liked to talk to Margaret, who was thoughtful and quiet. She shared a room on the ninth floor of the Beehive next to the press office and when I had time I would sit by her desk and we would talk about politics, or gossip. We had an easy working relationship, but I found it harder and harder to say goodbye to her every Friday. I am not sure exactly when I decided that I had to say something to her, though it must have been around October 1984. I did not know how to do it; she gave no sign of any more than friendly interest. I thought about it over Christmas and returned to Wellington a day before I was expected so that I could speak to her. When I found her I still did not know what I was going to say and I could have repeated all I did eventually say to the press gallery.

It was not until we travelled to the United States and Europe at the end of February that we reached an understanding. The delay only made me more confident. I knew exactly what I was doing. I knew the risk. I knew it would mean the end of my marriage but I did not feel married enough to care.

If I worried about the political risk, it would have been for about half a second. In those first two years in government, when I was happy in the job and enjoying myself, I felt that nothing could touch me. I was bulletproof. When things were going badly later on, there is no doubt that whispering about me and Margaret was damaging, and done with intention to damage, but again I was past caring.

The only one of my colleagues who ever spoke to me about my relationship with Margaret was Geoffrey Palmer, who thought it his duty to warn me. Sometime around the middle of 1985 he asked me if I knew that there was a lot of gossip about me and Margaret. 'I know,' I said. 'I'm flattered and she's embarrassed.' I changed the subject before he could ask me anything else.

There was not much else to take me to Wellington in January 1985. Very shortly before Christmas the American embassy wrote in the usual form to ask permission for a United States naval vessel to call at a New Zealand port early in the following year, but no individual vessel was as yet identified. The matter had long been under discussion among officials. On the New Zealand side there was a wish to maintain some form of military relationship with the United States, while the chief concern on the American side was the effect the New Zealand example might have on others. Its constitution required the Japanese government to shun a nuclear defence, yet American vessels which were almost certainly nuclear-armed visited Japanese ports. While the United States claimed that it respected the Japanese constitution, it refused to confirm or deny if its ships were armed with nuclear weapons. In January 1985 the Japanese prime minister was due to visit New Zealand and there was considerable diplomatic anxiety lest anything be said or done which might illuminate the hypocrisy of the Japanese arrangement.

Prime Minister Nakasone arrived with an enormous entourage. We held meetings of a formal nature at which the requirements of interpretation precluded any engagement. Nakasone spoke English almost as well as his foreign minister. I thought I would have some chance of a serious conversation with him when we drove to Turangawaewae and from there to lunch at Ruakura. We sat together in the back seat of the governor-general's elderly Rolls-Royce. He promptly went to sleep and woke up at Turangawaewae. He went to sleep when we left and woke up again for lunch. When we left Ruakura he slept until we got back to Auckland.

Soon after this visit I went to Tokelau, accompanied among others by Roy and Byron, the indefatigable Ken Richardson, and Trish Green, a press secretary. I could not resist the invitation to see this remote corner of the Pacific. We sailed from Apia on the *Avondale*, a wreck of a tramp steamer, and bumped slowly sideways across the water. Tokelau consists of three atolls. At every atoll we climbed down a ladder into a small boat which shot the reef and crossed the lagoon to be hauled ashore by the locals. The inhabitants were proud New Zealanders and wherever I went I was accompanied by a police officer carrying a pole which flew the national flag. The visit was a wonderful glimpse of a remarkable way of life. The *Avondale* was in worse shape than ever when it came time to go back to Apia; the crew were pouring oil over the drive shaft to keep the engine going. During the voyage I was summoned to the bridge and stood there while a radio operator tried to decipher a communication from New Zealand. Morse was the only available medium and the reception was poor. I learned that the United States had asked permission for a named ship to visit and that there were some matters about which I should be briefed. I was met by a military aircraft at Pago Pago in American Samoa and carried straight on to Wellington.

The American ship was the USS *Buchanan*. The New Zealand government's military advisors were as certain as they could be that the *Buchanan*, which was conventionally powered, would not be carrying nuclear weapons when she arrived in New Zealand. But the ship was capable of carrying them, and given the American refusal to disclose its armament it was not possible to assert without qualification that the *Buchanan* complied with the nuclear-free policy. When I got to Pago Pago I found a recommendation from the secretary of foreign affairs that the visit be accepted and one from Geoffrey Palmer, who was acting prime minister in my absence, that it not be.

None of this in itself would have made me go back early to Wellington. The cause of the urgency was a report in the *Sydney Morning Herald* which not only said that a request had been made but described the *Buchanan* in all but name. This report was attributed to unidentified sources in Washington. It made the visit a public issue and put the decision beyond diplomacy. When I got to Wellington I was driven to the Beehive and went straight from the car park in the basement to the cabinet room. I supported Palmer's assessment and the cabinet agreed. There was no immediate announcement because it was also agreed at cabinet that I should see the American ambassador the next day to ask him to send a ship which complied with the policy, an invitation he declined. The delay led to consternation among activists and some demonstrations by members of the public, but the decision which led to New Zealand's suspension from the ANZUS alliance and was in a real way a turning point in our foreign policy was already made. It was made the same day I woke on the deck of the *Avondale* somewhere off Pago Pago.

Misrepresentation and misreporting are hazards of public life. I have read so often that I sacked Roger Douglas that I have sometimes believed it myself. I have seen so much wrongly attributed to Tomorrow's Schools that I have long since given up trying to correct it. But I will not let the allegation pass that I was somehow pressured into refusing the visit of the *Buchanan*.

It is absurd to suggest that the day was carried by Labour Party activism. The last people I listened to at that time were the likes of Anderton and Clark. It is an allegation which makes sense only if it is believed that I intended to concede the nuclear-free policy to the Americans, and the only evidence for that comes from the disappointed or the disaffected. It was our policy to make the attempt to reconcile what proved to be irreconcilable, but when a choice had to be made between ANZUS and the nuclear-free policy I advised my cabinet colleagues to give the nuclear-free policy precedence. The advice of my officials was that implementing the policy would do great damage to our relationship with our allies and, while I did not go against that advice lightly, I did go against it. I made the case for the policy when I spoke at the Oxford Union only a few weeks after the *Buchanan* was rejected, but I had accepted that invitation before the *Buchanan* was ever heard of. I did not go to Oxford to be coy about being nuclear-free.

Considerable effort was made by officials to identify the source of the leaked story about the ship visit. There was a meeting of departmental heads in my office but none of them could offer more than speculation. Lin Smith suggested that special blinds be installed in the office which deflected long-range surveillance, and after some months they were fitted. Before I left for the United States and the United Kingdom on my way to speak at the Oxford Union, Gerald Hensley warned me that I should say nothing in hotel rooms and the like which I did not wish to be overheard. Hensley rushed into my office one day when I was on the telephone to Rowling in Washington. He said, 'Prime Minister! Don't use the word nuclear, or ANZUS or ships . . .' I put the phone down and said, 'What the hell are you talking about, Gerald?' These, it seemed, were among the words which triggered electronic eavesdropping of telephone communications.

The American response to our rejection of the *Buchanan* was given to me in Los Angeles on the way to London. By way of sending a diplomatic signal about how much offence had been taken, it was delivered by a junior official from the State Department in the dining room at the New Zealand consul's residence. It amounted to a severe limitation of military co-operation and diplomatic contact. Hensley, who joined us in Los Angeles for the meeting, was splendid. He tore into the American, spelling out to him the contribution made over a long time by New Zealand to Western interests. What mattered most to me was that the threat of economic reprisal which was hanging over us was dispersed. I was so relieved I could hardly speak.

I arrived in London with Margaret, Ken Richardson and Trish Green not long before the debate was to take place. In a life full of surprises it was almost unexceptional to be told that the deputy governor of the Reserve Bank wanted to see me. This was Rod Deane. I met him in a small office in New Zealand House. I knew before he said a word that he had come to recommend that the dollar be floated. It was an obvious fit with everything else we did and I told him we should get on with it. All that had to be done was to tell the cabinet. It was evening in New Zealand but we found them all, except for Douglas. We tried every number we could think of but nobody knew where the finance minister was. Wherever he was, he got back to work in time to make the announcement of the float not long after I finished speaking at Oxford.

I drove down to Oxford with Joe Walding. There was almost no colour in the sky or in the English countryside. The debate took place late in the evening and black tie was the required dress: my wardrobe had expanded to include a dinner suit but I never really felt comfortable in it. Joe wore his diamond studs. My cousin Russell Reid, a psychiatrist in London, was in the audience and I recognised many faces from New Zealand among the crowd; it was a full house. I had reports from home of the interest in the debate and I knew it would be shown live on television on a Saturday morning. I did not yet know how the general public would respond to the breach with the United States. I wanted to say something about the nuclear-free policy which would make people at home proud of it.

The Oxford Union speech was not the best speech I ever made but it was the one which mattered most. I was sure that if I faltered or made a fool of myself I would tip the balance of public opinion against the nuclear-free policy. If I did well I would help move public opinion away from its attachment to the American military alliance and make nuclear-free New Zealand a reality.

In the afternoon before the debate there was a bomb threat against our hotel, the Randolph in Oxford, and we had to wait outside while the police searched the building. I felt twinges of nerves about the debate and the disturbance did not help. The dinner which took place in the early evening was not very settling either. The student debaters and the two British members of parliament who took part were good company but my chief opponent Falwell was somewhat cold and humourless.

It was an enormous relief to me when the debate started and I got my first words off. I made my case and a young American on the opposing side came forward and said something so hawkish and earnest by way of interjection that he made me a gift of a riposte when he asked for an answer to his question. I said, 'And I'm going to give it to you if you hold your breath just for a moment . . . I can smell the uranium on it as you lean forward!' The audience was warm and well-informed and what I said went down well at home. It was a night when the abilities I had as a politician were most fully exercised. It was not a time for caution or compromise; it was a time when I could speak as I felt and win my point by what I said. This night was the highest point of my career in politics.

We had some diversions in London. Mrs Thatcher asked to meet me and I told her how pleased I was to see her. She put me right on nuclear deterrence. We went to see *Cats*. I enjoyed the performance but it had a different effect on Trish Green. She was absolutely exhausted after several days of doing nothing but work all hours and no sooner was she seated than she went to sleep. She woke up at the interval and then it was back to sleep. I also met John Henderson, who was working in London at the Commonwealth Parliamentary Association, and spoke to him about taking a job as head of the advisory group. He was a political scientist by profession and was close to Bill Rowling, but in the back of my mind that probably counted more in his favour than against him.

We went from London to Geneva where I spoke at the United Nations Conference on Disarmament. I walked with Margaret to the Reformation monument and looked at the statues of Calvin and Knox. This was the only overseas journey we made together while I was prime minister. We came home by way of Singapore and Malaysia, where I met Mahatir and visited New Zealand soldiers based in Singapore who were on exercise in the jungle of Johor Buru. In Singapore, Lee Kuan Yew invited me to a barbecue dinner, which was informal only in the sense that the men were advised to wear shirts cut in a style to be worn outside the trousers and I had to get one made. My diplomatic advisors often suggested to me that I ask certain foreign leaders why they chose to imprison people without trial, even though this was not always easy to do. When I eventually plucked up the courage to ask Lee Kuan Yew, I prefaced my remarks with a tribute to his background. I said, 'Prime Minister, you're a graduate of the most distinguished law school in the Commonwealth. Why are you still imprisoning people without trial?' He put his hand on my shoulder and smiled. He said, 'Because, David, it has become unfashionable to shoot them.'

A lot of my time in 1985 was taken up with Africa. I wanted New Zealand to identify with the states which were in the front line of the struggle against apartheid and put our association with white South Africa behind us. At the same time the rugby union was planning to take the All Blacks on tour to South Africa. To deal with these two issues I employed Chris Laidlaw, a former All Black who had worked for the Commonwealth secretary-general. He was assigned to work up a tour of east Africa. Laidlaw was a Labour Party favourite and Hensley refused to have him in the advisory group on grounds of his political associations. I thought at the time that Hensley was being unnecessarily obstructive but he may simply have been a good judge of character.

On the morning we left for Africa the rugby union executive came to the Beehive so I could lay out the consequences of their going ahead with the tour. I told its members that I would not look for a legal reason to bar the team from travelling and that I relied on their judgement and their concern for New Zealand's international standing. They said nothing.

We were a large party, the secretary for foreign affairs among us, which took off for Kenya in the air force 727 with stops for fuelling in Melbourne, Perth, Cocos, Diego Garcia and Mauritius. The journey round Africa was trial by travel. We visited five countries and in every country we went on safari: people at home must have thought we had migrated to a zoo. I could hardly bring myself to speak to Laidlaw after the second one. The official meetings were almost invariably heavy going and there was no chance of relaxation; when I tried to have a swim in the pool in the State House at Nairobi I was stopped at gunpoint by a guard.

Our journey took us to Kenya, Zambia, Tanzania, Zimbabwe and Botswana. In every country I asked its leader why people were being imprisoned without trial. In every country I was told that the government was using the same law the British colonial authorities used. It was not easy to persuade leaders who had been subjected to British rule that in a modern democracy it was not possible to deny permission to leave the country to rugby players, however misguided they might be.

There were some extraordinary moments. In Zambia I went to the headquarters of the African National Congress and met Oliver Tambo, its president. He was engaging and welcoming, but the sense of exile was almost palpable in him. He was one of those described as a terrorist by Jim Bolger, who followed Jim McLay as Muldoon's successor in the National Party leadership, and who as prime minister refused my request for a place on the air force 727 he took to South Africa for Nelson Mandela's inauguration. It was in Zambia that I heard for the first time the anthem 'Nkosi sikelel' iAfrika', so beautifully sung I could not stop myself from crying. In Zimbabwe I met the New Zealand-born Garfield Todd, once prime minister of Southern Rhodesia. I later recommended Todd for a knighthood and was present at his investiture at Buckingham Palace. He was a great optimist: I heard him say to the Queen that he would live to see the end of apartheid. I doubted he would, but he was right, although he also lived to be disappointed in the oppressive character of many African governments.

We left Africa at Nairobi, where Marjorie McDonald, my senior typist, was detained by police at the airport. She had a dispute with her hotel about the bill and mindful of the interests of the taxpayers had declined to pay the excess. We could not go home without her so Ken Richardson paid up. It was a long way back and we were in Australia when I heard that the rugby union was going ahead with its tour of South Africa. The rugby union was not of course the guardian of the national interest, but I found it hard to conceal my contempt for its disregard of it. In the end the High Court decided on application by two Auckland lawyers that the tour was adverse to the interest of the rugby union itself and I was enormously relieved. When we opened a high commission in Harare I sent Laidlaw there.

I got on well enough with Naomi while we were in Africa but I did not always do so. When I came home at the weekend I was always worn out. I went to the electorate office. I went to church. I went to party functions and other meetings. I had little engagement with her. At the Mangere Labour Party's midwinter Christmas dinner at the Metro theatre I declined to be ordered about by her and she told me very loudly exactly who was boss. I could not wait to go back to Wellington.

Sir Basil Arthur, the speaker of the house, was a rarity in New Zealand, a baronet. He was gravely ill in Wellington Hospital and a technicality in the superannuation scheme of the time meant that if he were to resign from parliament before he died, his estate would be entitled to a lump-sum payment it would otherwise be denied. I had to answer a question in the house and as soon as I was done I went to the hospital with a letter of resignation, only to find that he had died hardly a minute before I got there.

The death meant a by-election in Timaru, a seat with a large rural hinterland. It was not a propitious time for a campaign. The electorate was suffering cuts in farm subsidies and it was a dreadful time for farmers who were struggling under a growing burden of debt repayment. John Bayley, who was the farmer member of my advisory group, spent much of his energy securing refinancing arrangements for many who were worst afflicted. The human suffering involved in the restructuring of the rural economy was only too apparent.

To add to the political load, the Labour Party organisation insisted on the selection of a candidate who could hardly be less suited to the place. Jan Walker, who is now a judge in the Family Court, was a good lawyer but she did not live in Timaru and her opinions, and even her appearance, were at odds with the conservative character of the electorate. What I chiefly remember of the campaign was a scene which took place in a theatre where I was speaking. There was some heckling, and considerable unrest broke out in one quarter, ending when Tony Timms, general secretary of the Labour Party and a veteran of the Israeli army in the Six Day War, took it on himself to manhandle the chief offender out of the building.

We lost Timaru, a seat Labour had held for many years. I remember telling a television interviewer that the electorate spat Labour out with the medicine the government had administered. The loss though had one helpful result; it caused a repositioning among the left of the caucus. Anderton publicly blamed the defeat on the government's abandonment of traditional Labour policy. This produced some division between him and pragmatists like

Wilson and Clark, and led eventually to Anderton's isolation in the caucus.

Then came the *Rainbow Warrior*. I was as staggered as everyone else in the country in July when I heard that the Greenpeace vessel had been sunk at its berth in the port of Auckland. There was no suggestion of such a possibility from any diplomatic or intelligence source. It became known very rapidly that the sinking, and the death of a crew member, were the result of a bomb placed by a saboteur: the *Rainbow Warrior* was in Auckland on its way to the French nuclear-testing site at Moruroa. A French couple was arrested. It was not until September that the government of France, after persistent inquiries by the French news media, admitted that the two were its agents.

The agents were waiting trial under heavy guard in a military lockup, temporarily designated a civilian prison, when I went to my first Commonwealth heads of government conference.

It was very difficult to discern the purpose of the Commonwealth. Its heads of government met every two years and a more disparate group you could not imagine. The 1985 conference was held in the Bahamas, where the prime minister had acquired a low reputation and conference gatherings were always attended by demonstrators bearing placards. 'The chief is a thief' said one of them. We met in the casino. The formal opening of the conference and its public sessions were entirely stage-managed, although the remarkable Mahatir, who was one of the opening speakers, surprised me by saying, 'The Commonwealth is valued by Malaysia as the least of our international associations, but I'll stay if I like it,' and then sitting down.

Commonwealth conferences were dominated in those days by the continuing struggle between Mrs Thatcher and the Africans. The latter wanted the Commonwealth to do something about South Africa and she was determined to stop them. She really was not happy unless she was falling out with the whole African bloc. She always tackled them head-on, spitting phrases like 'unfit to govern' right at them. She was always easy on Caribbean and South Pacific leaders and later on she made a pet out of Samora Machel of Mozambique, but she did not seem to be close to any head of government. I thought she might get on with Mulroney, the Canadian conservative, but he was far too much of a wimp for her.

I enjoyed meeting Lee Kuan Yew, who was always shrewd and realistic. The other person whose company I greatly enjoyed, and whose presence made me feel that my time in the Bahamas was not wasted, was Rajiv Gandhi. I met him again soon afterwards in New York, where we went for the fortieth anniversary session of the United Nations.

There were seven speakers at the special session of the general assembly. Five were the heads of government of the permanent members of the security council. The other two were Rajiv Gandhi and me. It was a great honour for New Zealand and for this country's longstanding commitment to the ideals of the United Nations and, though I found it a daunting occasion, it went off well enough. It was followed by a lunch given by the UN secretary-general, Kurt Waldheim, the Austrian who was forever tainted by his Nazi associations. I sat at the left hand of president Ronald Reagan. In light of the diplomatic sanctions the State Department had imposed on New Zealand, he was not supposed to talk to me, and I assumed at first that he was complying with the department's wishes, but it soon became perfectly apparent that on that day at least he was not capable of engaging in conversation with anyone at the table. He rather mechanically ate his lunch and was taken away.

Whenever I was overseas, and I was away a lot in our first term of office, Geoffrey Palmer was acting prime minister. It was comforting to know that everything ticked over while I was away. I did not speak to him every day, though we would talk if there was anything out of the ordinary to discuss. In 1988, when I was taken to hospital and was feeling the first terrors of heart disease, I still had enough awareness to call Palmer back from overseas to act as prime minister. This led to my parting of the ways with Mike Moore, who was number three in the pecking order and who was hurt and disappointed at my passing him over. But God alone knew what Moore might do. There was no need for divine guidance when it came to Palmer's stewardship.

CHAPTER FOURTEEN

Palmer called me while I was in Fiji for the South Pacific Forum in August 1986 and told me that copies of Douglas's as yet undelivered budget were circulating among the business community. Douglas gave him a letter of resignation. Not yet knowing if there had been a deliberate leak of budget secrets, and wondering if we might be looking for a new finance minister, I flew back to Wellington, leaving Naomi in Suva with the two younger children, one of them too ill to travel. I got back to find that the release of material from the minister's office was entirely accidental and told Palmer that I did not think it was a resignation matter.

Losing Douglas at that point would have been a considerable blow. No successor was obvious. Caygill had the potential but not the profile; Prebble worked at white-hot intensity when he became a minister but he was volatile and touchy; Michael Cullen often provided an interesting counterpoint to the three finance ministers but he was hardly known and not in the cabinet. The government's reputation as an economic manager was embodied in Douglas's determination and single-mindedness and I backed him solidly at party conferences.

I also promoted the economic policy to the wider public. That was part of my job. I was the face of the government and its policies and it was my task to assure the electorate of our stability, our confidence, our unity and our competence. It was gratifying to be associated with success, but it was my responsibility to represent our least popular as well as our most popular policies. I had to sell the offal as well as the T-bone. If a defence were needed, it was my duty to provide it.

I enjoyed the campaign we ran in support of the new goods and services tax, in spite of the extraordinary television advertising which appeared at the end of it. For some reason I have now forgotten I went to a church hall in Miramar to watch the filming of a commercial featuring a dozen babies in nappies who could not believe their luck in having a consumption tax. Babies apart, there was a good case to be made for GST. Many Labour backbenchers were unhappy about it to begin with, but came to support it in light of the compensation which was to be paid to beneficiaries. There were predictable stoushes at Labour Party conferences, where objection was raised to the near-universal nature of the imposition, but as a general rule I found delegates at conferences in 1985 and 1986 supportive. It had much to do with the sheer joy of being in government. The union movement was different. A younger generation was moving into its leadership, but the change was not yet complete and engagement with it was as difficult as always.

The implementation of GST was well managed and deserved

to do as well as it did. One matter concerned me. The changes in income tax which accompanied its introduction meant that I was going to be about $500 a week better off. I wrote to the Higher Salaries Commission, which determined the remuneration given to ministers and the like, and said that I would be grateful if in its next review of my salary it reduced my income by the amount of the reduction in tax. At its next review the commission increased my salary by $500 a week.

There used to be a canard which had it that the government bought party support for its economic policy by adopting the nuclear-free policy. There may well have been party members whose support for the nuclear-free policy helped them swallow the economic policy, but that is not the same thing. If Douglas ever talked about foreign policy I cannot remember it, and in any case he needed no licence for what he did. I still see our economic policy and our foreign policy as complementary. The economic policy got us ready to do business in a world which did not owe us a living, while our foreign policy let us make our own judgement of where our interests lay.

I was foreign affairs minister for three years. I enjoyed it more than I did being education minister in our second term in office, although I got a greater sense of achievement from the education portfolio. I liked the travel which came with the job and I liked the chance it offered to meet the significant figures of the day. Wherever I travelled, however remote the place, I met New Zealanders planting forests or running dairy factories or working for any number of non-governmental or multilateral organisations and I was proud of their contribution.

I knew when I took the job as foreign minister that the connection to the United Kingdom which had coloured my childhood, while still valuable, had become less and less relevant. I did not want to replace it with dependence on the Americans. Even before the breach with the Americans over ANZUS it was my aim to reach out to places where New Zealand interests had not traditionally been advanced or even represented. That was what took me to Africa and India, and why I made long journeys to places like China, Indonesia and the Philippines. The nuclear-free policy made me unwelcome in some places where we might in the past have had a hearing, but it opened other doors and it proved to be critical in the development of an independent outlook.

I got on well with Merv Norrish and with most of his officials. Many of them I liked immensely. Some, like John Wood, later our ambassador in Washington, I distrusted for their inevitable posture of apology to the Americans. My only serious difference with the ministry was over the nuclear-free policy. The official view of ANZUS was deeply conservative. Officials believed that our membership of it gave us influence with the United States; 'punching above our weight' was the phrase they used. I did not accept that argument. I thought, and I still think, the more so now that the foreign policy of the United States has become more aggressively self-interested than it was in the 1980s, that it is spurious, and moved more by a desire for an entrée into the big world than by an objective assessment of New Zealand's interests.

The management of our relationship with the United States and other members of the Western bloc was a continuing preoccupation of my time as foreign minister. In 1986 Australia and the United States decided that New Zealand was to be suspended from its membership of the ANZUS council, and the United States formally withdrew from New Zealand what it called its security guarantee. This concerned me only in that it might create a feeling in New Zealand that we were somehow at risk, a feeling not to be taken lightly in those Cold War days. The government reviewed and restructured the country's military capability and established a committee to inquire into defence; the chief part of its brief was to assess public thinking on the issue. We sought more military co-operation with Australia, which was difficult at first given Australian reluctance to be seen by the Americans as providing solace, but it did prove possible.

Growing public support for the nuclear-free policy did more than anything to overcome the insecurity brought about by the breach with the Americans. The Americans could not help but sound like bullies. The more they protested, the more the New Zealand public backed the policy and in doing so came to question the value of the military connection.

I would be sorry to see the nuclear-free policy abandoned now that the threat of global nuclear war has receded and few American vessels are routinely nuclear-armed. The United States today reserves the right to arm its vessels with nuclear weapons and it will neither confirm nor deny their presence. It tests and deploys nuclear weapons, and its defence is based on the projection of nuclear force. There is still a need for an alternative to these doctrines, and for people to believe that an alternative is desirable. New Zealand's policy shows what is possible. The trade advantages of surrendering are speculative, to say the least, and there is none other which might even slightly compensate for the loss of independent initiative which is embodied in the nuclear-free policy.

The matter which caused me most difficulty when I was foreign minister was what followed the sinking of the *Rainbow Warrior*. I think I shall always be pursued by it. Whenever I speak and ask for questions from the audience, the one I least want to answer, and the one which is almost always asked, is 'Why did you give the agents back?' If it is put to me as an issue of principle, I can only acknowledge that it was not dealt with as such. If it was not an issue of principle, I have to ask myself why I made it one, and I cannot answer that.

The two French agents were charged with murder, but on their appearance in the District Court at Auckland in November 1985 the charge was reduced to one of manslaughter. Well before the trial started, the French government asked us how much we wanted for the release of the agents. I told the French privately, and said publicly, that our legal process must run its course. The agents pleaded guilty and would not let their lawyer make any statement in mitigation. I doubt the French government wanted the modus operandi of its agents thrashed out in open court. The agents appeared for sentence in front of the chief justice in the High Court in Auckland later in the month. At a time when most convictions for manslaughter led to a sentence of three years, the chief justice grandly gave them ten. I said that the agents would serve out their sentence in New Zealand, not imagining that the government of France would resort to extortion, but I should have known that a government which sent agents to carry out an act of terrorism would resort to anything.

The French reaction was to promise economic sanctions. In those days France had a power of veto in the European Community which it could use to put an end to our sales of primary produce in Europe. It would have been a crippling blow. When in difficulties with the European Community, we used to rely on British assistance, but it was clear in this case that the British were not inclined to intervene. New Zealand exports began to meet unexpected obstacles in French markets. Officials opened negotiations and the French offered a settlement – to apologise, to pay compensation, and to leave our export trade alone. In return the agents would be released to French custody for a period of three years.

The first place the French proposed to hold the agents was the island of Mayotte in the Comoros group in the Indian Ocean. A briefing from the foreign affairs ministry informed me it was home to a military establishment. John Henderson went to the parliamentary library to look it up and found that it was also home to Club Med. The island of Hao, which was a support base for the French nuclear-testing programme at Moruroa atoll, was substituted. Cabinet agreed to the settlement, which was dressed up for public consumption as the product of a mediation by the secretary-general of the United Nations.

There was a general outcry when the agents were released to French custody on Hao, and more was to come when the French breached the terms of the settlement and let the agents go home to France. Having said all I had, and having raised public expectations that the agents would stay here, I had to wear the contempt.

I was largely an observer of another drama of my time as foreign minister. This was the first of the coups in Fiji, which took place in 1987, hardly a month after the election there of a Labour government led by an ethnic Fijian and closely associated with Fijian Indian interests. The government was turned out by an army brigadier who was acting in collaboration with Fiji's traditional chiefly rulers. There proved to be little violence, largely because there was little resistance, but this outcome was not obvious in the beginning. There was never any question that New Zealand might use force to restore the democratically elected government, since we were not asked to intervene by its representatives and had we been, we did not have the military resources. I did however ask our military leaders to ready themselves to come to the assistance of any New Zealand citizens who might be endangered, and I met with considerable obstruction.

A frigate of the New Zealand navy was in port in Suva when the coup took place and there was another nearby, but frigates could not carry many passengers and would in any case appear threatening to the rebels. The obvious candidate to carry out an evacuation was the survey vessel *Monowai*. I was told by the government's naval advisors that the *Monowai*'s involvement was impractical so I asked the chief of naval staff how long it would take to get the vessel to Fiji. His answer was five days. It happened that I knew the *Monowai*. It used to be a banana boat, in which capacity it made the journey from Suva to Auckland in just over three days. Three days being the better estimate, a time for departure was agreed, but when the time arrived some failure of a propeller caused the departure to be delayed.

Events after the coup were further complicated when an

unstable individual seized control of the flight deck of an Air New Zealand plane on the ground at Nadi and held the pilots hostage. The rebels took no action to release the aircraft. I agreed with the chief of general staff that the SAS would be sent to Nadi to free the trapped aircrew and release the aircraft. The chief of defence staff literally ran across the road to countermand the order. The danger was defused when one of the aircrew knocked out the hijacker with a whisky bottle.

The defence chiefs tried to justify their inertia by arguing that the overwhelming numerical advantage enjoyed by the Fijian army meant that the government was recklessly sending its military forces into danger, a point which does not take into account the careful steps we took to avoid antagonising the rebels. I can only contrast the military view with that of an officer of the Government Communications Security Bureau, who went to Fiji to re-establish telephone communications which had been broken by the rebels. He arrived at Nadi with a large tin trunk containing satellite communications equipment, a bulky item in those days. He told all inquirers at the airport that the trunk contained canned food for the New Zealand high commission and asked for help to carry it to his rental car, which he then drove to Suva to set up the phone.

I met deeply felt resentment among many in the military. Retired Air Vice Marshal Morrison told an Anzac Day assembly I was an agent of the Kremlin. I invited him to repeat this endorsement at the Labour Party conference. Military recalcitrance was the product of a mindset which could not accept the government's breach with the United States and was unready to adapt to new ways of thinking about defence.

I further antagonised some military commanders by insisting that they did not discriminate between women and men. I thought I was doing well in carrying this point until I was accosted in the street by a member of the Labour women's council, who told me that feminism's goal was the peaceful resolution of conflict and not the equal right to kill and be killed.

The tone was set in the defence ministry by its permanent head, Denis McLean, who quite improperly for one in his position was on the public record as an opponent of Labour's nuclear-free policy, and made no secret of his antipathy towards the government. He was obstructive and unhelpful, and because of the conventions of the public service of the time, impossible to shift until he brought his end on himself. He was found to have briefed the National Party's defence spokesman on the restructuring of the armed forces without having first obtained the consent of the minister. Gerald Hensley became secretary when the defence bureaucracy was restructured. In 1991 McLean was sent by the National government to be ambassador in Washington. Public opinion obliged the National Party to adopt the nuclear-free policy and McLean's appointment was a way of signalling to the Americans that they did not really mean it. I said at the time of the appointment that he was going to Washington as a highly-paid shoeshine boy, and that he would not need a brush.

There is little to record here about the other ministerial responsibility of my first term of office, the Security Intelligence Service, not because it is a secret but because it seems unremarkable in retrospect. The greater part of the intelligence effort was aimed at the Soviet embassy and those who were thought to be its agents in

New Zealand. The embassy struck me as clumsy and ill-informed. Its suspected contacts were the obvious ones, the leadership of the Communist Party, the Socialist Unity Party, the Socialist Action League and the like. I do not remember being surprised by any warrant I was asked to issue by the SIS. There were no requests to tap the phones of radical feminists or Maori activists.

In 1987 the cabinet agreed to build an electronic interception facility at Waihopai, to complement the installation we already had at Tangimoana. We did this as part of our obligations under the UKUSA security agreement. Gerald Hensley was once disconcerted by a public mention I inadvertently gave to the UKUSA agreement, as protocol demanded that its existence never be acknowledged. I thought we should build the base because it seemed unwise at the time to further upset the Americans, who were the chief beneficiaries of the information it provided.

Foreign affairs and defence gave rise to several salient public issues in the government's first two years in office, but the cabinet's chief preoccupation was economic management. What we did was done quickly. Tariffs were lowered, the public sector was restructured, financial markets were deregulated. To control inflation, money supply was tightened. Interest rates soared and the exchange rate climbed. The human consequences of our approach were only too obvious. The export sector was squeezed and there was a rapid decline in manufacturing. The corporatisation of the public sector led to many more job losses.

I cannot remember any serious sustained discussion in cabinet of the human costs of our economic policy. Some in cabinet did not allow themselves to be sensitised to the politics of the issues we dealt with. Adversity was a provocation to Prebble in particular: the worse things were the more aggressive he became. Douglas talked about the ability of redundant forestry workers and the like to start successful small businesses and did not see the Timaru by-election as any kind of warning to the government. Some in the cabinet expressed concern about the jobs and businesses we lost, but the difficulty lay in the absence of any effective counterweight to the Treasury line, which said that measures to prop up employment while economic adjustment was in progress were palliatives which would hinder achievement of our long-term goals.

This was a matter of continuing difficulty. I would not have argued that the likelihood of job losses should stop, for example, the corporatisation of many public sector activities, and the departmental restructuring which accompanied it. But I could not ignore the cost. I talked about it at great length with the members of the advisory group. They were people from outside the government and the bureaucracy and they brought a different viewpoint to economic policy. They left me in no doubt about the immediate impact of the government's actions, and they often questioned the way in which policy was implemented. We started our discussions by accepting the government's commitment to its economic policy, but the question we increasingly asked ourselves was how we could make the economy fit for people to live in.

I was certainly not alone in this preoccupation. When I overcame the reservations which arose from her earlier association with Anderton and other activists, I found myself comfortable enough with Margaret Wilson, who was Labour Party president until after the 1987 election. She chose her battles carefully. She encouraged the selection of candidates from a trade union background, although there was no obvious common thread among her choices. She accepted that the thrust of economic policy could not be deflected and her management of the party reflected that acceptance. She put her effort into more limited goals like the labour laws. The Labour Relations Act 1987 stood out among other measures of our first term in office as an evolutionary rather than a revolutionary approach to reform. Alf Kirk, who was an economist with considerable expertise in labour relations and a member of the advisory group, was closely involved in the discussions between officials in which, remarkably enough for the time, the view of the labour department overcame that of the Treasury. There was resistance in caucus to a more radical approach, perhaps because labour relations was a subject understood by many Labour members of parliament.

It was plain enough by 1986 that there was a need for some kind of counterweight to the power of Treasury. Some departments had the capacity to challenge Treasury thinking, but their interests were necessarily limited to their departmental responsibilities. Others were hopelessly ill-prepared for the assault. There was an intellectual coherence about the Treasury point of view which other departments could hardly ever match, and all the momentum was with it. Its interest in social institutions was one of theory and its detachment amounted to indifference to the human consequences of what it recommended.

The Labour Party's 1984 election manifesto promised an inquiry into social security. This became the Royal Commission on Social Policy, which had a much wider mandate to inquire into what might be called our well-being as a society. In some ways the commission was a defensive measure. I did not want Treasury to take its knife to the social services and the commission was a way of fencing them off. But the case for it was compelling enough. There was a new economy and there would be a new society. Its institutions should be shaped by the people who lived in it. I wanted the royal commission to give them a voice. I wanted an alternative view in the form of an argument with some weight behind it.

Treasury was implacably opposed to the idea of the royal commission and members of my advisory group wore themselves out in the bureaucratic struggle behind its establishment. It was no easier getting its terms of reference and its membership through the cabinet process. The result was inevitably a compromise. The terms of reference were far too broad, although I told its members when I met them what I hoped for from them. The royal commission finally started work in October 1986.

This was a mixed year for me in my personal life. For the first time I found myself out of sorts with the Methodist church. Its leadership made much of its criticism of the government and announced its intention of coming to see me to tell me about it. I declined. If it had asked to see me first and done the grandstanding afterwards I would have been more receptive. I still went to services when I was in Mangere, but I found it hard to take seriously a church which insisted that a congregation of a few *palagi* and many Pacific Islanders sing and pray in the Maori language.

At the end of 1985 I tired of the drive to work from Lower Hutt and I moved into a flat in Hill Street near parliament. By comparison with Vogel House it was spartan, but it did me well enough and I lived there as long as I was prime minister. I was once again a smoker, following a visit to Manila. New Zealand was the first country to recognise the government of Corazon Aquino and the welcome was warm. President Aquino gave me a box of cigars; they looked magnificent, and so they proved. From time to time I had a glass of wine in the evening. It was not much more than that at first, and I drank it because I liked it.

I was happy with Margaret. It was difficult to meet outside the office and I used to look forward to Labour Party regional conferences which took the two of us on long journeys to provincial towns. When I had the chance I still liked to sit in the office she shared with Stephen Mills and talk to them about the job. I enjoyed Stephen's blunt assessments; he was honest and a good operator. I asked him after the 1987 election to go to a government department which was hearing pitches from advertising agencies and do anything he could to see that the agency which handled the Labour Party campaign did not get the contract. The party owed the agency thousands of dollars and I did not want it said that we used public money to pay it off. The agency was nearly good enough to get the job. 'That was close,' Stephen said when he got back.

I had a wonderfully enjoyable time when Rajiv and Sonia Gandhi came to New Zealand in October 1986. They were good company, though even in this country it was impossible to be unaware of the risks he constantly faced. An armoured car was needed for the visit. We did not have such a thing in the country and had to borrow one from the Australian government fleet in Canberra. The highlight of the visit was the making of an episode of *This Is Your Life* featuring Ed Hillary. Rajiv and I both took part.

The year ended in farce. Officers of the Maori affairs department attempted to raise an unauthorised loan of $600 million overseas. The story had the lot: con artists, Hawaiian middlemen and shady Middle Eastern financiers. Official inquiries followed the disclosure of the scheme in parliament, but the critical question for the government was the degree of involvement of the minister. Investigations found nothing conclusive and the minister himself denied all knowledge of the loan. It looked bad; if the minister was not a liar, he was hopelessly incompetent. The minister was Koro Wetere whose presence in the cabinet was an acknowledgement of the debt owed by the Labour Party to Maori voters. As he was formally responsible for the loan fiasco, he offered me his resignation from cabinet. The question was whether or not I should accept it.

I decided that it was best to take soundings of the Maori leadership outside parliament. I did this in deepest secrecy lest it become known that Wetere's future was in the balance. I went with Ken Richardson and Annette Dixon from the advisory group in the civil aviation department's Cessna to Napier, where I met Te Atairangikaahu and Hepi te Heuheu. Then we flew to Wanganui. As we circled the airport I could see an unmistakable military formation on the tarmac. It was a guard of honour. When we landed I told Ken to ask them to move, but he came back and said dolefully, 'You'd better inspect them, Prime Minister.' The soldiers were territorials on exercise and the control tower had told their commander of our arrival. Cover blown, we went on to Ratana, where the message from the church leadership was the same as from the others. What had happened was deplorable, but Wetere should be supported. So I started 1987 by inventing defences for the minister.

When I was a youngster I looked at the way my father lived and vowed that I would never do the same. He was at the call of anyone who knocked on the surgery door and, aside from the few holidays he took, there was never a day or night he could really call his own. When I was a lawyer I realised I was living exactly like my father did. There was no end to the demands on me and my time was never my own. There were certainly tedious times when I was prime minister, the days of the so-called Maori loan affair among them, and it always seemed that every moment of the day was accounted for, but I never found myself thinking that I was back on the treadmill again. The job was the difference. It is not easy to explain. I can only say that I was sustained by my sense of how privileged I was. I was honoured to have the job and I would have done it for nothing. I would have done it for much longer than I did if the chance had offered.

CHAPTER FIFTEEN

I took a risk when I asked Roger Douglas to stay in politics and made him Labour's finance spokesman, but I thought it was a risk worth taking. He had energy and ideas. I knew he would work hard, and I thought he would be moderated by the responsibility of being in government.

Douglas was a subdued figure for some months after the devaluation debacle which had nearly sent us off the rails before the 1984 election. He came close to the edge and the experience knocked him back. His first budget made him buoyant. It was a significant event and the old confident Douglas resurfaced. But in government it became apparent how narrow his vision was. This was the reverse side of the doggedness which characterised him; he heard what he wanted to hear and he closed his mind to the rest. His ideas were rarely tempered by any acknowledgement that their implementation would make a difference to the way society was ordered. He focused entirely on the economic indices and disregarded the others, talking about economic policy in cabinet as if we were sitting in a tutorial. He was fortunate in that his limitations suited him to the exigencies of our first term in office, when urgency was needed and boldness was at a premium. But when the temper of the times changed, he was not capable of changing with it.

He and I did not fall out over the Royal Commission on Social Policy. I did not see him as obstructive as much as unpersuaded of the commission's relevance, and we remained on good terms. Inside a year our relationship was to alter.

In April 1987 Douglas sent me a letter which set out three possible options for the budget he intended to present in the middle of the year. I cannot recall any detail of the first two, other than that the first was described by its author as a budget which would do very little but simply keep the ship afloat. It was accompanied by the observation that this was not to Douglas's taste, and that I should perhaps look for a new finance minister if this was the course I wanted to take. This addendum was a characteristic idiosyncrasy. The second option escapes my memory completely, although I imagine it was something like the budget he actually did present that year.

The third option Douglas offered is burned into my memory. Its content would come as no surprise to anyone familiar with ACT policy, or at least with ACT policy as it was in the days when Douglas was the head of that party, but in April 1987, when such things were unheard of in mainstream politics, it was a shock to me. He described it at some point as radical, but radical does not do it justice. He argued for the sale of almost every government asset, including roads, hospitals, schools and universities. Every social service was to be privatised. We were to have a single rate of income tax at 15c in the dollar, and GST would be raised to fifteen percent to match.

This was Douglas's preferred option. He offered to work on it in secret if that was what I wanted. I could hardly believe what I was reading. It was an unaccustomed addition to the burdens of office to have the finance minister take leave of his senses. I said as much to Bassett when I happened to meet him in a lift, expecting it to get back to Douglas, which it did. I asked members of the advisory group for their help in drafting a reply to his letter. His letter came to me under the cover of budget secrecy and I treated my reply the same way; I did not want it widely known that Douglas had even considered such schemes, let alone become their advocate.

The reply I sent was as strongly worded as I could make it. I told him that the adoption of his preferred strategy would shatter the unity of the government. I told him that the people of my electorate and his had not voted Labour so that in future they would have to beg for the entitlements of citizenship. I told him that I would rather raise taxes to pay our debts than privatise the social services. I said that the electorate did not expect miracles from us, and that we would be rewarded enough if we took a steady course.

An informal meeting of six senior ministers took place to consider the Douglas proposals. Palmer, Moore, Caygill and Prebble were there with me and Douglas. I cannot remember now what was said, but I can imagine what took place. Prebble was always solidly with Douglas, while Caygill was always cagey at meetings of this sort. Moore was more gung-ho when Douglas was present than when he was not. Palmer concerned himself with legal issues. I do remember he was outraged by a suggestion in the Douglas proposals that the government charge the State Insurance Office for the use of its own name. In any event, it was agreed that the radical option would not be pursued.

Douglas remarked in later years that he should have gone to see me when he heard of my reaction, as if my response were the result of some kind of misunderstanding. There was no misunderstanding. He wrote to me, I wrote back. He did come to see me and I told him what I thought. I asked him to think, if he could think of nothing else, of the politics of it. What he proposed could not be sustained in a society in which every adult had a vote. There was nothing he or I could talk about which would ever make his agenda acceptable to the public. In the first half of 1987 he appeared to accept, albeit with some carping, that the course he wished to pursue was closed to him.

Almost certainly I knew then that I had made a great mistake when I stuck by Douglas, but it was hard to face up to it. So much of my political capital was invested in him. If you set out on a course and you find yourself beset by doubt, it is not easy to concede that you are wrong and that the effort has been made in a losing cause. It is a concession almost never made in politics, not because politicians are more deceived or deceiving than the rest of humankind, but because such concessions are not rewarded with popular support. In its first term in office the public supported the Labour government in extraordinary numbers because of our unity and strength of purpose, qualities which were drawn in great part from the alliance between me and Douglas. I could not cut him loose; I consigned myself to a life of constant vigilance.

One concession was made to Douglas by way of solace for the loss of his radical option. We agreed that there would be reviews of the management of public hospitals and the compulsory education sector. There was a good case to be made for these reviews. Hospitals were run by locally elected but centrally funded boards and the proper balance between local and central authority was a long way from being achieved. School administration was based on a model devised in the 1870s. In both hospitals and schools it was sometimes hard to see where the money went and harder to measure the effectiveness of the spending. I spoke about the two reviews to members of the Royal Commission on Social Policy, as I did not wish them to see the reviews as taking precedence over their work. They took the news well enough, on the understanding that the reviews were to concern themselves with models of public-sector management and in that sense would complement the commission's inquiries.

I talked about the education review with the responsible minister, Russell Marshall, and we agreed to appoint as its head an Auckland businessman, Brian Picot. Picot was the head of the Foodtown empire, which had its headquarters in Mangere where it had a reputation as a thoughtful and innovative employer. He had a longstanding interest in education and had given much time to its service. The health review was chaired by Alan Gibbs, a wealthy friend of Douglas.

Gibbs was only one of many in the business community who were close to Douglas. Before the 1987 election Douglas asked me to host a dinner for potential donors to the Labour Party's campaign funds, and I agreed. All of the Business Roundtable types were there, Gibbs, Trevor Farmer, and the like, and shonky entrepreneurs of the time such as Bruce Judge. I left them to it as soon as I could. I could not stand the cant. In that company the pursuit of wealth was a public service and self-interest was a noble purpose. It was members of the Business Roundtable who were responsible in great part for the chorus of approval which increasingly greeted every suggestion Douglas made.

I do not know how much money Douglas raised from the business community since much of it was given to him personally and not to the Labour Party. He insisted that such donations be made by individuals rather than by their companies, which was as much as propriety demanded in those days. He gave some of it to the party organisation. Some he distributed to candidates, as I know from his giving $3000 to the Mangere Labour electorate committee.

The existence of this independent fund was an annoyance to the Labour Party organisation, which was short of money for the campaign. There were continuing disputes between ministers and party over the manifesto, which were resolved on the surface by having a summary of policy released during the campaign and the actual manifesto afterwards. At the party's insistence, the manifesto promised to take a consultative approach to labour relations and, while it allowed for the possibility of the privatisation of public assets, it specifically promised not to privatise any of the three corporations carved out of the old post office. The first of these promises was broken before the year was out, and the second later.

Cabinet, caucus and party did agree on the general thrust of our campaign, which was that the pain inflicted by the economic policy was to be rewarded by improvement in the quality of our social services. I was happy with that and Douglas seemed to have no difficulty with it.

The general election took place on 15 August 1987. It would be kind to describe the campaign, and my part in it, as lacklustre. It started badly and got worse. Before the formal campaign even started an extraordinary newsletter surfaced in the news media. It was written by Simon Walker, who was a former journalist and director of the Labour Party's parliamentary research unit, an associate of Douglas and a member of the Labour Party's policy council. He later went to the United Kingdom where he worked for the Conservative Party. The newsletter was published by Walker's public relations company and purported to set out Labour's real intentions if it won the election. It was very like Douglas's radical proposal of April. I condemned its content and its author as strongly as I could, but its publication did nothing for my state of mind.

I disliked almost everything about the campaign. More than anxiety about Douglas combined to deflate my efforts. The National Party offered no challenge, although I thought we might well lose some provincial seats to it. National could not get traction. The Labour Party had occupied its ground and it was simply thrashing about. My televised encounters with its leader did not feel like a contest and I could not lift myself. Our television advertising was an embarrassment, with me posing like a corporate highflier in a flash office. I do not know if it was ever paid for. The day-to-day activity of the campaign was almost entirely designed for television. It would have been pointless to do otherwise, but it was bad for me; I liked the challenge of a live audience yet the days of big public meetings were gone for good. To feed the demands of television I had to do what I did not like. I intruded on the public as they went about their business at work or in shopping centres. I had to perform as I ordinarily never would for the benefit of the cameras. The formal campaign lasted only three weeks, but it was an ordeal.

As I did in 1984, I waited for the results of the election in the Metro theatre in Massey Road. I was surprised when Douglas appeared at the hall. It was most unusual for a candidate to leave his own electorate on the night of a general election. He seemed happy; he was certainly relaxed, and we talked quite comfortably. When it was clear that we had won, and indeed increased our majority in parliament, I took him on to the stage with me to acknowledge the part he had played in the victory.

I did not imagine that we would ever do as well as we did in the 1987 general election, especially in the provincial areas which carried the greater part of the burden of economic adjustment in our first term in office. But there were grounds for concern. We came close to winning Remuera, and the Labour majority withered in some of our strongholds. That to me was a sign that caution was required unless we were to supplant the National Party entirely. It is the goal of every major political party to occupy the centre ground which is the key to longevity in government, but it cannot do that if its base is not secure, and it was plain in 1987 that we were at some risk of losing ours. It was self-serving to argue, as Douglas and his supporters did afterwards, that our victory was a mandate for yet more radical reform. Our campaign did not promise more radical reform. In terms of the electorate, and in terms of Labour's chances in the electoral contest, it made no sense at all to have us leap even further away from our home ground.

I do not see what happened between me and Douglas as anything other than a political contest. I thought that if we stopped to pick up the casualties of our first term in office we would get the politics right and we would be the government for a long time, but he thought otherwise. In terms of politics I came to see him as a fundamentalist, with all that the word implies. He was not an economist any more than I was. His politics lacked understanding and humanity, and I will always believe I was right to take issue with them. It was a contest which wore me out in the end, but my only regret is that I did not make a better job of it. I made mistakes, I was not always consistent, and I sometimes did what I knew was wrong or what I should have known to be wrong. Explanations I found convincing at the time are not convincing now.

I think of the State Sector Bill, which became the State Sector Act 1988. It was introduced without regard to the promise in our manifesto to consult about labour relations issues, and without regard to undertakings given by ministers to the state sector unions. It had a more radical effect on labour relations in the public sector than the Labour Relations Act had in the private sector. I do not remember the undertakings we gave being canvassed in the cabinet; I did not raise them. I had confidence in the responsible minister, Stan Rodger, who was contemptuous of the featherbedding which permeated the state sector unions. I was amazed to learn when we first took office that the government, the employer, was funding the two teacher unions and the police association. I put an end to that, but far more was needed to make work practices in the public sector more dynamic. I thought the Bill was timely and appropriate and that consultation would be pointless. The promise was broken and the Bill was introduced. I was no better than those who thought it was macho to laugh at the party's manifesto.

There was by then a new cabinet. Fraser Colman and Frank O'Flynn retired at the general election. They were both older, and good cabinet ministers, and I missed them greatly. Ann Hercus left to pursue appointments overseas. Kerry Burke was eased out of the cabinet and into the speakership left vacant by the retirement of Gerry Wall. Burke was a lightweight with little to offer the cabinet and his departure was a relief to nearly all. I could not believe it when he became the best speaker of any I ever met. Among the replacements elected by the caucus were Helen Clark and Michael Cullen.

The allocation of portfolios did not fall into place as easily as it had in 1984. I no longer trusted Douglas and wanted to use the allocation to put some restraints on him. I took Prebble out of his role in finance but made a misjudgement when I gave him responsibility for all the state-owned enterprises, thinking that he would find enough to interest him in their oversight. His chief interest proved to be in selling them. Cullen was made an associate finance minister as well as social welfare minister. It was an enormous burden to put on him. My greatest concern was to put ministers in place who would protect the social services from the onslaught I knew would be made on them, which was why I gave social welfare to Cullen, and why I gave housing to Clark.

The two major social service portfolios, health and education, were more problematic. Health had been Bassett's responsibility in our first term in office. He had a waspish manner and he was a staunch ally of Douglas. I made Caygill health minister in his place. Caygill was dry as dust on economic issues but I thought him too polite and cautious to drive a bulldozer through public health. I asked Bassett to see me in my office to tell him of the change. 'This is a mistake,' he said through very tight lips. He told me at one point he would never speak to me again unless he had to, so the news was not all bad.

Russell Marshall had no love for Douglas but he was not the right minister to defend the education portfolio. His department was a lumbering dinosaur, an easy target, but he was unable to distance himself from it, or from the teacher unions. I spoke to Palmer at length about the allocation of portfolios and asked him in the course of our discussions to take education. He refused and so I took it myself. I had felt little but resentment from Marshall since I beat him for a place on the party executive in the 1970s and this was compounded by his failed attempt on the leadership in 1983. I gave him more than he deserved when I gave him the foreign affairs portfolio by way of compensation; he was still inclined to grieve.

I doubt Douglas was happy about these changes, but he said nothing to me.

In October 1987 I went to Vancouver for another pointless meeting of the upper echelon of the Commonwealth. I could not walk around the beautiful waterfront because security measures were so tight, and at the mountain resort where the retreat took place we frittered the time away surrounded by hundreds of mounted police. I heard on the way home that the cabinet had decided to discontinue its subsidy to 600 post offices, which would close as a result, and not long after I got back, the stock market crashed and the bubble which did so much to sustain the government was burst. I thought then that I would never win another election. It seemed to me inevitable that Douglas would bounce back and say that the crash was a signal that the government had not gone far enough and that more must be done as proof against such adversity, and that is what he did.

I cannot remember exactly when he first brought me the package of measures he said were essential to restore confidence in the economy, but it may have been about the time that calls for action from his supporters in business began to appear in the news media. It was a lengthy document and I said I would look at it. I was in a low mood when I went to the Labour Party conference which was held in Auckland in November. Douglas was beyond reason and the left of the party, which was well represented on the floor of the conference, was sullen and unresponsive. When the time came for me to speak, I did not know what to say to the audience. I did not want to talk. I read the script and walked off. My useful life as a politician was coming to a close.

The Douglas proposals amounted to a reworking of his radical option of earlier in the year. In December they went to cabinet. He argued that we should liberalise the labour market, remodel the public sector, further reduce tariffs, and sell something like $14 billion worth of public assets. Personal income tax was to be levied at a flat rate of 23c in the dollar and the goods and services tax was to be raised to fifteen percent. His fiscal projections seemed hopelessly optimistic to me. Much as had happened with GST, when benefits were raised as compensation for the impost, Douglas offered a sweetener by way of a scheme he called guaranteed minimum family income, or GMFI. This was a form of subsidy for those who were in paid employment and was designed to keep a margin between those in work and those on a benefit. The economic argument behind the package, if I remember right, was that our boldness would inspire the country to greater effort, or it may have been that lower taxes were to have that effect. A tent evangelist could hardly have put it better.

The proposals went twice to cabinet where there was considerable contention. There were reservations about some parts of the package, but, in the way these things were done, deals were made and support was traded. Labour relations reform did not make it off the starting blocks, adventures in health and housing were abandoned, and some ministerial patches were protected at the expense of the rest. The rate of GST stayed for the time being at ten percent.

The centrepiece of the scheme was the flat rate of tax. I spoke with some feeling against it, but Cullen was the more trenchant critic. He argued its unfairness and put to flight the dubious economic case which was made for it. He explained its fiscal implications and its likely meaning for the government's ability to fund the social services. He did all that and more, but when it came to the crunch there were only the two of us. Dear God! What a terrible lot of people they were! It is hard to believe I used to think so much of them.

Douglas came to see me after the package was approved by cabinet. I think Palmer was with him. He said that if I was unhappy with the measures he would delay their announcement. I do not know what he intended by that, since nothing but their cancellation would have made me happy about them. I told him to go ahead but I insisted that the announcement make no reference to the proposed rate of personal income tax. He had no option but to agree to that, since cabinet had asked for work to be done by officials on the GMFI and this work might well impact on the package as a whole. In the end the announcement was made in the Beehive theatre on 17 December. It was deemed worthy of the presence of seven of us ministers.

Before Christmas I sent a memorandum to my cabinet colleagues saying that they were to regard our announcement as a statement of possibility rather than of firm intention. I thought it might prove that the figures in the Douglas package were unsustainable and that we should allow ourselves a way out if we needed one. I asked John Henderson to get some advice from outside the advisory group and the public service on the fiscal implications of the proposals and the workability of the GMFI. As a result of the various investigations John commissioned, it became clear enough that the numbers were unreliable and that the GMFI was conceptually deficient, a finding later confirmed by officials, but Douglas was not disposed to listen.

Ivor Richardson, the judge who was the chairman of the Royal Commission on Social Policy, came to see me. It was not a happy meeting. He told me that there was no point in the commission's continuing its work, given that the flat tax and the GMFI would in themselves determine the nature of social policy. I could only agree.

I thought for much of that summer on what I should do for the best. I considered resignation, and indeed resignation was the proper course. The conventions of cabinet government were simple enough. All members of the cabinet were bound by its decisions. Whatever their view of a matter, ministers had, when a decision was made, to uphold it in caucus; if called on, they had to speak in its support in parliament; they had to act in public as if it had never crossed their mind to disagree with it. The prime minister was bound by that convention as much as was the most junior minister, and that was right, because we were not a dictatorship. Convention demanded that those who disagreed resign their office if they could not submit themselves to the judgement of their colleagues.

When I first sat in that cabinet room I believed in the conventions of cabinet government and I did my best to put them into practice. It was not an easy matter for me to set them aside but I did, because I could not bear to think of the country we would have if the flat tax went ahead.

It was nearly the end of January when I made up my mind. I did not inform my cabinet colleagues. Douglas was out of the country when I made my announcement. I think that some effort was made to contact him before I spoke, but I did not care if he knew or not. I went to caucus, where I said nothing of moment, and then I held a press conference where I told the journalists there would be no flat tax. When the conference was over I felt nothing but relief.

CHAPTER SIXTEEN

I had a wonderfully enjoyable distraction in the summer of 1988. A vehicle company invited me to drive one of their cars in a motor-racing series. It was one of those glorious opportunities that sometimes come your way in public life: the chance to have someone else pay for something you dearly want to do in return for nothing more than the public interest your presence induces. David Slater was my tutor and managed the team which prepared the car. It was soon clear that I was not a talent lost to Formula One, but I kept out of trouble and I got a close-up look at the people who made their lives in motor sport. I liked being part of a team. I could not believe how hard its members worked, or what could be done to repair a motor vehicle if you really set your mind to it. It was a model of management in which you tried as hard as you could to get the best out of everyone. In the cabinet that year the challenge was to keep the worst from getting the better of us.

I was at the Levels raceway in Timaru when Douglas made his rapid return from Europe in response to my announcement of the finish of the flat tax. There was a lot of sound and fury and much scribbling of numbers on whiteboards as he made his protest. For a while I was not sure if the government would survive, but somehow an agreement was cobbled together in the cabinet. The tax rate would be reduced but not flattened. The GMFI could never be made to work and was abandoned. The announced intention to sell public assets remained in place.

Cabinet was never again what it was in our first term of office. Cohesion was gone for good, and any kind of philosophical unity. It was a place of contest. We could turn our collective mind only to inconsequential issues; anything of moment was subject to dispute and settled by shifting alignments of support.

Douglas as leader of the opposition group had the constant encouragement of Bassett and Prebble. He would sit silently, looking sour, plainly not enjoying himself. Bassett was always venomous, while Prebble kept himself under control. Douglas and his allies rarely engaged in argument: they were assertive, focusing on the adverse consequences if their proposals were not adopted. One of the new ministers, David Butcher, was a Douglas adherent, although as an advocate he was almost completely ineffective. Wetere was patronised by Douglas and usually followed his lead. Caygill supported Douglas on most matters of economic policy. He was more thoughtful than Douglas and not given to extremes of rhetoric or conduct. Stan Rodger was dry on economic issues but I always liked him and found him quite without animosity. Tapsell was conservative, but personally warm to me.

Some of them were hard to read. Moyle was withdrawn, while Bill Jeffries sometimes seemed like a lost soul. Others were hard to read for different reasons. Moore was as mercurial as ever. He did not take sides, preferring to present himself as above it all. Phil Goff liked to be in the majority and Hunt similarly kept his options open. Marshall was shallow, shabby, endlessly self-seeking. Douglas bought Clark off by promising her supply in her housing portfolio. She responded by putting her head down. I do not remember her buying into any fight we ever had in cabinet. She was by her own account a survivor: as long as her paddock had a good sole of grass the firestorm could consume the rest.

Tizard hated Douglas and never missed a chance to get a crack in. When I saw Margaret Shields recently she told me that she was away when the flat tax was discussed or there would have been three against it, and I have to credit that, because she was invariably supportive. Cullen continued his critical assessment of the Douglas agenda. More than once in cabinet I thought Cullen was close to tears, but it was not a sign of weakness. He was persistent, determined, articulate. There were times when I could have cried myself. I could not stand the frustration; I could not believe that intelligent argument could not shift them.

Palmer was my greatest support. He was my obvious successor, but he made it plain he was not interested in succeeding. Towards the end, when things were very fraught, Palmer became somewhat agitated and announced, as I had done when I was deputy, that he would make himself available if there were to be a vacancy. Even then I did not doubt his loyalty. His reputation was not enhanced when he became prime minister because he did not have the desire for the job and his abilities were not the ones it required. I am sorry that the burden fell on him.

It was of course caucus and not cabinet which elected the leader of the Labour Party. Cabinet could not move me as long as I had the numbers in caucus. Those numbers eroded as confidence faltered. The calculated gathering of support was what I least liked in politics and there was nothing I could do to improve my aptitude for it. I never acquired a taste for the social side of parliamentary life, nor the least interest in it. I could work with members I did not like, I could go to their electorates and speak at their fundraisers, but I could not pretend to enjoy their company. If caucus wanted me, it wanted me; when it did not, I would go.

The intentions of Douglas and his allies were soon plain enough, although there was little that was organised about their effort at first. What they did, and what happened to me, is what happens in politics; I saw it done to Rowling when I was the beneficiary of it. I had to bear it, although there is no point in asserting that I bore it lightly. As the months dragged past, rumours were forever being carried back to me that I was about to be toppled. There was a constant undertow of smear and innuendo. It was not surprising that Margaret was blamed by some in the Douglas camp for having turned me against their man, as it was a way of putting my relationship with her into the public arena under cover of concern about the influence she was supposed to have on me. In fact Margaret fretted endlessly about the boundaries between personal and professional responsibilities and would have left my office long before she did if I had not asked her to stay. After I fell out with Douglas, she did not bother to hide her disdain for him and his following, and I can hardly blame her.

The Royal Commission on Social Policy finished up in April 1988 by releasing what it said it had learned to date. The report was a profound disappointment and there was little in it to suggest that the commission would have had anything substantial to offer even had it finished the job. It was hardly coherent and its length made it an instant laughing stock. It ran to several fat volumes and one of Douglas's offsiders publicly proclaimed its usefulness as a doorstop.

In the same month I received what proved to be a splendid gift – the report by Brian Picot and his committee on the administration of schools. It was in every sense what the report of the royal commission was not and it described a robust model of the public sector. I used to wonder if I had made the right choice when I had made myself education minister but when I saw the report I knew I had.

Things did not start off very well in the education portfolio. It was the practice when elections drew near for government departments to write a report which might serve as a briefing for a new minister, if there was one. In 1984 these were all published as part of an exercise in openness in government. Treasury must have spent a large part of the next three years writing its 1987 version, a work in two volumes under the title *Government Management*. The second volume was entirely given over to the study of education. This was the work which Bruce Jesson described as social theory without any concept of society. As the new minister, I looked forward to reading the education department's response, but there was none. This significant department, with its budget of many millions, was the only one which did not manage to produce a briefing for its minister.

I was rather daunted at the beginning, but the department's staff were pleasant and I got a feel for the place. Early in 1988 I went unannounced one lunch-time to see my departmental chiefs at the old wooden building over the road from the Beehive. As far as I could tell, the building was abandoned; I left notes on various desks and went back to my office. At four o'clock that afternoon an apologetic deputation of senior management arrived; they said that as former teachers they were not used to working during January. The management structure they worked in was cumbersome and its resources were used up in many layers of administration. Picot memorably described the education bureaucracy as 'good people, bad system', and I had to agree with him.

I met Picot and his colleagues several times in the course of their inquiry. I also had a range of new advisors. I relied greatly on Noel Scott MP, himself a former teacher and a man of broad humanity. He was made an undersecretary for education in August 1988. Anne Meade joined the advisory group. She was a distinguished educator whose work was critical not only in the emergence of the new school administration but also in the reshaping of the early childhood sector, for which she had a sympathy that was contagious. I asked Harvey McQueen to join my staff because I was impressed by his writing on educational issues. He was tireless and enthusiastic, and put up with being used as a straight man at the public meetings we held to discuss the Picot report. Vivienne Smith was the press secretary employed to handle education issues. She was good at the job, and when

Ross Vintiner's successor left she took over from him as chief press secretary.

The Picot report proposed a model of administration which was based on local control. Above all it was a democratic model, aimed at harnessing the most powerful force in education – the desire of parents to see their children do well at school. It set up a number of institutions through which not only the school but the agencies of central government were obliged to respond to parental wishes. It depended on school zoning, because every school had to have a discrete constituency to which it was accountable; if you abolish zoning, as the National Party did in government, you are left with the gimcrack accountability of the marketplace.

Having read the report, and being impressed by it, I decided it would be released to the public as a proposal which, subject to consultation, the government intended to adopt. It met with great enthusiasm from the general public and something like 20,000 written submissions were received inside six weeks. They were overwhelmingly positive. I went to public meetings all over the country to explain the report and answer questions from the audience. It was hard work but I enjoyed the meetings, and it seemed more useful than anything I was doing in Wellington.

The reaction of the teacher unions was far less encouraging. The burden of the change fell on the primary sector while the governance of the secondary sector hardly altered. This made little difference to the Post Primary Teachers Association. I found it difficult to engage with that union in any constructive way. This was the soft left at its worst: middle-class, shrill and platitudinous. Its representatives gave no credit to my observation that change was needed lest the weaknesses of the existing administration turn into its death warrant. Their bête noire, bulk funding, was removed from the original proposals, but this did not placate them. The low point for me came at the PPTA's annual conference at Trentham racecourse. It was the custom to invite the minister to speak. Ken Douglas was there, in token of the solidarity of teachers with the wider union movement. The president of the PPTA, who was helpful enough when I saw her in my office, delivered a blistering attack on the government. The detail escapes me now, but I am sure that treachery was invoked, and the ruin of the lives of honest hard-working schoolteachers. My patience was in short supply by then. I thanked the president for her speech and said that I understood why she had to say what her audience wanted to hear, but I wanted to assure her of my gratitude for her private agreement and support for the proposals. The audience was silent and I heard Ken Douglas say, 'That was a bit bloody rough, mate.' I told myself that not all secondary schoolteachers could possibly be as unprepossessing as their union delegates.

After the consultation, a scheme was adopted which was based on the Picot report, tempered by the views of the public and interested parties. A number of names were offered for it and I chose Tomorrow's Schools. The scheme was in place before the end of 1989 when nearly 3000 boards of trustees were elected.

The name has stuck but not much else. I shudder when I hear it applied to the schools of the 1990s, when the National government did away with zoning and schools were allowed to pick and choose their students. It also did away with the mechanisms by which parental voices could be heard and acknowledged, and in doing so it subverted the democratic element which was the essence of the original model of Tomorrow's Schools.

One reason I found the consultation process arduous was that I did not feel well. I think it was in February or March 1988 that I started to feel pains in my stomach. I felt unaccountably tired. I was sure that it was some uninvited consequence of the stomach surgery and tests were carried out but nothing was revealed. As the months went past I felt worse and worse.

Douglas had the 1988 budget under preparation. The tax cuts which were to take the place of the flat tax were due to take effect in October. Provision was made but not yet announced for new spending in the education portfolio and in other social services. In spite of the efforts of our first term in office we were still some way from getting the budget into surplus, but the deficit was expected to be a manageable amount. Treasury projections had the deficit at not much over $1 billion. Then in the middle of the year I suddenly learned that the Treasury figures were wrong – the deficit would in fact be $3.2 billion, an unacceptably high amount. Douglas reported that the difference was the result of unavoidable errors in the projections and recommended that we cut the deficit by cutting spending.

I did not trust Douglas and I did not trust the numbers he presented. I thought that our spending on social services was going to be the victim of a premeditated ambush. I would rather have postponed the tax cuts than taken the axe to the social services, but there was little hope of carrying that view in the cabinet. I could not risk another unilateral announcement, but there was nothing to prevent my talking about the problem and in that way appeal to a wider constituency, and that is what I decided to do.

I was due to give a speech to a group in Wellington called the Press Club. I used my speech to describe what had happened to the budget figures. I said that the government was dealing with the problem and emphasised that there was no way we would allow the deficit to reach the damaging figure of the latest forecast. I explained that we would look at all our options on both the revenue and the expenditure sides. Before I gave the speech I circulated a copy of it to ministers and invited their response. Douglas came to see me in my office on the morning it was to be given and read through the final version of it without making any comment. About an hour before it was to be delivered he called my office to say he did not agree with it, but by then it was far too late. I went to the Press Club and spoke. It was not a convincing performance and I felt dreadful. I was shivering and shaking and I thought I had the flu. As soon as it was over Douglas's office flooded the news media with assertions that there was nothing wrong with the budget projections; whatever problem there might have been had been solved some time ago.

I did not have the chance to take things any further, I was too sick. I flew to Auckland the day after my speech was delivered and the day after that went to a consultant's rooms for tests. It was on the treadmill there that the classic symptoms of angina made their first appearance. An angiogram at the Mater Hospital disclosed some degree of blockage in the blood vessels of the heart. I was admitted to Greenlane, where a procedure called angioplasty was performed and the obstruction in the blood vessels pushed aside.

I was not long in the hospital but I was unwell for some time, and more significantly perhaps my confidence took a battering. I was frightened, and I felt vulnerable in a way I never had before. Once again I gave up smoking, and I felt the loss.

Cabinet in my absence patched up a budget deficit of a little under $1.5 billion. The October income tax reductions remained in place. There were some cuts to spending, and there must have been some wishful thinking on the revenue side, as GST had to be increased in 1989. The government's commitment to the sale of public assets in the name of the reduction of debt was confirmed.

Early in August 1988 I made a visit to Australia. The purpose of the travel was to acknowledge Australia's 200 years of settlement, but there were other engagements, chief among them a speech to the National Press Club in Canberra. It was here that I made an unscripted aside which became well known as a form of shorthand for what I tried to do in our second term in office. It was time, I said, to stop and assess our situation and let those who had fallen behind catch up with us. It was time for a cup of tea.

The Douglas camp saw nothing but provocation in those words. By now the opposition was more organised. A grouping appeared which called itself the Backbone Club; its members were members of the Labour Party who supported the Douglas agenda and their aim was to advance it. Many of them left with Douglas when he formed the Association of Consumers and Taxpayers.

There were several in the caucus who were cheerleaders for Douglas, just as there were some who were his declared opponents, but there was an irreducible number in the caucus, and one or two in the cabinet, who believed that Douglas and I should simply kiss and make up. I thought it a bizarre response at the time and my view has not altered since. It is understandable that children are unhappy when mum and dad are at odds, but the members of the caucus were adults and I can only explain their behaviour in terms of their inability or unwillingness to face up to the issues which divided me and Douglas.

Just as Palmer was my shield, Caygill was Douglas's. I could do nothing about Douglas unless there was a successor. Caygill was the only credible choice, but he said plainly that he would not take over from Douglas unless Douglas did not want the job. I told Douglas towards the end of August that one of us would have to go and he agreed, but he came back later and told me that he was not going to make it easy for me. I decided that it was time to reshuffle the cabinet, and during discussions about this adopted a scheme whereby the finance portfolio would be split and the Treasury divided, in accordance with its own principles, into a ministry which gave economic advice and another ministry which implemented it. I proposed to make Douglas responsible for the advisory agency. I discussed this plan with any number of people on a strictly confidential basis and of course it became widely known that Douglas's position as finance minister was under threat. In fact it was not, because Caygill refused to budge, but after this episode Douglas seemed to lose the plot. Rage made him incoherent and bile spewed out of his office.

That year's Labour Party conference was an exercise in irony. Anderton, who by then was isolated in the caucus, decided to make one last push for control in the party by contesting the presidency on the floor of the conference. He had considerable support among the delegates. His opponent was Ruth Dyson, an activist from the South Island who in terms of the politics of the time was a moderate. She had no liking for the Douglas faction but, for some reason I can only explain in terms of an atavistic dislike of Anderton, the Backbone Club threw its weight behind her and she won. The right of the party would have been far better placed with Anderton as president, because it would have cut off the party from me and the caucus, but thinking more than one step ahead was never its strong point. Dyson offered a bridge between party and caucus. The party offered its continuing support in return for consultation and a voice, particularly in the sale of public assets. I agreed on behalf of the caucus.

This meeting in Dunedin was the last time I spoke to the Labour Party conference apart from a few words I said in response to a presentation by Ruth Dyson in 1989. I did not enjoy the conferences and I was not a particularly good attender of them when I was a backbencher in the 1990s. After I left parliament in 1996 I let my membership of the party lapse.

The sale of public assets led to the next eruption in the cabinet. The sales were urged on cabinet as a matter of economic urgency, the argument being that we needed the money to repay debt. There was a case to be made for some of the sales, but the process by which the sales were made was a debacle, to put it mildly. It cost us more political ground than any other single issue. The rush to sell was nothing more than bloody-mindedness. If the process was not corrupt, it was certainly open to corruption, or the appearance of corruption. Ministers were too close to the sales process and in some cases too close to prospective purchasers. It was an improper exercise of political responsibility. Towards the end of the year I took it on myself to announce a review of the sales process and put a proposal to cabinet which was intended to distance ministers from the process. It was hardly tabled when Prebble, who oversaw the disposal of several public enterprises and took my proposal as a personal affront, refused to consult the Labour Party about the sale of the Shipping Corporation, in disregard of the agreement made at the Dunedin conference. I dismissed him from his responsibility for the state-owned enterprises. He went on television and asserted in his unpleasant way that I was acting dictatorially and not rationally and I dismissed him from the cabinet. I called his cabinet colleagues to tell them what I intended. Douglas said little or nothing, Caygill, in his six-of-one, half-a-dozen-of-the-other manner of speaking made some defence of Prebble. But it was done.

I cannot remember exactly what it was that provoked Douglas into resigning at the end of 1988 – some trivial matter involving his staff. I do remember that he came into my office and handed me his letter of resignation from cabinet. He said nothing, I said nothing, and he slammed the door when he left. He was filled with righteous indignation, born of his frustration at my having thwarted his ambition; to prove that his and not mine was the mandate, he invited journalists into his office and let them read through cabinet papers until Palmer went down to stop him.

Caygill was appointed finance minister, but, in spite of his integrity and his lack of interest in privatising the social services, the change meant little to me in the end. On economic issues he was as dry as Douglas. As far as I could tell he wanted Palmer to be prime minister so that order, and indeed Douglas, could be restored to the cabinet.

The year of struggle took its toll on me. The joy of having the job sank in the conflict and anxiety which surrounded it. Nothing marks a political party down harder than disunity, and the Labour government had been disunited and dysfunctional for the better part of a year. Nor was there any end in sight of our difficulties. Douglas, out of office, launched himself at a public rally of the Backbone Club as a candidate for leadership. I could not unite the caucus and I could not win the next election. I doubted I would be allowed to try. I sometimes found myself crying, for the same reason I had cried in Mick Connelly's office ten years earlier. I could not believe that my life had become so meaningless and tedious. At the end of the year I thought I would have to go; the question was how my going would be decided.

CHAPTER SEVENTEEN

In the summer of 1989 I was forty-six years old. My state of health was good but my state of mind was not.

Naomi and I lived in two worlds. She looked after our children and kept the household going in Mangere, where she was still active in the church and the local Labour Party. We hardly spoke about politics or Wellington. Some time in that summer, I told her about Margaret. She asked me to stay in the marriage until our children left school, but I could not promise her that.

I resented a lot of the time I gave to the job, but the job carried on whether I resented it or not. I met distinguished visitors, I travelled overseas, I went to dinners and party functions, I visited schools, I held press conferences, I chaired the caucus and I chaired the cabinet.

Caucus was a battleground. The Douglas camp was in rebellion and the ranks of those who hoped for reconciliation were swelled, as the polls worsened, by the panic-stricken. 'Poll-driven fruitcakes' was the name I gave to them. At the same time there were many in the caucus who gave me support, some with reservation and some unconditionally, or close enough; I did not do enough to tell them of my gratitude. Cabinet meetings were shorter and more orderly with Douglas and Prebble gone. There were no more papers which demanded the attention of cabinet without notice. But there was no satisfaction in it for me. To avoid the appearance of instability after the departure of Douglas, there was little choice but to emphasise the continuity of economic policy. In the cabinet room there were pockets of discontent, and there was never enough money to do what we wanted.

In the middle of it all there were still things to enjoy. Towards the end of my time as prime minister I went to Kiribati for the South Pacific Forum. Kiribati itself was a ruin, as a Japanese aid programme had built a causeway to link the islands around the lagoon and thereby destroyed the capacity of the lagoon to flush itself clean. Swimming was not possible on Kiribati, as there were steep cliffs on the seaward side and the beaches inside the lagoon were filthy. HMNZS *Monowai* was there to provide support, and the sailors and hydrographers on board were a friendly bunch. The ship's helicopter flew me and two officers out over the ocean, well out of sight of land, and dropped the three of us and a rubber dinghy into the water. We spent several hours swimming from the boat in the middle of the Pacific. I have never felt such freedom as I felt miles from anywhere as I floated in that extraordinary turquoise pool.

In Wellington, I liked my regular press conferences. They were a challenge in the same way the crossword was a challenge, and usually as consequential. As always, it was what appeared on television that counted. The membership of the press gallery changed over the time I was in parliament: there were fewer representatives of the print medium as its ownership was concentrated, and more young journalists representing radio and television. There was always a hard core of solid and reliable reporters in the gallery, but it was not a place you would look to for considered inquiry or investigation. That is not a reflection on gallery journalists, as it was the product of the policy of editors and owners, which was perhaps itself a reflection of the small size of the market for serious journalism. I would go to London and be interviewed by a senior political commentator and nothing might appear in print until several weeks later when I would find myself quoted in the course of a long article which carefully canvassed many aspects of the topic. The video clip, the sound bite and their written equivalent were the currency here. It had to be immediate, which left little room for judgement.

I did not like the pack mentality of the gallery journalists and I preferred to keep them at a distance. I never spoke to journalists off the record. It is different now, but in those days I thought it was beneath the office of prime minister to cultivate reporters.

The press gallery could turn like a tide and it was running against me in 1989. The Backbone Club openly campaigned to put Douglas into the leadership, while Douglas set himself up as a commentator on the government. His camp followers spread their poison; rumour and allegation were put to me at press conferences by way of question, and denial achieved nothing. The sense of division was heightened, and uncertainty and instability were compounded.

Opinion polls were deeply damaging. It is customary in politics to profess your indifference to them, and I did, but I was not indifferent.

In April I suffered a setback from which I did not recover. I travelled to the United States and Canada after accepting an invitation to deliver a lecture named in honour of the father of the president of the day, George Bush Senior, at Yale. My subject was New Zealand's military relationship with the United States. I spoke about our long history of shared military goals and made the point which had occurred to me when I made my tour of the Pentagon: in all of the conflicts we took part in together the ANZUS alliance was not actually invoked. We had a good relationship with the United States long before ANZUS, and we could have a good relationship now that ANZUS was inoperative. Cabinet decided before I left that there were to be no policy initiatives made while I was overseas, so I contented myself with stating the obvious. By their actions in suspending New Zealand from the ANZUS council, Australia and the United States had made the treaty into a dead letter as far as New Zealand was concerned. To let our relationship develop on its new footing, it would be best to put the treaty and its associations behind us, which raised the question of whether or not New Zealand should give formal notice of withdrawal from the ANZUS council.

The speech was well received by the university audience and I was happy with it, until I heard how it was reported. It was given at Yale on the afternoon of 24 April, which meant reports of its content were relayed back to New Zealand early on the morning of Anzac Day. I said in my speech that ANZUS had left New Zealand, but Richard Griffin of Radio New Zealand told his audience that New Zealand had left ANZUS. I could not believe it. There was nothing apolitical about Anzac Day in the 1980s and the outrage of conservatives at the news that we had withdrawn from ANZUS sped the rush to judgement of cabinet ministers who believed that I had gone beyond my mandate. It did not matter what I said afterwards: the damage was done, and could not be put right. In 1984 or 1985 I could and did say what I thought about our foreign policy, or even muse aloud about it, and cabinet came along for the ride, but in 1989 I could not work that trick.

It was over quickly after that, although it dragged on like an agony at the time. When I got back to New Zealand, Palmer met me with his somewhat startling announcement that I did not have the numbers. He was concerned that cabinet would become unworkable. He told me that he must withdraw assurances he gave me earlier that if I were not the leader he would not remain in politics, saying that he would never challenge me directly but if I were to leave he would make himself available to fill the place. If I have the order of things right, I went from seeing Palmer to the Labour Party's Auckland regional conference. A number of the Auckland members of parliament were close to Douglas and the Backbone Club was strongly represented; the next day there were fist fights among the delegates.

Late in June there was a vote of confidence put in the caucus, and I won, but not by much. In July it was plain that the caucus wanted to fill the two vacancies in the cabinet and I agreed there should be a vote. It took place early in August and Douglas was re-elected to the cabinet. I did not put it to the members of caucus as a choice between him and me, as it was hard to believe any of them could be so stupid as to see it in any other way. The majority chose Douglas. When I heard the result I knew that my decision had been made for me.

I went back to Auckland the day after the caucus. I told Margaret I was going and she said she understood. I told Naomi. I called Ruth Dyson and told her in confidence of my resignation. I went to church on Sunday and found myself overcome with sadness, not because of any feeling I had for the place, but because it brought back to me the memory of the visit Donald Soper made to New Zealand in the summer of 1985, when he sat with me in that church and I was elated by his company and the thought of all the opportunities in front of me. I went to Wellington on Sunday afternoon and to cabinet on Monday morning. It was the only cabinet I ever went to that I did not prepare for; I did not bother to look at the papers. I told the cabinet I was going, Palmer spoke, others spoke, I left. I went back to my office to tell my staff, and that was hard, because they were loyal and hard-working and I was abandoning them to the uncertainty of new management. The press conference which followed was much easier. Several former members of staff came to the office in the afternoon, Trish Green and her new baby among them. It was a bittersweet occasion. Naomi and the children came down on Tuesday morning to see the last of it all. The staff made me a presentation. When they thanked me, I could not hold back my tears, the only time I lost my composure. I went to the house and made my farewell speech. I drove to Government House to tender my resignation and that was the end of it.

Caucus elected Palmer leader of the parliamentary Labour Party in a comfortable victory over Moore, while Clark narrowly defeated Douglas for the deputy leadership.

Palmer was most generous to me, offering me a knighthood, but I could think of no use for it. More to the point, he made me attorney-general and a minister outside the cabinet. There is a case for having the attorney-general outside the cabinet, as the office provides legal advice to the government and its head should not be constrained by decisions of cabinet, but like many fine constitutional points it has long since been lost to sight. I enjoyed my time as titular head of the legal profession, although not enough to imagine that a return to the practice of law was an option. I moved to an office in a small building between Parliament Buildings and Broadcasting House where a number of ministers and undersecretaries had their rooms. Lorna Best came with me as private secretary, and Vivienne Smith as press secretary.

It was all a great change, but not a wrench; I knew it was coming and I had a long time to get used to it. What I felt more than anything else was relief. The struggle was over, for good or worse, and the responsibility of the job belonged to someone else. My blood pressure, which was high enough to be a cause of some concern, was tested about a week after I left office and was back in the normal range.

I went to caucus, where after nearly ten years of sitting at the front, I took a seat at the back. I was not well disposed towards a good number of my colleagues, but again that feeling did not come over me suddenly. I took little part in caucus discussions. I read the paper or did the crossword and made the occasional comment. In the house I had a seat at the back of the block of ministers.

I spoke very little, mostly on education issues, and I neither asked nor was asked to do more. If I was sought out by journalists for comment I tried to say nothing which was not to the credit of the government.

The attorney-general was minister in charge of the Government Printing Office, because the government printer published bills, parliamentary papers and the like. Over many years the printing office had grown into a sizeable enterprise with plant in Wellington and Masterton. It had many substantial contracts. It was put up for sale by the government in 1988 but a buyer was not found until the latter part of 1989. As minister in charge, it was my responsibility to sign the agreement for sale, but I refused to sign it when I read it. The price did not reflect the extraordinarily generous terms being offered to the purchaser. It went back to cabinet, which directed me to sign, and again I declined. Cabinet changed the rules so that another minister could put his name to the agreement. That was as much resistance as I chose to make. I did not want another fight.

The solicitor-general was John McGrath, who later became a judge of the appeal court and the Supreme Court. He was open and collegial. His office was engaged in preparing a brief for the arbitration which was about to take place between the government of New Zealand and the government of France in the matter of the *Rainbow Warrior*, and McGrath suggested to me that I should be personally involved in it. The French had breached the agreement between the two governments when they removed their agents from the island of Hao and sent them home to Paris; the agreement provided for arbitration in case of a dispute. A tribunal was appointed to hear argument from both sides in New York in

October 1989. I took up the task with some enthusiasm, although I knew before the arbitration started that its findings would be less than satisfactory. International law applies to the powerful only so far as the powerful choose to let it apply to them, and there was no possibility in this case that the French would return the agents to the island. The New Zealand side had the benefit of considerable legal expertise and the presence of a distinguished English specialist in international law, but after much effort in the construction of our argument and ten laborious days in New York, the tribunal awarded us monetary compensation we did not seek and various forms of acknowledgement that the agreement had indeed been breached.

Before I went to New York I told Naomi that I was going to leave her. She had everything on her side: the promise I made to her when we married, the memory of my Methodist upbringing, the expectations of many people I cared about, the hardship she had gone through when we were young and short of money, our children and the care she gave them, the way she was whirled around the place when I was prime minister. It was my duty to stay but I did not want to. When I came back from the arbitration we agreed that there would be a formal separation and I made a short written statement to the news media. This was duly reported, for the most part without embellishment, until a television item suggested that Naomi's decision to stay in Auckland rather than move to Wellington when I became prime minister had contributed to the breakdown of the marriage. She called a reporter who worked on one of the Sunday papers and poured out her anger about me and Margaret. It was a sensation for some time. Paul Holmes went out to Takapuna to interview my mother at her home in the retirement village. She said she wished I had never been born. I was once in church on Mother's Day when the minister read the first verse of Psalm 23 and told the Sunday school that children should see their mother, as much as the Lord, as their shepherd; but my mother was my sheepdog.

A lot was said and written about the end of my marriage by people who knew none of us. Naomi's anger gave them licence. Then an odd thing happened. I was asked to go to Government House to see the governor-general, Paul Reeves, formerly the Anglican archbishop of New Zealand. I had no idea why he wanted to see me. He showed me a letter he had received from my father-in-law which asked him to remove from me my honours and appointments. I suppose he meant well in showing it to me, but I had to bite my tongue.

Margaret and I travelled to get away from it and that too was not easy at first, because she was the worst traveller I ever met. When I first knew her she got unsettled if she went beyond Masterton. We were in Hong Kong in January 1990 when I received two messages: one which said that my mother was in hospital for surgery, the other saying that the Queen would like to confer on me personally the Order of the Companions of Honour which was given to me in the New Year's list.

I was pleased to have the order, because it was unusual and did not carry the burden of a title, and I was moved by the Queen's offer of a private investiture. I used to think of myself as a monarchist, but in fact I am someone who admires the Queen, and not only because of my memory of the royal tour of my childhood. She rarely drops her guard and her public image does not do her justice. I found her far more warm and intelligent than she ever allows herself to appear. She asked to see me at Vancouver in 1987 to tell me that Fiji was leaving the Commonwealth, and it was clear that she knew the principal figures well and understood the issues thoroughly. It seems almost certain that the monarchy in this country will die with her and I would not be distressed to see it, but it is probably time to start thinking seriously about the alternatives.

The Queen presented me with the insignia of the order at Government House in Wellington. I took the medal and its ribbon to Auckland and showed them to my mother. It was the kind of thing Mum liked. For the first and only time in my life she said to me how well I had done.

Mum soldiered on despite the cancer which eventually killed her later in 1990. She lived an active life until the week of her death, driving her car vigorously and reasonably accurately. I was surprised when the King of Tonga arrived for her funeral; he mistook her for the widow of my Uncle Harold. Her ashes are next to my father's in the cemetery at Meadowbank, not far from the last place they lived together; Pop often pointed out the smoke from the crematorium as he sat on the back porch of their unit at Kohimarama.

Towards the end of 1989 Palmer asked his ministers to tell him if they intended to retire at the general election the following year, as he wanted to reshuffle the ministry and replace the retirees with new blood. I told him I intended to stand again. My political ambitions had long since burned out and I had no illusions about the backbench life which faced me after the election, but I could not afford to leave. I did not want to go back to the law and I did not see how I could make a living in any other way. I decided to become the country's highest-paid social worker.

Palmer reconstructed his ministry but little else altered. He inherited a bankrupt estate. It would have been hard enough for the government to win an election after the crash of 1987 and its aftermath, and the disunity we displayed from 1988 onwards destroyed what was left of the confidence the public had in us. More than anything else, voters in our second term of office wanted reassurance, but in policy and demeanour we offered exactly the opposite. The public could not rely on us. At the general election of 1990 we got exactly what we deserved and no amount of window-dressing could ever have saved us.

The government's poll ratings lifted after Palmer took office but soon began to slide back downwards. He was not an instinctive politician and could do little to correct the course. I once went to the Papatoetoe town hall to hear him speak. The place was full of Labour Party members. It was not hard to read the audience. It wanted to warm to him, but his delivery was wooden and repetitive and he could not make the connection. He did well enough on television before he became prime minister, but after he took over he seemed to lose his compass. His poor public performances led him to be blamed by many in the caucus for the government's low ratings; it was an analysis as shallow as it was deficient, but caucus by then was floundering in face of polling which suggested that even the safest seats were at risk. Clark among others withdrew her support from Palmer, and Moore engaged in frantic lobbying in his own interest until Palmer stepped aside and Moore became leader of the parliamentary Labour Party and prime minister for all of seven weeks.

It was distressing, because it devalued the office of prime minister and made us an international laughing stock, and it was destructive, because Palmer was perfectly willing to carry the burden of defeat and then give way to a new leadership which might have had a better chance of starting again among the ruins. There are hardly ever any happy endings in politics but there was something particularly sad and cynical about the end of the fourth Labour government.

A woman called Karen Lane came to see me in my office in Wellington just after the general election. Her husband was being held hostage by the Iraqi government. Saddam Hussein's army had invaded Kuwait in August 1990 and had taken a large number of foreign nationals hostage as a way of staving off attack by Kuwait's friends and allies. A coalition of rescuers was being assembled under the leadership of the United States. Edward Heath, the former British prime minister, went to Baghdad to ask for the release of the British hostages, and Karen Lane asked if I would go to ask for the release of the thirty New Zealanders held prisoner in Iraq. The incoming National Party government was less than supportive of the venture. It would not let me have a diplomatic passport and the costs of the journey were eventually met by Barry Colman, the publisher. I put this down to official unwillingness to upset the Americans and I said bitter things about the foreign affairs ministry when I got back. I regret that now, because the New Zealand diplomats I met along the way to Baghdad could not have done more to help.

I travelled with Margaret by way of New Delhi and Amman in Jordan. I did not want to be seen as a supporter of Saddam Hussein, but I did have a lot to say to foreign journalists in Amman about the debilitating influence of American diplomacy in the region. Whether or not this helped secure our admission to Iraq or the eventual release of the hostages I do not know, but we did go to Baghdad, where we were the guests of the regime at the Al Rashid hotel, an oasis of considerable luxury in the centre of the city and a landmark among much tragedy in time to come. I spoke to Iraqi officials and we were taken to see some of the monuments of the Saddam regime. It was a bizarre experience, made tolerable only by our meeting with some of the hostages whose release I hoped our presence might achieve. We went back to Amman without any word from the Iraqis; they were letting hostages go in batches and I hoped that they might at least set some of the New Zealanders free. It was wonderful to get word that they were all to be released.

We had to wait in Amman for three days until word came that we would be allowed to travel to Baghdad. It turned out to be an extraordinary interlude. We were looked after by Maurice Khalaf, who was New Zealand's honorary consul in Jordan. He was a most generous host and indefatigable in his efforts to secure our admission to Iraq. We dined with Maurice's family at a restaurant overlooking the city and I smoked a hubble bubble, a kind of pipe in which the smoke is cooled by passing it through water. We went to see Jerash, the extensive remains of a Roman city; we had it almost to ourselves, so I took the opportunity to stand and say a few words in its amphitheatre. We visited the Dead Sea and I floated in its astonishingly supportive water. There was a hotel by the shore, abandoned by tourists because of the possibility of war, and we sat on its terrace for a while, looking over at Israel. As I talked to Margaret I wondered for a moment how it was possible to be so happy.

CHAPTER EIGHTEEN

My parliamentary career after 1990 was very much a footnote. After that year's general election there were fewer than thirty of us in the caucus. Though there were some new faces, it was remarkable how quickly we lapsed into the habits of opposition. Mike Moore was leader of the parliamentary Labour Party and Helen Clark was his deputy. Moore treated me as if he saw me as a threat to his leadership, which was nonsense in the circumstances, and I found it hard to take him seriously. I voted for Clark when she replaced him as leader in 1994.

There was little to like in the politics of the day. Labour eroded public confidence in the institutions of government and National came close to destroying it. On election night in 1993 it was unclear which party would have the majority. Before the special votes were counted and the result finally decided, the National government was saved by the support of the Anderton vehicle, the Alliance. Anderton had left the Labour Party in 1989 and set up a party of his own; after the general election in 1993 he invented a constitutional principle which demanded he give his parliamentary support to National rather than to Labour. As it turned out, the special votes gave National a buffer, as long as it could induce one of the opposition to serve as speaker. Bolger offered the job to me and I had to laugh. Peter Tapsell took it.

Financial commitments again kept me in parliament for another term after 1993. By then I was more confident of my ability to earn an income outside of politics, but the settlement which was made at the end of my marriage and the purchase of houses in Wellington and Auckland left me heavily in debt and I needed the assurance of the parliamentary salary. I also had an annuity paid to me as the result of having served five years as prime minister. I wrote to the Higher Salaries Commission and pointed out that the payment could not be justified while I was still in public employment and would be far more useful when I actually retired. The commission paid as much attention to me as it did when I wrote to it about my unsought increase in income in 1986.

I did my best for my constituents. On Saturdays I went to my electorate office where there was now a full-time electorate secretary, Denise Hodgkinson, and through her efforts and those of volunteers the office worked its way through the many difficulties which faced people in Mangere in the early 1990s. The perennial issues of dependency, immigration and unemployment were made more demanding by the National government's benefit cuts and its policy of charging market rentals for state housing. If I had to, I used my public profile to advance the cause of people in my electorate, like the school principal who was subject to an extraordinary and unwarranted attack by the social welfare minister when he remarked on how her department had failed a student. I pointed out to some effect that it was not the job of the Ministry of Education to pay a local wide boy to run a bakery in the belief that he was providing pre-school education, and when I received an invitation from the local branch of the Department of Social Welfare, at the height of its commercialisation, to the opening of its 'fast and friendly lane', I could not help but wonder in print when my constituents might see the last of the slow and surly alternatives.

From 1991 onwards I wrote a few hundred words every fortnight for the *Dominion* and some other papers in the same ownership. I did so at the invitation of the editor, whose interest was engaged by letters I wrote to him pointing out the inaccuracy of his newspaper's reporting. I enjoyed the writing. Some of it was anecdote from my life in politics, much was commentary on the issues of the time, and some was lampooning of figures on the other side of the issues from me. I also wrote about the Labour Party, usually in the interest of spurring some resolution of the divisions which still troubled us in the 1990s, or sometimes in the hope that we might light on the alternative approach to economic management which was so elusive in the 1980s. By then I liked writing about politics far more than taking part in it, and when I left parliament in 1996 I felt no sense of loss.

I made a comfortable living for several years by writing and speaking and had agents in New Zealand and Australia. The Australian market was rewarding; political issues there were similar enough and audiences close enough to audiences at home to make frequent travel worth the effort. I spoke in Europe as well as Canada and the United States, and I went several times to Japan and Taiwan. I did some television work, but it was less to my liking than speaking. I always found it hard to put up with the tedium of filming and nothing in a studio could ever come close to the satisfaction I got from speaking to a live audience.

In 1991 Margaret and I bought a house in Mangere Bridge. The house was a place I knew of in my younger days, when it was something of a landmark among the market gardens of the district. Built in the 1880s by an immigrant from Yorkshire, its poured concrete walls are nearly ten inches thick. It was somewhat run-down when we bought it, but it was always an attractive property with its trees and its old barn and a paddock large enough to keep a pony, if we ever wanted to. In the nature of these things it took more than ten years to get the place close to the way we wanted it, and there is hammering on the roof above me as I write this, but it is a comfortable home.

Margaret and I were married in Glasgow in 1992. In July 1995 I had leave from parliament, which I used in part to teach a short course in South Pacific political issues at a summer school at Portland State University in Portland, Oregon; after that Margaret and I and our friend Murray Cotter, who was for some time my political manager in Mangere, attempted to see as much as we could of the United States by driving something over 12,000 kilometres across it and back in eighteen days. It was a great journey, marked by only two encounters with American traffic cops, but Margaret was more than usually homesick; the reason for this became apparent when our daughter Edith was born early the next year. Margaret and I were both past the age when such events are usually planned for, and Edith has put up all her life with people mistaking me for her grandfather.

Edith without knowing it saved my life. I am not sure exactly when I discovered the anaesthetic effect of alcohol; it may have been in 1988 but I think more likely it was 1989 when I found it to be more effective than any sleeping pill in blotting out the memory of the day and the thought of the day to come. In those times I never drank in company and I thought far too much of the job to drink when I was working or at any public function. The trouble was that when I lost the job I did not lose my dependence on alcohol. There were times when I could go for long periods without it, but when I started drinking I could not stop. I made all kinds of promises and I told all kinds of lies, but I have not had a drink since Edith was an infant because I did not want her to grow up with a father who lived like that. I went to my first AA meeting in a Baptist church hall, sure as I walked towards the hall from the car park that every eye in the nearby pensioner village was on me. In 2002 I was in Bombay with my son Roy and I asked him to find me a meeting to go to. He found one in a church hall in Colaba and, as we walked towards it down a dark street littered in the Indian way with victims of drug and alcohol abuse, I consoled myself with the thought that here at least I was not going to meet anyone who knew me. But nobody should discount the power of television. This was the time when the United States and other countries issued warnings to travellers that nuclear war between India and Pakistan was imminent. I went on local television in Bombay and denounced the stupidity of this view, so that when it came my turn to introduce myself at the meeting and I began in the usual way by saying, 'Hello, I'm David and I'm an alcoholic,' a dozen voices said, 'Good evening, Mr Lange.'

There are other unhappy memories of the 1990s. I became involved in two long and expensive actions in defamation. It was a time when the law of defamation was in transition: the law has always sought a balance between freedom of speech and the right of individuals to preserve their reputation, and in the 1990s the balance was shifting. The result was that my name was attached to leading cases in both Australia and New Zealand, but it was not something I wished for.

You cannot take part in political life if you cannot cope with hard words being said about you, up to and including abuse and ridicule, but it used to be the law that such commentary, were it not to be defamatory, had to be founded in truth. In 1990 a Television New Zealand programme suggested that I had a corrupt involvement in the sale of public assets. Its allegations were not put to me before they were broadcast. The programme met so few of the tests of responsible journalism that the local broadcaster settled my action against it fairly quickly, but the Australian Broadcasting Corporation, which re-broadcast the programme in spite of warnings of its defamatory conduct, defended itself by maintaining that it was exercising its constitutional right to freedom of political communication. Richard Fowler was my lawyer, and with his colleagues in Sydney he took the case all the way to the High Court of Australia, which upheld the constitutional principle but pointed out that its exercise had to be balanced by reasonableness of conduct, a finding which was sufficient to induce the ABC to settle.

The next case arose from an article in a magazine owned by Australian publishers. Its thesis, supported by some fanciful illustrations, was that I did not work at the job of being prime minister. It seems trivial now and I should have let it go, but it hurt in a way that better informed and more pointed criticism did not; whatever I did in that job, I gave it everything I had. The truth of the article was never tested in court, because the case was argued around the question of how far the law might allow untrue or unsubstantiated comment to be made about public figures. Statute law at the time the article was published was quite clear that the publishers would have to justify what was said about me, but that was no obstacle to Justice Sian Elias, nor the judges of the Court of Appeal, who declared that members of parliament past present or future were fair game for the news media; belief in the truth of what was said was not an issue. I had no choice but to take the case to the Privy Council in London, where my counsel Peter McKnight won the point on my behalf that the New Zealand court went too far in allowing the news media a free hit at politicians. Unfortunately for me the Privy Council chose not to determine the case but sent it back to the Court of Appeal. That court then decided that the law in New Zealand should be closer to its Australian equivalent, but it was not gracious enough to admit that it had been in error and went so far as to require me to pay for its mistake. I can only suppose that the court had become accustomed to the news media fawning on it. In any event I could not afford to risk carrying on with the case. That was hard to take, as was sanctimonious bleating among the news media about the hard-won victory for freedom of speech, which would have been more convincing had it been won against an opponent with more resources than I had.

When I was still in parliament I tried to find something to do in a voluntary way, and with that in mind became vice-president of the New Zealand Rugby Football League. The pleasure of that was short-lived. Before Gerald Ryan became its president, the NZRFL was a body which inevitably surrendered judgement to enthusiasm, or worse, and in which the conventional principles of governance and management were scarcely recognised. This was the time when the Murdoch media interests in the guise of Super League were attempting the takeover of the game. There was money about, and it did not take long for matters to get out of hand. I had to force the resignation of a senior official by threatening exposure of the improper financial arrangements he had made. I complained to the police about misappropriation by an official in a provincial league, only to be asked by the police to hold back as the man in question was one of their informers. When the Murdoch interests settled with their rivals in Australia, I was able to get some money out of them to put the NZRFL's finances on a sounder footing, but after that my only concern was to leave while the money could still be accounted for.

I could not have had a more different experience on the board of the Rally of New Zealand. The rally is perennially one of this country's best-run sporting events, and Morrie Chandler, the force behind it, has an international reputation as a sporting administrator. It was a pleasure to help in a small way with the effort which goes into the event every year. Only ill-health made me give it up.

I was for several years on the judging panel of the School of the Year Awards, and this was rewarding in more than one way as it reintroduced me to Gary McCormick, who suggested to me in 1999 that I should do some performances with him at a number of venues around the country. I was happy to agree. Our first performance was in Cambridge, and the format we used has not changed since. He speaks, I speak, there is a break and then the audience is invited to ask us questions. I could not believe how much I enjoyed the experience. It was akin to the part of politics I liked best, in that there is engagement with an audience, and while there is a lot which is meant to entertain, there is often something which is more serious and reflective. It was a great boost to work with Gary, who never seems to flag and who must count as one of the sharpest and wittiest commentators there is on life in this country. In recent times when by any test I was hardly fit to speak in public, yet being able to do it meant so much to me, he has carried our performances.

The election of the Labour-led government at the end of 1999 brought several pleasures to me. Helen Clark called and asked if I would like to be high commissioner to India. I did not accept, because Margaret would have hated it and I owed her too much to argue the point, but in a sense the offer itself was enough. Nothing else in the government's gift could ever have meant as much and the offer let me draw a line under all the disappointments of my last years in politics. After that, Mark Gosche, an Otahuhu friend from trade union politics, appointed me to the boards of Housing New Zealand and the Land Transport Safety Authority. They were both in their very different ways satisfying occupations, but like everything else I have done in the last few years my work on them was hampered by illness.

I had several bouts of ill-health in the 1990s. When I came back from the United States in 1995 my angina became unstable. My cardiologist was Warren Smith, who travelled with me in the United States when I was prime minister, and although he is as trim as any cardiologist should be he is the only one I have seen eat a 32-ounce steak. This time my condition was beyond the reach of angioplasty and I was placed in the care of Alan Kerr at Greenlane Hospital. Alan is a leading coronary surgeon and more than that a great humanitarian. He performed bypass surgery on me and my recovery went well. I was fit enough until 2001 when the angina came back. I was in Taranaki with Gary McCormick when I felt at my worst; for some reason, and this is no reflection on the place, I could not stand the thought of dying in a motel in Hawera and Gary drove me back to Auckland early in the morning. Alan Kerr did a second coronary bypass not long afterwards. The second time, of course, I knew what to expect, but it was arduous and my recovery was much slower.

The year after the second bypass I went to India for the last time. I travelled with my son Roy, who lived there for many years. I stayed with him often and I was never once disappointed in what I found in that extraordinary country, no matter how challenging it was. There is so much resilience in its people, so many who never surrender no matter what the odds against them are. The absence of tourists scared away by warnings of imminent nuclear war made this last journey particularly enjoyable as comfortable hotel rooms were to be had for a trifle and many popular places were comparatively uncrowded.

On the aircraft back to New Zealand I became aware of

significant swelling in my legs and the lower part of my body. I did not feel particularly well. I was working with Gary McCormick one night in Wellington when I lost my voice. It was raspy and croaky but there was no response to any conventional treatment. Pat Frengley arranged for any number of tests. The results were given to me by a renal specialist who told me I had a disorder I had never heard of called amyloidosis. He had to write it down for me. He had a gloomy view of my prognosis. I had to prepare myself for the possibility that in the worst case my life would be over in a few months.

Amyloidosis is a disorder of plasma cells in the bone marrow. It creates insoluble proteins which cannot be passed out of the body in the usual way but are deposited in the vital organs, impairing and eventually preventing their functioning. In comparatively recent times it was almost inevitably a death sentence, but these days it is treated by bone marrow transplant, or as in my case by chemotherapy, and there have been some remarkable successes. The course of chemotherapy lasted over a period of seven months. It was debilitating, and I was weak for a long time afterwards, but the result was the suppression of the disorder. Its reappearance can never be ruled out, but for some time it has been stable at a manageable level.

I was still getting over the chemotherapy when I was invited to Stockholm to receive an award created by a philanthropist with Swedish and German connections. The foundation he set up honoured many who were not particularly favoured by the Western political establishment and I was moved to be asked to accept an honorary award in recognition of what I had done on behalf of the nuclear-free movement. I tried to make it plain in my acceptance speech that what happened in New Zealand was the result of a popular movement created by the efforts of countless dedicated individuals. The award was presented in the parliament in Stockholm and was made happier for me by the presence of my son Byron and his fiancée whom I met for the first time there. I enjoyed the visit to Sweden and the brief visits to Berlin and Brussels which I made immediately afterwards on behalf of the foundation, but the effort was considerable and I came back to New Zealand in a state of some exhaustion.

There were a few days in 2004 when I felt well, but for the most part there is little to tell except continuing deterioration in my health. My heart gave further trouble and a pacemaker was put in place to control arrhythmia. I began to suffer from the effects of kidney failure. One remarkable evening gave me great encouragement. I was invited early in the year to speak at a meeting organised by a Dunedin inter-faith group about issues which complicated the relationships between the world's great religions. It was held in August and I was not sure I would be able to do it, but I wanted to try and the organisers were happy enough to have someone read my notes for me if I could not speak. My topic was the war in Iraq. The long flight south was tiring, but something wonderful happened when I got to the lecture theatre. It was full to overflowing, there were familiar faces in the audience, my voice came back and I stood and talked for an hour and a half. It was something I have done so many times in my life, and never tired of, and it was a great gift to enjoy this last time as much as I did.

My kidneys finally gave up the struggle at the end of 2004. I am kept alive by peritoneal dialysis; a little machine hums away by my bed every night. It is a limited kind of life, because my general health is not good and I find it hard to walk very far. I do not choose to drive myself much further than the local shopping centre. It is possible to travel, with a great deal of planning, and I have done some performances with Gary McCormick to keep my spirits up. I enjoy the visits of friends. I still follow politics, although its new rules have almost put an end to my near life-long interest in parliament: when members are allowed to read their speeches, and we are represented by so many of the incoherent and incomprehensible, the contest which attracted me to it in the first place has mostly gone. I am yet again a smoker. As there is little else which can possibly go wrong with my health there is nothing to keep me from my cigars. I do not need to worry about keeping up appearances. I wear my most comfortable clothes and I shave when I feel like it. After 1989 I ceased to be a regular attender at church and I have never gone back to the Methodist church as such, but I have more recently gone to services at a combined parish close to my home, where there is something familiar and comforting about the organ music, and wisdom in the sermons.

After a time of some estrangement I am able once again to talk freely to Naomi. Our three children live abroad. Roy married in India in 1996 and now lives in Melbourne with his wife. Byron and his wife live near Birmingham. Emily lives in London. It has been a long journey for the three of them and me, but we stay in close touch and see each other as often as we can and they are remarkably loving and tolerant. Edith is nine as I write this. She looks after her mouse Salt and goes to the local school. I was never one for tucking my children up in bed and reading to them, but if I am lucky this evening Edith will read to me.

CODA

About fifteen years ago the publishers of this book paid me an advance to write about my life and I had to pay it back because I was too unsettled by many of the events I should have described to want to write about them. But now I have at last achieved some ease. I do not have to pretend about anything any more, and I can write as I feel.

When governors-general finished their term in office they used to get on the boat and sail back to England, never to be seen here again, and the best way to leave the job of prime minister is probably with a state funeral. I left in the usual way, not very happily, and what I did in the job has been contested, sometimes acrimoniously. For all of that I value every minute I spent in it. It had its burdens and its duties, and in later times my possession of it, or rather the desire of others to dispossess me of it, put me into a state of constant anxiety, but I was never once disappointed in it. The job gave me unimagined opportunities and equally unanticipated responsibilities. It was often exhilarating and often moving. I was from the first moment to the last proud to be prime minister. It will be plain from this book that what I actually did in the job was sometimes a matter of satisfaction and sometimes not, but the job itself was far more than I ever wished for when I first imagined myself in it.

It was not my intention in writing this book to muse on the currents of history. I have written about events as they seemed to me at the time. I have recorded what I thought or said or did and what I remember other people saying or doing. For the most part I have relied on my memory. A lot has been left out, but it is not always because I have forgotten what happened.

Many events which for one reason or another were significant to me have not found a place in this book. I have not written about the devastation made by cyclone Bola, or the inauguration of Nelson Mandela as president of South Africa, or my good fortune in meeting any number of remarkable or idiosyncratic visitors to New Zealand. I have not described my visit to the Invermay Agricultural Centre, where the local president of Federated Farmers made a pitiful speech attacking the government, and when I said I would come back when farmers elected a representative who belonged to the twentieth century, the rural community responded by running across a field and pounding on my car as I left. A good public service garage driver got us out of it, one of many skilful people who drove me.

I find as well that I have left out places which mean a lot to me. It seems odd to look back over the finished work and see that I have not made any mention of the Cook Islands and Aitutaki, which when I first went there was for me the most magical place on earth. I have included some odd incidents but omitted others, like the banquet in China where the snake we were to eat was beheaded and skinned in front of us and I felt obliged as New Zealand's representative to consume the first course of deep-fried embryonic chicken; or the time I opened a plant which on that day was bottling bulk imported rum, and my mother's hand must have been on the switch, because when I pressed the button the line ran for a moment and then backed up, sending bottles crashing to the floor and rum splashing all over the distinguished visitors.

There are people missing too. I have mentioned some whose work or company I valued but left out far too many others. As if those omissions were not enough, what I have written does not give a full picture of the people in my life. Ken Richardson and Lorna Best, for instance, appear in the narrative as officials, but my three older children knew Ken as Uncle Ken, and Lorna is Aunt Lorna to my youngest. I have written about some people to whom I have not done justice because of the limits imposed by my viewpoint. Mike Moore is one, but he rose higher in the international community than any other New Zealander and he does not have to care what I say about him. Because I have written here about my difficulties with the defence establishment I did not mention people in the military I did respect, like John Mace, or even Ewen Jamieson, who was a bitter political opponent after retirement but was straightforward and reliable before it.

What I have written in this book is subjective, and that is its only perspective. I did not set out to write a history of the fourth Labour government. I have hardly touched on wider social and economic issues. I have written about my part in the implementation of New Zealand's nuclear-free policy without explaining how the policy ever came to be adopted by the Labour Party, but that does not mean I do not know how the party arrived at its policy, nor give credit where it is due. I have written about the nonsense which followed a misguided attempt to borrow money overseas and not about the Maori renaissance of the 1980s; but when I convened a meeting of Maori leaders and something close to a fist fight broke out in front of me, and the deputy prime minister, who had asked me to convene the meeting, handed me a note which said 'I am not of this planet' and left the room, I did not think about the swirling tides of history: I wondered when I could decently bring the meeting to a close. I might say much the same about the Labour women's council and the achievements of feminism in the same decade, except that its meetings were a lot more orderly.

In politics perhaps more than any other occupation, friends and supporters become enemies and opponents, and the other way around. It was not always easy to write about people in the way I saw them at a given time, rather than through a prism of what happened afterwards. I have done my best, although it is easier to remember the good points in some than it is in others. I was pleased to speak for a while to Roger Douglas a few months ago, because whatever happened between us in the end, he is someone who tried, and achieved, and was once very important to me.

Margaret I know would be happiest if she did not appear at all in this book and I have as a result said less about her than I wanted to. She means so much to me; she always has.

This year Auckland like me has had an Indian summer. I can see through my windows that the elm trees are shedding their leaves and that the ivy on the barn has reddened and will soon disappear. If I see its leaves green again I shall be very happy.

May 2005

INDEX